Caustic Comedies

PLAYS FOR THE STAGE

BY ROBERT SHEARMAN

First published in November 2010
by Big Finish Productions Ltd, PO Box 1127, Maidenhead, SL6 3LW
www.bigfinish.com

Editor: Xanna Eve Chown
Managing Editor: Jason Haigh-Ellery
With thanks to Jenny Westwell

ISBN
Numbered edition: 978-1-84435-539-6
1-84435-539-X
Hardback edition: 978-1-84435-542-6
1-84435-542-X
Paperback edition: 978-1-84435-540-2
1-84435-540-3

Cover photography © Katie Cooke, 2010
Cover design by Xanna Eve Chown

Printed and bound in Great Britain by Biddles Ltd, King's Lynn, Norfolk
www.biddles.co.uk

*

ACKNOWLEDGEMENTS

A huge thank you to all the long-suffering casts and crews who have staged my plays over the years - and have put up with me in those long, Diet Coke fuelled rehearsals. But in particular I'd like to give curtain call like applause to: Alan Ayckbourn, Rosalind Ayres, Christie Baugher, John Binns, Lyn Boundy, Nicholas Briggs, Vanessa Brooks, Martin Bruce, Owen Bywater, Patrick Carpmael, Debbie Challis, Xanna Eve Chown, Alan Clements, Katie Cooke, Sue Cowley, Russell T Davies, Karen Davison, John Durnin, Karen Edwards, Steven Elder, David Farnsworth, Ian Forrest, Nev Fountain, Michael Friend, Mark Gatiss, James Grant, Simon Guerrier, Toby Hadoke, Jason Haigh-Ellery, Steven Hall, Lisa L Hannett, Malcolm Hebden, Hannah Houghton-Berry, James Humphreys, Martin Jarvis, Tanya Lemke, Rob Lines, Kath Mattock, Adrian McLoughlin, Suzanne Milligan, Steven Moffat, Ian Mond, Simon Murgatroyd, Chris Myles, Liz Myles, Iain Ormsby-Knox, Connal Orton, John Primrose, David Richardson, Jody Richardson, Rebecca Riley, Roger Ringrose, Aubrey Scrace, Will Shindler, Leigh Shine, Kai Simmons, Andy Sinclair, Angela Slatter, Heather Stoney, Jeannie Swales, Tommaso di Thellung, John Ursu, Beryl Vertue, Sue Vertue, Lucy Warren, Janet Whitaker, Jessica Willcocks, Clive and Pat Wolfe, Philip Wolff.

For my family - Mum (Joyce), Dad (Dennis), and Barely-Still-Kid Sister (Vicky). Who attended most of my first nights, laughed as often as they were able, and usually stayed past the interval.

But mostly, as ever, for Jane Goddard, who has known me as playwright, director, producer, and accommodation organiser - and yet married me in spite of it.

**For further information on Robert and his work,
check out www.robertshearman.net**

FOREWORD

It all began with a stammer.

I don't think I'd been especially shy as a little kid; all the photographs and home movies always show me grinning away, or burbling about something. And my father confirms that it was quite an effort to get me to shut up. But some time in my pre-teens the words just stopped. Oh, they were still there inside of course, my head was full of them. Perhaps there were too many, perhaps that was the problem. But whatever the reason, they wouldn't come out. And it changed everything.

If you've got a stammer, then you'll know the exasperation of it. It's hard to explain otherwise because people mercifully free of the thing can't understand logically why you just can't speak at will. You feel your heart beating faster, and a part of your brain goes into panic mode, and tells you that the words on the tip of your tongue just won't be formed, no way, no chance. And you're left gaping in restaurants at waiters asking for your order. It actually becomes a physical hurdle to get over, you can feel yourself at last forcing the sounds out – assuming, naturally, that by this time the waiter hasn't given up and wandered off to another table.

I don't know when the stammer took. It ought to be one of those great dramatic moments of crisis, a hitherto relaxed and happy child wakes up one day to discover his mouth no longer behaves the way it used to. It's the way I'd write it if it were a story. But what I do know is that it drew a line separating the me then and the me now; I'd never really take talking for granted again. I was quite bright at school. But even though I could produce the goods on paper, it's strange how differently you're treated when you can't articulate your answers out loud. I felt stupid.

My way out of it was to try acting. I'm not quite sure how I came to the conclusion that the terror of attempting ordinary conversation with teachers or classmates would be so much easier trying it in front of hundreds of strangers in a school concert hall instead. But I fell in love with it. I wasn't very good, really – my way to avoid the stammer was to talk very very very fast in an often incomprehensible gabble. But at my school persistence was applauded, and I kept on getting cast. Usually in amiable parts that had one or two scenes of melodramatic temper loss. I liked shouting on stage. As a cuckolded husband in A Month in the Country I nearly lost my voice through shouting. My initially amiable Capulet pushed Juliet through the set backdrop when she told me she wanted to run off with Romeo. Shouting was brilliant. I was like a teenage Brian Blessed.

I loved acting so much I tried to join the National Youth Theatre. My obvious passion for it got me through to the final auditions, where I was told (very regretfully) that the best actor I could ever hope to be was a mediocre one. And thuddingly mediocre at that.

So I began to write plays instead. At that age, it's that simple. I still needed to be part of the theatre, but didn't want to let the side down. I wrote parts for myself at first; my early stuff is bursting with amiable shoutyness. But pretty soon I realised I wanted these plays to be good, that the last person I'd want to cast in them would be someone like me holding everybody else up.

My first 'proper' play was called Sentimental Gushing, and I wrote it when I was seventeen, and my school allowed a lunchtime production of it. It was about a married couple who only had conversations within the TV commercial breaks, and it all got very surreal when the commercials began taking over. It sounds better than it was. (No, really – and even if you don't like the sound of it.) But the commercials were quite funny, especially the bits where plucky Wanda rises up from obscurity as a housewife asked to identify different brands of soap powder to become a fascist ruler of the world.

That play is not in this collection. Thank God.

What we do have here is a selection of scripts written between 1992 and 2001, my first decade as a full time writer, and the decade in which I pretty much devoted myself exclusively to the stage. I wrote plays obsessively. I wrote about sixty of them. Only half of them have been produced in any form, mind. And of that sixty, I think there's about fifty too many. (Oh, let's say forty-five. I'll be charitable.) These aren't necessarily my most successful plays – there are a handful that did rather well but repeat themes too clearly elsewhere in the book – and there are a couple I have collected which – frankly – bombed. But I hope this is an interesting bunch nonetheless.

I'm not going to preface these plays with explanations or justifications. To be honest, if it's not immediately obvious what any given scene is about, your guess is as good as mine. And I don't want to justify the work of someone else – because they do feel the product of another writer, sometimes I think I'm barely on nodding terms with the Rob I was then. The funny thing is I often don't remember what happens in my plays. I went to a revival of one a little while ago and I genuinely couldn't work out what might happen after the first act. I spent the interval in a state of excited anticipation, hoping that the younger me hadn't dropped the ball. So the prefaces will be a collection of anecdotes and memories – and, no doubt, vague inaccuracies and bare-faced lies.

I wrote a play about a stammerer once. There was a vicar, and it caused him great anguish that whenever he addressed his congregation from the pulpit he could barely get a word out. The only time he could relax and talk normally was when he prayed to God. So he begged the Almighty to free him from this curse, just so he could express his devotion to the world all the better. And, miraculously, the stammer lifted. The vicar's word could be heard. But the awful truth was, he was so boring a speaker that he drove the congregation away. It was the Devil who had answered his prayer – and God had kept the amiable shouty man mute for the greater good.

That's not in here either; hey, it runs for three and a half hours, and it's a bit gory, there's a weird bit where parishioners' heads turn up in the font. But if I permit myself the indulgence of analysing my work, just this once – I can see my twenty-two year old self's anxiety now he'd found a way to express himself that he'd actually have nothing to say.

Let's see.

Robert Shearman, 2010

Caustic Comedies

BY ROBERT SHEARMAN

Contents

Easy Laughter
(1992)

WINNER OF THE SUNDAY TIMES PLAYWRITING AWARD

OPENED AT ST LUKE'S THEATRE, EXETER,
ON 22 JANUARY 1993, WITH THE FOLLOWING CAST:
DENNIS KAI SIMMONS
PATSY JESSICA WILLCOCKS
RALPH JAMES HUMPHREYS
TOBY PHILIP WOLFF
JUDY LUCY WARREN
DIRECTED BY ROBERT SHEARMAN

ITS FIRST LONDON PRODUCTION OPENED AT THE MAN IN THE MOON THEATRE
ON 10 JANUARY 1995, WITH THE FOLLOWING CAST:
DENNIS MAX GOLD
PATSY ANNA KIRKE
RALPH EDWARD JEWESBURY
TOBY GARY WHITAKER
JUDY ERICA ROSSI
DIRECTED BY KATH MATTOCK

ITS FIRST AMERICAN PRODUCTION OPENED AT SPACESPACE IN MINNEAPOLIS, MINNESOTA,
PRESENTED BY PETER PETER PUMPKIN THEATER,
ON 1 FEBRUARY 1996, WITH THE FOLLOWING CAST:
DENNIS SHAWN MARTIN
PATSY SARAH PHEMISTER
RALPH JEFF REDMAN
TOBY KYLE CHRISTOPHERSON
JUDY ELLEN APEL
DIRECTED BY JOHN URSU

Act One

(The play is designed for traverse. The set is an apparently normal suburban living room. The only furniture in the room is a drinks trolley, and a single armchair with side table. This armchair stands at one extreme of the stage, facing at the other extreme a worryingly large Christmas tree, decorated with hundreds of fairy lights, hanging chocolates and pink ribbons. A large selection of wrapped presents are at its base.

(A sickeningly upbeat version of Winter Wonderland *plays as* **Patsy** *enters in half light. She is a woman in her forties, dressed plainly with a pink ribbon in her hair. She walks straight to the drinks trolley, pours a glass of whisky. She walks stage centre, visibly anxious. So anxious is she, in fact, that she sips at the drink and finishes it without realising. She starts, rushes back to the trolley, pours another glass. She walks to the armchair, sits bolt upright on the edge of her seat, ready to leap up whenever necessary. She holds the glass so rigidly that it suggests an unfamiliarity with the very action itself.*

(The music comes to an end, the lights brighten to full. Christmas tree lights are on, having slowly risen during the song.)

(There is a long pause.)

Patsy   *(softly)* Twenty-seven.

(Pause. She sighs audibly. Then, with sudden force:)

Judy! Aren't you ready yet?

(The reply from offstage is **Judy**, **Patsy's** *eight year old daughter. She has a brother called* **Toby**, *ten. These are acted by actors in their twenties, who play up the youth of their characters to the boundaries of grotesquerie.)*

Judy   Yes, I'm nearly ready, thank you very much indeed.

Patsy   Yes. Just approximately how nearly ready is that? Do you have your dress on?

Judy   Yes, I have my dress on.

Patsy   The pink one your father likes?

Judy   Yes, I have my dress on, thank you very much indeed.

Patsy   And your pink ribbon in your hair?

(Short pause)

Judy?

Judy   No... I can't manage it properly.

Patsy Judy, do you realise what time it is? Do you realise what the time is?

Judy Yes, sorry most kindly...

Patsy Your father will be home any minute. Any second. Any minute now, any second now. And you won't have your ribbon in your hair...

Judy It gets all so tangled, mother.

Patsy *(with some panic)* Well, we don't want it all tangled! We don't want it all tangled! Any minute now, any second now, your father will be here. Any second now and there will be the key in the lock, and shoes wiped on the mat, and he'll be here, and we don't want it all tangled with his key in the lock!

Judy No, sorry most kindly...

Patsy Any second. He's already late. Twenty-seven, no, twenty-eight now, twenty-eight minutes late, nearly twenty-nine, and you haven't got your ribbon in your hair and when you have it's all tangled!

(Short pause. Forcing herself to calm down:)

Could you go and ask your brother to help you, please? Could you go and ask him to help you with your ribbon, your pink ribbon, so it won't be tangled when your father comes home any second now?

(She resumes her rigid position. Pause)

Any minute now...

(Short pause)

Any second now...

*(And **Dennis**, her husband, enters. He is carrying a briefcase.)*

Oh, that's a relief. You're home.

Dennis Good evening, Patsy.

(She approaches him, takes his briefcase. And continues to hold it until instructed.)

Thank you very much indeed...

(And she gives him his whisky. At length he sits in the armchair during the exchange below.)

And thank you very much indeed.

Patsy I was worried. You were late.

Dennis Well, home now, eh? All safe now, eh?

Patsy I was worried. You're never normally this late.

Dennis Well, remember, I told you, I had to stay late tonight.

Patsy Yes, I know...

Dennis A further fifteen minutes. So the office manager could wish us all a happy holiday.

Patsy Yes, I know. I remembered. I did remember this year. I mean, not like last year when I forgot about that and got really frantic...

Dennis No.

Patsy No. But you were more than fifteen minutes late. I was worried.

Dennis Well, different train timetables to follow when you leave the office fifteen minutes later.

Patsy Yes, I know. But it's all right. I wasn't frantic. I was only worried.

(Short pause)

Are you enjoying your whisky, Dennis?

Dennis Thank you, Patsy. Yes, I am. Thank you very much indeed.

*(Short pause. **Patsy** stands still, looks at **Dennis** hopefully.)*

Would you like one?

Patsy *(delighted)* Well, I shouldn't...

Dennis Well, it is a holiday now, isn't it?

Patsy Are you sure? I know I shouldn't. Are you sure?

Dennis Just a half. I think we can allow you a half, can't we?

Patsy Well, just a half. I shouldn't really, but if you're sure...

Dennis It is the beginning of the holiday.

Patsy Just a half then.

*(**Dennis** rises, goes to the drink trolley.)*

Oh, no, I didn't mean you had to pour it as well...

Dennis No problem, Patsy. I'm up now.

Patsy *(warmly)* Well, that's very kind. Thank you very much indeed.

Dennis *(inspecting the bottle)* Just a minute...

Patsy I'm so glad I married you. You're the best husband in the world.

Dennis Patsy, isn't the whisky level a little low?

(Short pause)

Patsy Yes, I'm...

Dennis Have you had a drink?

Patsy ... A very little one. I was worried when you weren't home...

Dennis Yes, I see...

Patsy Only worried, not frantic.

Dennis No.

Patsy And I had poured you your whisky, and I don't know why... I was worried, remember... I just took a sip and carried on sipping... I don't know... I was worried, though not frantic.

(Short pause)

It's all right. I gave you another glass.

Dennis Good.

Patsy There's no saliva of mine in there.

Dennis Well, all right. But if you've already had your half glass of whisky, do you think it wise I pour you another?

Patsy Well, it wasn't a half, it was less than that, I'd say it was a half of a half...

Dennis So you've already had a quarter of whisky?

Patsy Yes, about a quarter, I suppose...

Dennis Well, Patsy. Now it's up to you. You can have another quarter now if you want to, I'm not stopping you.

Patsy No.

Dennis *(sternly)* But before you decide, I think you had better just ask yourself whether you're sure you want it.

Patsy ...Yes.

(Short pause)

Dennis *(kindly)* Well, have you decided?

Patsy Yes. I'll... I'll do without.

Dennis You're absolutely sure?

Patsy Yes.

Dennis Quite quite sure?

Patsy ... Yes.

Dennis All right then. It was your decision. I had no part in it. But I think I can tell you now that you have made your decision, that that's all over, I think that you made the correct decision.

Patsy *(softly)* Thank you very much indeed.

Dennis And Christ, looking down on us, I have no doubt at all that He too, in His infinite compassion, will also think that you made the correct decision.

Patsy Yes.

Dennis Well done.

(He pours himself another glass of whisky.)

Patsy I just wish... I just wish I could have had my whisky with you rather than on my own...

Dennis Well. That was your decision, wasn't it?

Patsy Yes.

Dennis Too late for regrets now. No point in that.

*(**Dennis** moves back to his armchair.)*

Never mind. Maybe you can have a half tomorrow.

Patsy *(brightening)* Oh yes. Please. Thank you very much indeed. You're the best husband in the whole world.

(Short pause)

So... how was your day at work?

Dennis Oh, fine. Everything just as normal.

Patsy Everything just as normal, yes.

Dennis Yes.

Patsy Except for the fact you were kept fifteen minutes late.

Dennis ... Yes.

(Short pause)

Patsy I don't mind telling you, I was worried.

Dennis Yes, I know.

Patsy I don't know why the firm has to keep you fifteen minutes late every year to wish you a happy holiday.

Dennis Well, that's the way it works, isn't it?

Patsy But if they want to wish you all a merry Cristtide, why couldn't they all let you go home at the normal time? It'd be much more festive.

Dennis *(slowly)* It's good custom to wish us a merry Cristtide. It's a kind and generous sentiment on the part of our employers.

Patsy Yes.

Dennis And it just happens to take fifteen minutes.

Patsy Yes, I know, but if they were to let you go fifteen minutes earlier, wind up work fifteen minutes earlier, and then they were to wish you all a merry Cristtide, and still take fifteen minutes, then you'd be able to leave at the usual time, wouldn't you?

(Pause)

Dennis Yes. Patsy, are you sure you only had a quarter of whisky?

Patsy ... Sorry most kindly. It's just that I worry...

Dennis You see, Patsy, I work very hard at the office.

Patsy Yes, I know you work very hard...

Dennis We all do. We all work very hard.

Patsy Yes, I know you all work very hard...

Dennis And Christ, in His infinite compassion, still doesn't give us enough minutes in the day. He doesn't give any of us enough minutes in the day. Today, for example, at half past five the bells sounded, and I laid down my pen in the middle of a memo.

Patsy Dear me.

Dennis So you see, I could have quite well done with a few more minutes in the day. We all could. And not just in the middle of a memo either, but in the middle of a sentence. We all work very hard.

Patsy Yes, I know you all work very hard.

(Short pause. Sympathetically:)

Was it a difficult sentence?

Dennis Not an especially difficult sentence, no. When these two days'
holidays are over, I know precisely how I'm going to finish it.

Patsy Good.

(Short pause)

Yes, I know you work very hard...

*(Short pause. **Dennis** rises to pour himself another whisky.)*

Dennis And how was your day?

Patsy Oh, very good, thank you very much indeed for asking.

Dennis Good.

Patsy Mother phoned.

Dennis Did she now?

Patsy Yes.

Dennis That's nice.

Patsy She bought another goldfish.

Dennis Oh good.

Patsy Oh, and yes! I must tell you!

*(She goes over to him in excitement. **Dennis** watches her indulgently.)*

Dennis Yes?

Patsy I was able at last to get those wrinkle-free balloons!

Dennis Oh... really?

Patsy Yes! You remember how I told you I'd tried to order some in the
shop?

Dennis Hmm...

Patsy And they'd said no, because there wasn't enough demand, and I
said oh go on, please...

Dennis Hmmm...

Patsy And they carried on saying no, and I said please again...

Dennis Yes, yes...

Patsy Well, they got some in stock anyway. And I bought the last bag!
Isn't that wonderful?

(Short pause)

Dennis Wonderful.

Patsy That's what I thought!

Dennis Christ, in His infinite compassion, has been particularly compassionate to you today.

Patsy That's what I said!

Dennis *(gently, stern)* But Patsy, please. Do try to remember. If the balloons do wrinkle this Cristtide...

Patsy They won't, there's a guarantee on the bag...

Dennis Good... but if they *do* wrinkle, if something goes wrong... please don't overreact like last year. Especially not this year.

Patsy But I...

Dennis Don't.

(Pause)

Patsy *(lamely)* Well, they won't anyway, there's a guarantee on the bag.

(Short pause)

I do love you, Dennis. I'm so glad I married you. You're the best husband in the whole world.

Dennis And you're the best wife too.

Patsy I do think you're ever so nice.

(She approaches him.)

May I?

*(And they take positions facing each other. They lean forward from the waist, feet unmoving, raising their arms behind their backs – and peck each other on the lips. **Patsy** intends this to take a little longer than **Dennis**, who pulls away with a laugh.)*

Dennis Wait, wait! No Frenches. It's not Cristtide yet.

Patsy Sorry, it just slipped out...

Dennis Yes, well, keep your tongue within your own body until Cristtide.

Patsy Sorry most kindly...

Dennis No exchange of saliva until then.

(They both take a footstep backwards, perform the same operation again – this time, naturally, with greater difficulty.)

Patsy I was so worried when you were late.

*(And she kisses him again for a second, until **Dennis** pushes her away gently.)*

Dennis Time to stop now, Patsy.

Patsy Yes. Thank you very much indeed.

Dennis There'll be plenty of time for that later. It is Cristtide!

(Short pause)

I see that you've decorated the tree.

Patsy Do you like it?

Dennis It's very festive.

Patsy Judy gave me a hand. She worked very hard.

Dennis Oh, really?

Patsy All the pink ribbons on the tree are hers.

Dennis Well, they're very festive.

Patsy Well, that's nice that you've said that.

Dennis Yes.

Patsy When she comes down, Dennis, when she comes downstairs, do point out the pink ribbons.

Dennis Yes, I will.

Patsy It would mean so much to her. She dotes on you. Absolutely dotes.

Dennis Well, she deserves the attention. The pink ribbons are very festive indeed.

*(**Dennis** approaches her, then kisses her on top of the head.)*

Very festive. Very well done.

Patsy Oh, Dennis...

Dennis Very well done.

Patsy Thank you very much indeed. Oh, you're the best husband in the whole world. I love you, I think you're ever so nice.

Dennis Mmm. And tomorrow, maybe you can have half a whisky.

(Short pause)

I think it's time to see the children now.

Patsy Right. I'll give them a call.

(Enthusiastic shout:)

It's time for your father to see you!

*(To **Dennis**:)*

I hope everything's all right, but we had a little accident...

Dennis Accident?

Patsy Well, I hope it's all right, but Judy's hair may have got a little tangled...

Dennis I'm sure it'll be fine.

Patsy Just to let you know, I'd hate to let you down.

Dennis I'm sure it will be satisfactory.

*(Enter **Judy** and **Toby**. **Judy** is wearing a bright pink dress and her hair is tied back neatly by a pink ribbon. **Toby** is dressed smartly, wearing a navy blue blazer, with a small, unidentifiable badge pinned on his lapel. Unlike his sister he is not dressed specifically to match his age.*

*(**Toby**'s voice may not have fully broken yet, and so might be slightly higher pitched than that of the actor. At times, however, when **Toby** is being particularly stern, his voice will deepen, suddenly and disconcertingly.)*

*(They march in, and take up positions in front of **Dennis** as if on parade. It is clear that **Toby** leads **Judy** in, who follows with some respect. Both stand rigidly to attention as **Dennis** freely walks around them; at instances, both will swivel around to face him in strict unison.)*

Patsy Children. You'll be pleased to learn your father has arrived home.

*(**Dennis** approaches them.)*

Toby Glad to renew your acquaintance, sir.

Dennis Glad to renew your acquaintance, son.

(They shake hands.)

And how's my little daughter? How's Judy?

Judy Good evening, father.

(He affectionately grasps both of her cheeks between his forefingers and thumbs.)

Dennis Little chubby cheeks.

Judy Thank you very much indeed, father.

(He lets go, and ruffles her hair with a smile. Then he manoeuvres her head to look at the ribbon.)

Dennis No sign I can see of a tangle with the ribbon...

Patsy *(embarrassed)* Well, that's good...

Judy *(even more embarrassed)* No, no tangle, no...

Dennis I heard that there might be a little tangle. I was told to expect a little tangle.

Toby Oh, mother...

Patsy I only said a little tangle. It wasn't a big tangle, just a little tangle...

Toby *(coolly)* And when have I ever allowed Judy to come downstairs with her hair in a tangle?

Patsy I only said a little tangle...

Dennis Well, Judy, did you have your hair in a little tangle?

Toby I straightened that out, sir.

Judy It was only a little tangle, father. But Toby straightened it out for me.

Dennis I hope you thanked him.

Judy Oh yes. I did very much indeed. He's the best brother in the whole world.

Patsy *(nervously)* Maybe you should thank him again.

Judy Thank you very much indeed, Toby. You're the best brother in the whole world.

Toby *(soberly)* That's perfectly all right, Judy.

Dennis That's very well done, Judy. You thanked your brother very nicely.

Toby Very well done, Judy.

Judy Thank you very much indeed.

(Short pause)

Dennis Yes. So tell me, children, are you both looking forward to

Cristtide?

Toby Thank you very much indeed, sir.

Judy Yes, I'm very excited, father. Do you think maybe I'll see Santa this year?

Dennis *(laughing)* Well, you never know, little chubby cheeks, you never know.

Patsy Remember that your grandfather will be staying this year.

Toby We are looking forward to that very much.

Judy We love Gramps very much.

Toby We love him very much indeed.

Judy And we love Gran very much indeed too.

Patsy Of course you realise Gran won't be staying for Cristtide this year.

Judy Yes.

Patsy Because she's dead.

Judy Yes.

Dennis But I've no doubt that she'll be with us in spirit. Now, when your grandfather arrives tomorrow, Judy, you must make sure you wear just that pink dress.

Judy Yes, father.

Dennis It's a very pretty pink dress. And I think tomorrow you should wear a red ribbon.

Patsy Oh yes. Listen to your father, Judy.

Dennis Your grandfather always liked red ribbons.

Patsy Your Gran used to wear red ribbons.

Dennis That's right. So a red ribbon for tomorrow.

Toby I have a red ribbon already prepared, sir.

Dennis That's excellent, Toby. Very well done.

Toby Thank you very much indeed, sir.

(Short pause)

Dennis *(uneasily)* Yes... Very well done...

Patsy Judy. Tell your father where you've been today.

Dennis Oh. Where have you been today, Judy?

*(**Judy** clears her throat.)*

Judy Toby took me to the Grotto.

Dennis Oh, that was nice of him, wasn't it?

Judy Yes. Thank you very much indeed, Toby.

Dennis And did you get a present?

Judy I wasn't strong enough to get a present, but Toby got one for me.

Patsy Wasn't that nice of Toby?

Judy Toby is the best brother in the whole world. He is ever so nice.

Toby And you're the best sister too.

Judy He is ever so nice.

Dennis *(laughing)* Well, of course you weren't strong enough to get a present! You're just my little chubby cheeks, aren't you?

Judy Yes, father. I couldn't have done it without Toby.

Dennis Just my little chubby cheeks.

(He holds her cheeks again, then ruffles her hair. He speaks to her with a sudden, contrasting formality.)

How old are you now?

Toby She is eight years old, sir.

Judy I'm eight, father.

Toby And I'm ten years old, sir.

Dennis Eight years old. Well, well. But still my little chubby cheeks.

Judy Yes. Thank you very much indeed. Christ, in Your infinite compassion, keep me so.

Dennis Yes.

(Short pause)

A red ribbon for tomorrow, Toby.

Toby It shall be done, sir.

Dennis I'm sure it will.

(Short pause)

Patsy Your father was just saying how festive he found the Cristtide tree...

Dennis Yes, that's right. I was just saying, it's very festive.

Patsy Especially the pink ribbons.

Dennis *(irritated)* Yes, I was just about to say that, that I was just saying, the pink ribbons were particularly festive.

*(**Dennis** approaches **Judy** from behind, at last putting his hands upon her shoulders affectionately. **Judy** jumps, startled.)*

Now, I don't know, but I have a feeling... a hunch, call it if you will... that Judy may have had something to do with that...?

Judy *(timidly)* Yes, a little...

Patsy That was all Judy's work, the pink ribbons.

Judy Well, yes...

Dennis Well, very well done, Judy. I was just saying, it looks very festive.

Judy Thank you very much indeed...

Dennis I think that Christ, looking down upon us, would agree with me on that. It all looks particularly festive.

Judy Well, Toby gave me a lot of help...

Patsy Did he?

Judy Oh yes. I'm not very good at tying the knots, I get it all in a bit of a tangle...

Patsy Yes...

Judy So Toby very kindly helped me with that. And some of the taller branches, I couldn't reach those.

Dennis Well, of course you couldn't reach those. You're just my little chubby cheeks, aren't you?

Patsy I didn't know Toby helped you, Judy.

Judy Yes, he did.

Toby Yes.

Judy He's the best brother in the whole world.

Dennis I hope you thanked him, Judy.

Judy I did. Thank you very much indeed, Toby. You're the best brother in the whole world.

(Short pause)

Dennis So it all looks very festive. As I was saying. Very well done, both of you.

Toby Sir.

(Short pause)

Dennis *(enthusiastically)* Well, I can see that we're going to have a good Cristtide. It all looks very festive. That's excellent. Very well done, all of you. The fairy lights, the pink ribbons, the lot.

Patsy And remember, family, I also have the wrinkle-free balloons!

Dennis ...Yes. Now, you know that this Cristtide is going to be a little bit different. Somewhat unusual. You know that my father... your grandfather... your father-in-law, Patsy...

Patsy Oh yes.

Dennis ... That he is going to stay with us. Now it goes without saying that you will all do your best to make him feel welcome and comfortable. He is a guest. A visitor. He is also the most senior member of the family.

Judy I love Gramps. He is the best grandfather in the whole world.

Toby *(reprovingly)* Judy, be quiet! Your father is still talking. Apologise to him.

Judy *(abashed)* Sorry most kindly, Toby... Sorry most kindly, father.

Dennis However, I would like you all to bear in mind that this will be his first Cristtide he has spent without his wife. My mother. Gran. And so whilst you are making him welcome and comfortable, which it goes without saying you will do, I would like you to remember that if he could be made welcomer and comfortabler even than that then it will be all the better.

Patsy That's right.

Dennis They were very much in love. Almost as much in love as your mother and I are currently.

Patsy That's right.

Dennis So I ask you to bear that in mind.

Toby It shall be done, sir. I can assure you that Judy and I shall do our utmost to be of service to Gramps.

Dennis If you could also remember ... The red ribbon, Judy. The red ribbon is very important.

Toby Yes.

Dennis My mother would always wear a red ribbon. It would be nice for him.

Toby Yes, sir.

Judy Father.

Dennis He is getting older, this may be his last Cristtide. Make that red ribbon stand out.

Patsy And shall I wear a red ribbon too, dear?

*(Pause. **Dennis** turns to stare at her, scandalised.)*

Dennis *(icily)* You will continue to wear the pink ribbon that I enjoy, Patsy.

Patsy Yes ... sorry most kindly...

*(Short pause. **Dennis** returns to his former affability.)*

Dennis But as I say, I'm sure that this will be a perfect Cristtide. And I'm sure that when everything looks so festive, Christ looking down will share a perfect Cristtide with us. And that my father shall too.

Patsy It will be a perfect Cristtide even with him here.

Dennis I'm sure it will be a perfect Cristtide *because* he's here. The whole family gathered around the home, sharing.

(Short pause)

Very well. You may both go now.

Toby Thank you very much indeed, sir.

Judy Thank you very much indeed, father.

Patsy Goodbye, children.

Toby Come on, young Judy. I shall check your homework.

Judy Thank you very much indeed, Toby. You're the best brother in the whole world.

(They exit. As they do so:)

Dennis *(calling)* And don't forget. The red ribbon!

Patsy *(calling)* And no tangles! No tangles at all!

(Pause)

Dennis Good. Would you pour me another whisky, please, Patsy?

Patsy Yes, of course. A full glass?

Dennis A full glass would be just the ticket.

Patsy Certainly.

*(She struggles to pour him a whisky whilst still carrying the briefcase. **Dennis** allows her a good few seconds' abortive attempts before he gives her further instructions.)*

Dennis Oh, and I think you can put down the briefcase now if you like.

Patsy ...On the armchair?

Dennis For the while, yes, I think the armchair will suffice. But you'd better move it later.

*(**Patsy** puts down the briefcase, and begins to pour **Dennis** a whisky.)*

Patsy It was ever so nice of you to comment upon Judy's pink ribbons on the Cristtide tree.

Dennis Yes...

Patsy Did you see the way her face lit up? Her whole face lit up. She dotes on you. Absolutely dotes.

Dennis Yes. Just one thing. I did detect that my comment was in some way prompted by you.

Patsy *(uneasily)* ...Was it?

Dennis Most definitely.

(Short pause)

Patsy Well, I wanted to see her face light up... Her whole face, that is. ... I was a little worried. Just a little worried. I thought you might have forgotten...

Dennis Patsy. You know full well that I don't forget things.

Patsy No, I'm sorry...

Dennis I can't afford to in my job, can I? At present I'm in the middle of a memo. In the middle of a sentence even...

Patsy Sorry most kindly...

Dennis And in two days' time I shall remember precisely how to finish it. The memo. And the sentence. How to finish *them,* the memo and the sentence. You know full well that I don't forget things.

(Short pause)

Remember that.

Patsy Yes... Sorry... I'm truly...

Dennis Yes. Well. Never mind. Too late for regrets now. No point in that.

Patsy Sorry most kindly.

Dennis *(with sudden anger)* It's just that I don't want to have my credibility challenged in front of the children...! But never mind. Too late for regrets now. Too late for that.

*(Short pause. He stoops towards **Patsy**, apparently gently, actually menacingly.)*

Could I have my whisky please?

Patsy Oh... yes ...

(And she gives him the glass. He drains it in one gulp.)

Dennis ... Thank you very much indeed.

Patsy Would you like another?

(He hands her the glass.)

Dennis No. You can wash this one.

Patsy Right...

Dennis *(laughing, affable once more)* Not now, Patsy! There's no rush! It is Cristtide after all. ...You can take it to the kitchen in a minute.

Patsy *(relieved)* Yes. Yes, it is Cristtide.

Dennis Exactly.

Patsy Thank you very much indeed.

Dennis And it is going to be a perfect Cristtide. The whole family together. All five of us.

Patsy ... Yes.

Dennis You are looking forward to my father arriving, aren't you?

Patsy Yes. Yes, yes, of course.

Dennis Good. I am. I most certainly am.

(Short pause)

Oh yes.

Patsy Yes... Dennis, this may be the wrong moment...

Dennis *(affectionately)* What is it, Patsy?

Patsy Well, I mentioned to you earlier... my mother phoned...

Dennis Yes, I remember.

Patsy No, I know you remember, I know you don't forget... But you remember she bought herself a goldfish...

Dennis Yes, of course.

Patsy ...Do you have any names for it?

Dennis She asked you to ask me again.

Patsy ... That is what she phoned for, yes...

Dennis She is pushing her luck, isn't she?

Patsy Oh, please, Dennis. It's just what you said. That she had a woefully small, erm...

Dennis I said... I always say, that your mother has a woefully minimal imagination.

Patsy That's right. As you say, my mother has a woefully mimimal imagination. But she was hoping you might have a name for it...

Dennis I don't know. What use was that Book of Names we bought her last Cristtide, that's what I want to know...

*(**Patsy** shrugs helplessly. Short pause)*

Very well. Wayne.

Patsy *(delighted)* Oh, that's perfect. Yes. Wayne! That's a perfect name!

Dennis Yes. I just hope she's grateful.

Patsy Oh. She is. She is. I'll phone her back. She's very grateful.

Dennis So I should hope.

Patsy She'll speak to me on the phone, and she'll say she's very grateful. She's already very grateful.

Dennis After all, she's not my mother.

Patsy I'll tell her.

Dennis Tell her too that she has a woefully minimal imagination.

Patsy I will. I'll tell her that. And she'll say she's very grateful.

Dennis And tell her too...

(Short pause. He smiles.)

Tell her too that I wish her a merry Cristtide...

Patsy *(touched)* Oh, Dennis. That's wonderful. Oh, you're ever so nice. You're the best husband in the whole world.

*(**Dennis** moves to exit. **Patsy** scurries after him.)*

Dennis This year, a perfect Cristtide...

Patsy And Judy thinks that you're the best father in the whole world...

*(**Dennis** calls to her offstage.)*

Dennis Patsy. Don't forget the briefcase.

Patsy Oh.

*(**Patsy** scurries back, puts down the glass, and picks up the briefcase. She makes to exit again.)*

Dennis *(offstage)* And the dirty glass...

Patsy Oh yes.

(She doubles back, picks up the glass as well. To the audience:)

Sorry most kindly...

(And she hurries after him with both glass and briefcase.

(Lights dim. Upbeat version of Rudolf the Red-Nosed Reindeer. Lights rise again. It is Cristtide Eve, in the late morning. Christmas tree lights off in this scene.

*(Enter **Patsy**, with **Judy** close behind her, both carrying balloons. All of them are red, all of them blown to the same size. **Patsy** manages a couple, but **Judy** can hardly be seen, struggling beneath several of them. **Judy** now wears a red ribbon in her hair.)*

Patsy All right, Judy? Are you behind me?

Judy I'm behind you, mother.

Patsy You're managing with the balloons?

Judy Yes, mother, thank you very much indeed. I'm managing very well indeed.

Patsy ...Right. Put them down here.

*(She has reached a far edge of the stage. She drops her balloons, and **Judy** does the same, with relief.)*

Right. Good. That's good. That's perfect. Now what we need to do now, Judy... Are you listening?

Judy Yes, mother.

Patsy We need to scatter them over the room. We need to take these balloons and scatter them over the room. Over the room we have to scatter them liberally.

Judy ...Yes, mother.

Patsy You do that side, I'll do this side.

*(**Judy** takes some balloons, and decorates behind the armchair.*

*(**Dennis** and **Toby** enter by another door, make their way towards where **Judy** is working.)*

Dennis Yes. So. Toby. You are looking forward to the Cristtide celebrations.

Toby Yes, sir.

Dennis All excited about what Santa is going to leave you this year, eh?

Toby Yes, sir.

Dennis Yes, I remember when I was your age... Every Cristtide Eve, there I'd be, with my father, and he'd ask me whether I was looking forward to Cristtide, and whether I was excited about what Santa was going to be leaving me. And, of course, I was. I always was. Mind you, I was your age then. I was just a little boy.

Toby Yes, sir.

Dennis And here we are now, and you're as excited as I was, looking forward to the Cristtide celebrations.

Toby *(smoothly)* Another cycle of history is evidently repeating itself, sir.

Dennis Yes, Toby, it is. It certainly is.

(Short pause)

Look, Toby... I must have a word...

Toby Sir.

Dennis Privately.

*(They both look at **Judy**, working nearby.)*

Judy, would you please excuse us?

Judy *(startled)* I'm sorry, father?

Dennis Would you please work somewhere else for a moment?

Judy *(confused)* But mother told me to work here...

Toby *(sternly)* Judy. Do as your father tells you.

Judy ...Yes. Sorry most kindly, Toby.

(She hurries over to her mother.)

Dennis ... Thank you very much indeed, Toby. Very well done.

Toby Sir.

Patsy What are you doing back here, Judy? I thought I told you to work over there...

Judy Father sent me back, mother.

Patsy *(softening)* Oh. Oh. Quite right then. Very well done, Judy.

*(**Judy** helps **Patsy** with the balloons.)*

Dennis I wanted to say very well done with Judy's red ribbon, Toby.

Toby Thank you very much indeed, sir.

Dennis It is very impressive, it certainly stands out. I think that your grandfather will appreciate it.

Toby Yes, sir.

Dennis You understand that your grandfather likes red ribbons and such like, and, well, we're not so much humouring him...

Toby Yes, sir.

Dennis Yes. Well. It's just I wanted to ask you to keep a special eye on Judy this Cristtide. See if you can make sure she spends a lot of time with her grandfather...

Toby Yes, sir.

Dennis It's not that we're humouring him so much... but still. If you could do that.

Toby Certainly, sir.

Dennis You understand what I'm saying, don't you, Toby?

Patsy You know what I like about these balloons, Judy?

Toby Quite quite fully, sir.

Judy No, mother. What's that?

Dennis Good. Good lad. Good boy. Very well done.

Patsy These balloons are wrinkle-free. Do you know what that means, Judy?

Judy That they don't wrinkle, mother.

Patsy That's right. That's right. And these balloons won't wrinkle. There's a guarantee on the bag. And I do so much hate balloons that wrinkle, Judy.

Judy I know, mother.

Patsy When you reach my age you'll understand, Judy. But I do dislike wrinkles. When the skin gets less taut and all the grooves appear. You understand?

Judy Yes, mother.

Patsy *(cheerfully)* And when balloons wrinkle, they look just like old women's breasts. And I don't want to look at that.

Judy No.

*(**Dennis** stands in the centre of the room and surveys it.)*

Dennis Very festive.

Patsy Oh, sssh, Judy, now. Your father's talking.

Dennis I think it's all very festive.

Patsy Thank you very much indeed.

Dennis I think that Christ must be looking down on this and finding a lot to be infinitely compassionate about. Very well done indeed.

Patsy Thank you very...

Dennis But before we get blasé... let's just check everything off. Patsy, have you and Judy vacuumed under the furniture as well as around it?

Patsy Check.

Dennis Have you cleared my father's room so that he has plenty of space for all the little artefacts he might have brought with him?

Patsy Check.

Dennis And you have remembered to disinfect and air freshen the lavatories?

Patsy Check.

Dennis Good. At his age, family, you must bear in mind, at his age his urea smells like dog food. And I'm sure he has no wish to be reminded of that, so make sure that the lavatories are regularly disinfected and air freshened.

Patsy Judy and I have set up a rota.

Dennis Excellent. Very well done. Well then. Just a few general notes before he arrives. Gather around.

*(**Patsy**, **Judy** and **Toby** simultaneously take a step forward.)*

My father is very old. He has also recently lost a spouse to whom he was devoted. The mixture of this age and this grief is almost certainly going to kill him. If this mixture doesn't kill him now, it is likely that it will kill him later. I hope obviously that it won't kill him while he is a guest here, but if it does, it is something that we as a family will just have to compensate for. Whatever else happens, he is likely to have a short attention span, a need to be indulged beyond normal expectation, and a tendency to be prone to great tiredness. He is likely, for instance, to be very tired from his journey when he arrives. This tiredness may lead him to doze off in the middle of a conversation, or to keel over fast asleep before he is able to reach a bed. I want none of you to make him feel embarrassed about this. I have already pointed out the certainty of urea stench: there shall be no reference to this in his presence, nor to any other smells he may emit for which I have not prepared you.

(Short pause)

Bearing this in mind, I am sure that this will be a perfect family Cristtide. Merry Cristtide, one and all.

Judy I love Gramps. Whatever he does, he is the best gramps in the whole world.

Dennis Yes. Thank you very much indeed for that sentiment, Judy.

Judy He has always such funny stories to tell me.

Toby Yes. Please bear in mind, Judy, that these stories he tells must not be accepted as gospel truth. He is likely to lie a lot.

Dennis Toby... I don't think that you should say that of the senior member of our family...

Toby *(with quiet ferocity)* And I don't think that I am prepared to have Judy's education threatened by an old man's love of hyperbole.

*(Pause. **Dennis** clearly does not risk challenging him. Calmly, to **Judy**)*

You see, Judy, when a man is old, just as his urea begins to smell of dog food, so his grasp of truth is discoloured.

Judy Does that mean I can't enjoy his stories, Toby?

Toby Of course you may enjoy his stories.

Judy Oh good. I do enjoy his stories.

Toby I just advise you not to remember them.

Judy Oh, thank you very much indeed, Toby. You're the best brother in the whole world.

Dennis *(cheerfully, nervously)* You will treat him with due respect, won't you, Toby? He is your grandfather. He is my father.

Toby Of course, sir. I shall treat him with far more than his due respect.

(Pause)

Dennis *(awkwardly)* Well, I suppose... I suppose that's as much as I can ask really...

Toby Yes, sir.

Judy I'm confused. More than his due respect...

Toby Not you, Judy. You will treat your grandfather like a god or you shall have me to answer to.

Judy *(happily)* Oh, that's all right then. I enjoy that. I think that Gramps is the best Gramps in the whole world.

(The doorbell sounds – a doorbell of such suburban normality that it strikes a comic contrast.

*(All but **Judy**, who does not register anything at all, start to become very animated.)*

Patsy That can't be him!

Dennis If it is him, he's early.

Patsy Eighteen. He's eighteen minutes early.

Dennis Well, children, come on, get in line to greet him...

Patsy Oh dear, oh dear me, have I got everything straight...?

Dennis Come on, Patsy. Go and get the door.

Patsy *(panicked)* I can't remember if everything's ready!

Dennis *(impatiently)* Well, it's too late now, isn't it? Too late for regrets now. No point in that.

Patsy Oh... Oh, all right...

Dennis It's all very festive, Patsy. Don't worry.

*(The family have lined up, as if for inspection, with closest to the door, **Dennis**, a space for **Patsy**, **Judy** and **Toby**.*

*(**Patsy** takes her position in the line-up. A few seconds' pause, then all the members of the family turn to look at her expectantly. With realisation, she hurries off.*

*(**Patsy** re-enters with **Ralph** behind. He is seventy-eight years old, and carries a suitcase and a plain plastic bag, neither with any discomfort.)*

Patsy! Take my father's bags!

Patsy Oh, sorry most kindly...

Ralph There you are, my dear...

(He gives her his suitcase. From her reaction we can judge it is very heavy.)

Thank you very much indeed... No, thank you, I'll keep this bag on me.

*(Half-carrying, half-dragging the suitcase, **Patsy** takes her place in the line-up. Then the family all approach him one by one, **Dennis** first.)*

Ah... my son.

*(**Dennis** offers **Ralph** his hand, which **Ralph** accepts. They shake.)*

Dennis Very pleased to renew your acquaintance, sir.

Ralph Very pleased to renew yours as well, son, believe me, yes, yes, yes.

Dennis Did you have a good journey?

Ralph I must admit, I'm very tired.

Dennis Not unpleasantly, I hope, sir.

Ralph I missed the first train. So I caught the second train. And I don't know why, but the second train went quicker than the first train.

Dennis Really, sir?

Ralph Yes. The people in the first train were very put out when we overtook them. So we got in earlier than they did.

Dennis ... Well, that must make you even more tired, sir.

Ralph And this must be your beautiful wife who opened the door to me.

Dennis That's right, sir.

Patsy *(nervously)* Hello, Mr Simpson.

Ralph What a very beautiful lady you are, my dear.

*(He offers her his hand. **Patsy** looks at it with apprehension for a second, then with considerable difficulty frees one of her hands from the suitcase, forcing her to hold it with extreme awkwardness. In this position she can hardly stand, but is able to shake his hand. Afterwards, she gratefully rescues the suitcase.)*

Still in love with my son, are you?

Patsy Oh yes. Yes, he's... he's the best husband in the whole world...

Dennis We are deeply in love, sir.

Ralph Must be looking forward to Cristtide, the pair of you, eh? Soon able to exchange saliva again... I used to love Cristtide for that, when Fiona and I could be lovers again... ah, no more, no more... Still. Never mind. Enough of that. Enough of that. Never mind...

*(Underneath this, both **Patsy** and **Toby** have had to push **Judy** out of the line-up, to meet **Ralph**.)*

And hello, young... Good Lord.

Judy Very pleased to renew...

Ralph No, no, please. Please, don't say a word. Be silent.

(He looks at her intently. Short pause. Then, with increasing delight, walking around her, prodding her a little:)

Well... Well. Good Lord. I would never have... I never noticed that before. The spitting image of my Fiona. My word. The face, everything about it... The eyes, oh dear me yes, ha ha, those are Fiona's eyes, I'd recognise them anywhere... Oh, and the ribbon! Even the red ribbon! Fiona always wore a red ribbon like this...

(He inspects her head.)

And not a slight tangle, not even a hint of a tangle. Very well done, yes...

Judy Very pleased to renew your acquaintance, Gramps.

*(And she offers him her hand. **Ralph** doesn't take it.)*

Ralph ...Yes, but the voice is all wrong, isn't it? Never mind... I beg your pardon, little girl... Judy, isn't it?...

Judy *(nervously)* Yes.

Ralph Yes, that's right... Could you try speaking in a deeper voice for a moment?

Judy *(confused)* Well, I...

Toby Come on, Judy. Do what your grandfather tells you.

*(Short pause. **Judy** clears her throat, speaks in a lower voice.)*

Judy Very pleased to renew your...

Ralph No, no, no, no. That's all wrong. Never mind. Never mind. Extraordinary likeness. Dennis, you must be very proud of this one.

Dennis Indeed I am, sir.

Ralph I bet you are.

Dennis She's my little chubby cheeks, sir.

Ralph I beg your pardon?

Dennis She's my little chubby cheeks, sir.

Ralph I bet she is. Yes. How old is she?

Dennis How old is she, Toby?

Toby She is eight years old, sir.

Ralph Eight. Well, well.

(He offers her his hand.)

Very pleased to renew your acquaintance, Judy.

Judy Very pleased to renew your acquaintance, Gramps.

(They shake, then he bends to kiss her on the cheek.

*(**Judy** is startled, does not know what to do. **Toby** walks out of the line-up, perfunctorily elbows her out of the way.)*

Ralph Extraordinary... And you must be...

Toby Toby, Gramps.

Ralph *(unhappily)* Really. Well, well.

Toby Very pleased to renew your acquaintance, Gramps.

*(He offers **Ralph** his hand.)*

Ralph ... Yes. You'll pardon me, I know, if I don't shake your hand. This old body of mine gets very tired. Especially in the hand.

Toby Of course. Gramps.

*(But **Toby** does not return to the line-up. Instead he takes a step forward, so that he and **Ralph** are only inches apart. Short pause.)*

Ralph Well, you're older than when I last saw you.

Toby Yes, Gramps.

Ralph And bigger too.

Toby Yes, Gramps. I'm four months older and indeed, four months bigger than when you last saw me.

Ralph That must have been at the funeral...

Toby Yes, Gramps.

Ralph At Fiona's funeral... Oh dear Lord...

*(He turns away from **Toby's** stare, who with satisfaction returns to the line-up. Pause. The family watch **Ralph** uneasily.)*

Still. Never mind. Never mind, eh?

Judy I'm very sorry that Gran is dead, Gramps. I loved her very much. She was the best gran in the whole world.

Patsy *(hissing)* Judy...!

(Short pause)

Ralph ... Yes. Yes. I loved her very much too. You know what she used to call me ... ? No, no, you don't want to know that. Still. I don't mind telling you all, admitting to you. I miss her very much. There. I've said it. Still. Never mind. Never mind.

(He takes from his plastic bag a framed photograph, and looks at it with affection: it is of a stereotypical smiling grandmother, with a red ribbon in her hair. Short pause)

There she is. There she is... Christ... In His infinite compassion... Well, maybe anyway. Well, I can say one thing. I can say one thing for sure. Not a day of my life was wasted. Not a day. Not with her by my side to share it. I've no regrets. Not one. How many others can say that? How many, I wonder?

(He looks at the family, expecting a response. They all continue to

look forward, uncertain of how to react to any of this. With some disappointment:)

Oh, please, fall out if you want...

*(**Patsy** and **Dennis** bustle around him, **Patsy** with some difficulty. **Dennis** tries to lead **Ralph** to the armchair, though **Ralph** is still looking at the vacant **Judy**.)*

Dennis You must be tired, sir...

Patsy Shall I take that plastic bag, Mr Simpson?

Ralph No, I'll keep this a second...

Dennis Would you like the armchair, sir?

Ralph Yes, yes. In a second.

Judy I love you too, Gramps. I think you're the best gramps in the whole world.

Ralph Thank you very much indeed, Judy, yes...

Judy Are you going to tell me one of your stories?

Toby Judy. Quiet.

Ralph In time. In time I will, my dear.

Dennis But not now, Judy. Gramps is tired, aren't you, sir?

Ralph ... May I put this photograph in the room?

Dennis Yes, yes, of course ...

Patsy Of course.

(He stands the photograph on the table beside the armchair.)

Ralph There you go, my love...

*(He looks at it fondly for a second, then takes more framed photographs – all exactly the same picture – out of his plastic bag, and offers them to **Patsy**.)*

And I'd like these around the room. Anywhere you can find. You can put the suitcase down now.

Dennis Put the suitcase down, Patsy.

Patsy Yes. Sorry most kindly.

(She does so, and takes the photographs.)

Thank you very much indeed...

(And she begins placing them around the room – on the drinks trolley, hanging one on the tree, etc.)

Dennis Would you like a whisky, sir?

Ralph Thank you very much indeed.

*(**Dennis** goes to the drinks trolley. **Ralph** looks at the photograph again.)*

A handsome woman isn't she, son?

Dennis ... Yes. Yes, sir.

Ralph *(pointedly)* Wasn't she, Toby?

Toby Certainly, Gramps.

Ralph *(smiling)* Mustn't ask you, should I, Judy? After all, you'd only be flattering yourself. You look so much like her. Yes, you even stand still just the same as her...

Dennis There you are, sir...

*(He hands him his whisky. **Ralph** sits down in the armchair with it.)*

Ralph Thank you very much indeed. Yes, I can tell you though, with her by my side, not a day wasted. Yes, my life was a success. I can tell you that much. A handsome woman, no denying that. Such nice eyes, such nice hair... and that lovely way she had of wearing a red ribbon, oh yes... She was a lovely woman to be with. And... a very elegant woman... When I think of her by my side, oh yes, it nearly makes me shiver, I tell you, I used to look forward so much to Cristtide, so hard, I used to look forward so hard...

Dennis Yes, sir.

Ralph Still. Never mind. Never mind. This old body of mine gets very tired. Never mind. Though I tell you, I haven't entirely lost my looks.

Dennis No, that's right, sir.

Ralph The woman down the street ... Mrs Davis ... I see her looking at me a lot. Out of the corner of her eye. But I want no part in it. I'm telling you. Christ, in His infinite compassion, He would know. Looking down on us, He would know. And if Christ has infinite compassion, and He has it in bundles, I know that Fiona is with Him. Now as we speak. And if He is looking down on us, she too is looking down on us. And she would know.

*(Short pause. He swigs his whisky. **Patsy** has by now rejoined her husband and picked up the suitcase again.)*

That makes me feel better always.

Dennis Yes, sir.

Patsy *(nervously)* If you're having problems getting over Mrs Simpson's death, Mr Simpson, you could do what my mother does.

Dennis Patsy! My father is not interested...

Ralph Why, what does your mother do?

Dennis Oh, Patsy...

Patsy Well. My mother. Her husband, my father. He died. And she was very upset. So she started buying goldfish.

(Short pause)

Ralph I beg your pardon?

Patsy She buys goldfish. One a week.

Dennis My Christ.

Ralph She buys goldfish?

Patsy Yes. Every week she goes out and buys herself a goldfish. And then she puts it in her aquarium.

(Short pause)

Yes... Erm, and then she names them. And talks to them. And gives them food at mealtimes.

Ralph ... I don't understand.

Patsy She says it fills a gap...

Dennis Patsy's mother, sir, is a woman of a woefully minimal imagination...

Ralph Yes.

Dennis Woefully.

Patsy *(hastily, nervously)* Oh yes. A woefully minimal imagination. Sorry most kindly. Sorry I just thought I'd... It takes her mind off it, you see... Yes. Sorry most kindly. I'll... I can take the suitcase out. Yes.

*(Pause as **Ralph** and **Dennis** watch her struggle to the exit with the suitcases.)*

Ralph ... You still love her, Dennis?

Dennis Oh. Yes, sir. Yes.

Ralph Well, that's good.

Judy Are you going to tell me one of your stories now, Gramps?

Toby Not now, Judy. Gramps is tired.

Ralph *(winking at her)* Later, my dear. Eh? A little later.

Judy I enjoy hearing your stories, Gramps.

Ralph Well, I enjoy telling you them.

Judy Thank you very much indeed.

Ralph Yes... The spitting image of her grandmother. Pity about the voice. Never mind. Never mind...

(Short pause)

Dennis Would you like another whisky, sir?

Ralph ... No. No, I'll tell you what I'd like.

Dennis Yes, sir?

Ralph I think I'd like to take Judy to the Grotto. How about that? I think I'll take Judy to the Grotto.

*(Short pause. **Dennis** and **Toby** exchange glances warily.)*

That's all right, isn't it? Come on, it's Cristtide. It wouldn't be very seasonal, would it, if Judy didn't go to the Grotto.

Judy I went yesterday, Gramps.

Ralph You remember me taking you to the Grotto, Dennis. I know your memory's poorly... You remember me taking you to see the Great Yid at the Grotto and sitting on his knee...

Dennis Yes. Well, what a good idea, sir.

Judy Toby took me to the Grotto yesterday, Gramps.

Ralph What's that?

Judy Toby took me to the Grotto yesterday, Gramps.

Ralph *(sternly)* What's that? Did you?

Toby Yes, Gramps.

(Short pause)

Ralph Oh. Well. Never mind. You can go again, can't you? You can go again. You'd like to go again, wouldn't you, Judy?

Judy Yes, Gramps.

Ralph Go to the Grotto again with your grandfather and sit on the Great Yid's knee. I've never seen you sit on the Great Yid's knee before.

Judy Yes, Gramps.

Ralph That's good. That's excellent. It wouldn't be Cristtide without seeing the Great Yid, would it?

Judy It's just that He'll know I've been before.

Ralph Well, he's not going to mind, is he? He has lots of little girls sitting on his knee every day.

Judy No, I don't mean the Great Yid. I mean Christ. Looking down on us.

Ralph ... Oh. Christ. Him. Well... Christ isn't going to mind. Not in His infinite compassion.

Judy No, Gramps.

Ralph That's right.

(He gets out of his armchair.)

Dennis Do you want a hand, sir?

Ralph No, thank you very much indeed, son. This old body of mine gets very tired. Especially the bones. But I'm all right.

Dennis Sir.

Ralph Well, young Judy ... You lead the way.

Judy Toby can come too, can't he?

(Short pause)

Ralph What, Toby? Why?

Judy He's my brother. He's the best brother in the whole world.

Ralph Oh, surely he's too big for all that now...

Judy But he's ever so nice, he always goes with me.

Toby *(slowly)* I really think that I should accompany little Judy, Gramps.

(Short pause)

Ralph Well, if you insist. Yes. Never mind. Never mind. Yes.

Judy And will you tell us one of your stories on the way, Gramps?

Ralph Maybe I will, maybe I will... You lead the way then, children.

*(**Judy** and **Toby** exit. **Ralph** watches **Judy** as she goes.)*

Extraordinary... Walks just like her grandmother too...

Dennis You're sure you're not too tired, sir?

Ralph No, son, I'm fine. You can have this if you want.

(He gives him his unfinished glass of whisky.)

Dennis ... Oh. Thank you very much indeed, sir.

Ralph Very well done, son. Looking around the room. It's all very seasonal. That's the word for it. It's all very seasonal.

Dennis Yes, sir. That's the word I always use. It's very seasonal.

Ralph *(clapping him on the shoulder)* Very well done.

(He hobbles off to the exit, calling:)

Wait for me, Judy! This old body of mine gets very tired... Especially the legs...

*(**Ralph** exits. And **Dennis** sighs with relief.*

*(Lights to half. Music. **Dennis** sits in the armchair, drinking the whisky, relaxing back. Fade to blackout.)*

Act Two

(In half light, upbeat version of Santa Claus is Coming to Town. **Dennis** *enters, walks to drinks trolley, pours himself a whisky. He turns away, drains it. He goes back to the drinks trolley, replenishes his drink, walks to armchair. He takes off his jacket, and relaxes into his seat.*

(Lights up full, music off. **Patsy** *enters carrying a couple of wrapped presents. She stoops and puts them under the tree, unaware that* **Dennis** *is watching her curiously. She then straightens the other presents with pride.*

(Christmas tree lights are off.

(It is Cristtide evening. Suddenly:)

Dennis Boo!

*(***Patsy*** *is startled.)*

Patsy Oh... Dennis, it's you!

Dennis Yes. Hello.

Patsy I didn't know you were in here.

Dennis No.

Patsy You were in here. I didn't know you were.

(Short pause)

Dennis No.

(Short pause)

Did I make you jump?

Patsy Oh, yes. Yes.

Dennis When I said 'boo'?

Patsy Oh yes. It was very funny.

Dennis Well, that's what I thought. It is Cristtide after all.

Patsy ... I've just been doing some last minute wrapping...

Dennis It's all very seasonal, this, Patsy. Very well done.

Patsy Seasonal?

Dennis Seasonal. All very seasonal. That's what I said.

Patsy Well, thank you very much indeed.

(Pause)

How long do you think they've been at the Grotto now?

Dennis Oh, I don't know...

Patsy It's half past eleven. It must have closed by now.

Dennis They're probably walking home even now.

Patsy There can't be many children left awake to sit on his knee. They're all going to be asleep ready for Santa.

Dennis Well.

(Short pause)

Patsy I'm worried, Dennis.

Dennis What for?

Patsy They're very late back.

Dennis What's there to worry about? Look round this room. Look how seasonal it is.

Patsy Yes...

Dennis Look.

(She does, turning around in a tight circle. Short pause)

Patsy *(slightly reassured)* Yes, it is very seasonal.

Dennis What can there be to worry about? My father is probably just telling the children a few of his stories. That's all.

Patsy Yes.

(Short pause)

Dennis?

Dennis Yes?

Patsy Are any of the stories true that your father tells?

Dennis ... Well, I don't know. Toby's probably right. You know, my father probably does exaggerate...

Patsy Yes.

Dennis But then Toby's very clever. He's the cleverest son in the whole world. He's much cleverer than I am.

Patsy Yes, and he's cleverer than me too.

Dennis *(amiably)* Yes, well, quite obviously.

(Short pause)

Stop worrying. You worry too much.

Patsy I'm not frantic or anything. Just worried.

Dennis Well, don't be. You don't need to be.

(Short pause)

Patsy Would you like a refill?

Dennis Mmm.

*(He offers her his glass. She comes over to him to accept it. As she reaches for it, **Dennis** grabs her by the wrist gently.)*

Patsy Dennis ... ?

Dennis *(sexually)* Mmm.

(And he lets her go. She goes over to the drink trolley and refills his glass.)

Why not have one yourself?

Patsy What, a whisky?

Dennis Why not? If you're feeling worried.

Patsy Well, I am feeling a little worried...

Dennis Well then. Have a whisky.

Patsy ... Yes, all right. Just a half.

(She begins to pour a second.)

Dennis Why not a whole one?

*(**Patsy** turns round to him, surprised.)*

Patsy A whole one?

Dennis Sure. Why not? If you're feeling worried. It is Cristtide after all.

Patsy Well... it is Cristtide after all...

Dennis That's right.

Patsy I am feeling worried.

Dennis There you go.

Patsy And it is Cristtide, isn't it? After all.

(She turns back and pours herself a full glass. As she does so:)

Dennis Toots.

Patsy Dennis?

Dennis ... Come over here, Toots.

(Short pause)

Patsy But Dennis... it isn't Cristtide yet...

Dennis Very nearly.

Patsy Yes, it's very nearly...

Dennis I want to give you a kiss.

Patsy What, now?

Dennis And I want you to give me a kiss. Each other a kiss. With tongues. With your saliva mingling with my saliva.

Patsy But we're not allowed to exchange saliva before midnight...

Dennis Who's going to know? Everyone's out.

Patsy Christ, looking down on us, will see.

Dennis Christ, in His infinite compassion, be damned. I'm fed up of only satisfying myself on His birthday. Come here.

Patsy Oh Dennis... You are ever so nice...

(She approaches him, drains her whisky in one gulp.)

Dennis Come here.

Patsy I love it when you're rebellious. You're the most rebellious husband in the whole world...

(He pulls her down to him, and he kisses her fiercely on the mouth for a few seconds. She collapses on top of him, as they continue kissing. At last they break off.)

Oh, what a relief. My lips didn't stick to yours.

Dennis No.

Patsy I never understand why that never happens. But year after year...

(He pulls her down again. They kiss.)

Do you love me, Dennis?

Dennis What was that you're asking?

Patsy Do you love me?

Dennis Well, yes, naturally.

Patsy Our marriage is just getting better and better, isn't it?

Dennis Better and better.

Patsy Every year it gets better and better.

Dennis Better and better annually.

Patsy Better and better annually and annually.

Dennis Christ, you have good breasts.

Patsy Thank you very much indeed.

Dennis Still not at all wrinkled, I'll be bound.

Patsy No, I don't have old women's breasts...

Dennis ...Come on. We've exchanged saliva. It's time we exchanged more than that.

(He gets up, takes her by the hands, and starts to sashay across the room with her.)

Patsy But Dennis, we can't.

Dennis Why not?

Patsy What if I get pregnant?

Dennis The child will still be born around September. No-one will know it wasn't Cristtide Day.

Patsy But they will, Dennis. They have machines that can tell.

Dennis What are you talking about?

Patsy Inside the baby, they can tell from the layers of skin, the exact day of conception.

Dennis Where did you hear that?

Patsy It's true. It's true. They carve up the baby and count the layers.

Dennis They'd never suspect us. There's no-one to see.

Patsy Christ, looking down on us ... Christ, in His infinite compassion, might be an informant.

*(Pause. **Dennis** and **Patsy** raise their heads simultaneously, look up to the heavens. With sudden realisation, they let go of each other and stand apart.)*

Dennis *(slowly)* There's certainly nothing in the Bible which says He doesn't make reports to the State...

Patsy I'm frightened, Dennis.

Dennis Don't be frightened, Patsy. No point in that.

Patsy Well, I'm not frightened then, just worried. Just a little worried...

Dennis We'll just have to make sure you don't get pregnant, that's all. That's all there is to it.

Patsy How can we do that?

Dennis Wait a minute. Let me think.

(Short pause. He paces the room slowly, methodically.)

What we need... surely, is something that catches the sperm... like a little bag...

Patsy A little bag?

Dennis Do we have a little bag?

Patsy I'm right out of little bags.

Dennis There are no little bags in the house?

Patsy I'm sorry most kindly, Dennis, I didn't realise we'd need any...

Dennis Or some wrapping paper. I'll make a little bag out of some wrapping paper.

Patsy *(delighted)* Oh, Dennis, you are so clever!

Dennis That's right. Now run and find some.

Patsy You're the cleverest person in the whole world. Even Toby would never have thought of this!

Dennis Toby wouldn't need to, my dear, he's only a little boy. Now quickly, quickly!

Patsy Yes, yes, sorry most kindly...

(She runs off excitedly.)

Dennis Nice breasts, but not a mass of intellect...

(He calls:)

You better bring two sheets!

Ralph *(offstage)* Give me a hand here, Judy! It's quite a big doorstep...

Dennis *(deadpan)* Oh, Christ.

(Hurriedly he puts his jacket back on.)

Ralph *(offstage)* That's right. Very well done. Just as Fiona used to do...

*(Enter **Ralph**, holding hands with **Judy**, with **Toby** trailing.)*

Dennis Oh, good evening, sir, pleased to renew your acquaintance...

Ralph Son.

Dennis Did you have a nice time?

Ralph Very, thank you very much indeed.

Judy Gramps took us to the Grotto to meet the Great Yid.

Toby And then he took us to a public house.

Ralph A very nice time, thank you very much indeed.

Judy Go on, Gramps, you were going to tell me your story...

Dennis Would you like a drink, sir?

Ralph Probably had enough. A single will be enough.

*(**Dennis** pours **Ralph** a whisky at the drink trolley.)*

Judy Gramps...

Ralph What, Judy?

Judy The story, you were going to tell the story.

*(**Dennis** gives **Ralph** the glass.)*

Ralph Ah, thank you very much indeed... I'm a little tired now, Judy. This old body of mine. Especially my mouth, you know...

Judy *(stamping her foot)* But you promised, Gramps!

Toby That's quite enough, Judy. You've had several whiskies too many.

Ralph Well, at least she had some, young man! At least she had... All right, young Judy, I'll tell you the story...

*(**Patsy** rushes in with two sheets of wrapping paper.)*

Patsy Ta-dah, wrapping paper! ... Oh, my Christ...

*(Pause. All look at **Patsy**. **Ralph** lets go of **Judy's** hand and walks up to her.)*

Ralph And very nice too. May I see?

*(**Patsy** nervously hands him a sheet of paper.)*

Oh yes. How nice.

Patsy *(lamely)* It's got little Santas on...

Ralph Yes. And the other one?

(She hands him the other sheet.)

Oh yes. It's exactly the same.

Patsy Yes... it is...

Ralph Well, it balances better, doesn't it?

(Pause)

Patsy I think... I think I had better be going to bed... If you don't mind... If that's all right with you... All of you, that is... Before Santa arrives ... Yes.

(Short pause)

Toby *(prompting)* Good night, mother.

Ralph Yes, yes. Good night.

Dennis You'd better leave your door unlocked tonight, my dear... erm, in case, maybe, my father wants anything...

Patsy *(eagerly)* Oh yes. Yes.

Judy Good night, mother.

*(Short pause. **Patsy** waits awkwardly for the wrapping paper **Ralph** is still holding.)*

Ralph ... Yes? May I help you?

Patsy *(whispering)* May I have the wrapping paper back, please?

Ralph I beg your pardon?

Patsy May I have the wrapping paper back? With the, erm... little Santas...

Ralph Certainly.

(He hands them back.)

Patsy *(nervously, announcing)* I may have to... do some wrapping in the night. Yes.

*(She exits briskly. Short pause. **Ralph** turns to **Dennis** quizzically.)*

Ralph ...Son?

Dennis *(desperately)* ... Tell me what happened at the Grotto. Did you enjoy yourself at the Grotto? Tell me what happened there.

Judy Gramps was going to tell me...

Toby Well, sir, we arrived in perfect time. There was no longer much of a queue, as most parents seemed to have already taken their children and gone home to prepare the celebrations proper for the next day.

Dennis Yes, yes. Good, good...

Toby Judy sat on the Great Yid's knee, underneath his long, flowing beard. He asked her if she wanted to purify Cristtide for Christ and Judy said she did.

Ralph She said that bit very well.

Toby And she reached up and took a firm grasp of the Great Yid's beard, and pulled it very hard. Much harder than yesterday. But she was still unable to pull it off, and so she wasn't allowed to have a present. But Judy lost her temper. It was very creditable.

Judy Thank you very much indeed, Toby.

Toby Tell Father what you said, Judy.

Judy *(nervously)* I said that I wanted to purify Cristtide. Christ, in His infinite compassion, was looking down on me and He wanted me to purify Cristtide. And the Great Yid said that I was still too young, but maybe next year I would succeed in pulling his beard off. And I said... I said that pulling his beard off didn't kill him anyway, didn't do anything at all to purify Cristtide...

Dennis *(dubiously)* It's a ceremony, Judy...

Judy *(defiantly)* But it *doesn't* hurt him. I've seen other people pull off his beard, and he just gives them a present as if nothing had ever happened. So I decided to hurt him properly.

(Short pause)

Dennis What did you do?

Judy I kicked him.

Toby In the groin, sir.

Ralph ...Yes, I'm afraid so.

Judy His beard fell off.

Toby I think it was very well done.

Judy I won a present after all. It was a little doll.

(She shows the doll.)

Her name's Betsy.

Dennis ...That's very nice.

Judy She's my daughter. She's the best daughter in the whole world.

Ralph I think it important to point out, Judy, that the Great Yid wasn't a real Yid.

Judy *(playing with her doll)* What do you mean, not real?

Toby *(warningly)* Gramps...

Judy The shout he gave when I kicked him was real enough. I hate Jews.

Ralph But he wasn't a real Jew, my dear. He was a man dressed up as a Jew.

Toby Gramps, I don't think that Judy need know that yet...

Ralph The Great Yid doesn't really exist.

*(**Judy** looks away from her doll and stares at **Ralph**.)*

Judy ... Of course he exists. I kicked him.

Ralph There are no more Jews, my dear.

Judy *(fiercely)* I kicked myself a real Jew! I helped to purify Cristtide!

(Short pause. To the doll, innocently:)

Didn't I, Betsy?

Ralph *(laughing)* But you must understand, Judy, that's the whole point. That's what Cristtide is all about. We are celebrating the birth of Jesus Christ Our Saviour, and the death of the race that killed Him. It's nonsense to believe the Great Yid is a real Jew...

Judy I kicked myself a real Jew! I kicked myself the Great Yid!

Toby Judy...

Judy That's why I've won Betsy! I want to kill a Jew! Just like you did, Gramps! Just like you. Are you going to tell us the story now of how you killed a Jew?

*(Pause. All look at **Judy** uncertainly.)*

Toby *(calmly, soothingly)* Judy. I want you to know how proud of you I am.

Judy *(happily)* ...Toby?

Toby You kicked that Jew good and hard. Christ, looking down upon us, must be smiling very hard. Now Cristtide is purified, and you have had a huge part in it. Very well done.

Judy Thank you very much indeed, Toby. You're the best brother in the whole world.

Toby That's all right.

Judy Really. I love you very much. And so does Betsy.

Toby And Betsy is very proud of you too. But I think you should go and get into your nightie now, don't you? It's very late for you and you should be thinking about sleep.

Judy *(yawning)* Yes, all right.

Toby I've left your nightie for you on your bed. Now say good night to everyone.

Judy *(tired)* Good night, father. Good night, Gramps. Betsy says good night to you all too.

Toby *(soothingly)* That's good.

(He steers her towards the exit.)

Judy You'll tell me the story tomorrow, won't you, Gramps? Of how you killed a Jew...

*(And both **Judy** and **Toby** exit.*

(Pause)

Dennis It is very late, sir. I must be going to bed.

Ralph ...Yes. Yes.

Dennis Are you all right, sir?

Ralph Hmm? Oh yes. Yes. Just... a little tired, son. You know... this old body of mine!

Dennis Yes, sir. Are you going to come up now?

Ralph I'll just be a minute.

*(Re-enter **Toby**, silently, unnoticed.*

*(**Dennis** hesitates, then makes to leave. He is checked, as **Ralph** begins to laugh gently to himself.)*

I was just thinking, Dennis ...

Dennis Sir?

Ralph Do you remember that every year when you were a little boy you used to be so excited about Cristtide?

Dennis Oh yes, sir.

Ralph I'd ask you if you were excited, and you'd tell me you were. And your little face was red and flushed. And you'd tell me how much you were looking forward to Santa coming. You remember that?

Dennis Yes, sir. It was very... nice.

Ralph ... Yes. Fond memories, fond memories.

Dennis Yes.

(Short pause)

Well, if that's all, sir... Good night.

*(And he exits, leaving **Toby** behind.)*

Ralph *(to himself)* And then you'd go to bed, and I'd look across to Fiona, and she would to me, and we knew it was nearly Cristtide, and that we could touch... nearly kiss and make love... and we'd no longer be husband and wife, but lovers again. And we'd sit up and wait until midnight, and no Santa would come, but at midnight we would kiss each other... And that was beautiful... And we'd go up to our separate bedrooms knowing that the next night it would be to the same room... And she'd take off the red ribbon and her hair would stream...

(He sighs.

(Short pause)

Toby Good night, Gramps. Sleep well.

Ralph *(startled)* Oh my Christ, Toby...

Toby You should get some sleep soon.

Ralph I didn't realise you were there...

Toby Don't worry, Gramps. There is still yet nothing officially incorrect about talking to yourself. Good night.

(He turns to go.)

Ralph Toby... Toby, could I... Could I have a quiet word, please?

Toby A quiet word, Gramps?

Ralph A little conversation. Would that be all right? You weren't too busy?

Toby I was going to go to bed now...

Ralph Yes, yes... A big day tomorrow...

Toby *(coolly)* Yes. I need my sleep. I am, after all, only a little boy.

Ralph Yes... Look, I hate to be... I hate, on Cristtide Eve to... Here, take a seat, son...

(He indicates the armchair.)

Toby Grandson.

Ralph Grandson, yes... Here, take a seat, grandson...

Toby Thank you. I prefer to stand.

Ralph Yes, of course... Standing to attention, yes? The more alert the body, the more alert the mind... Not like my body, this old body of mine... Yes. Very good. Very good indeed. Very... very proud of you, son.

Toby Grandson.

Ralph Yes.

(Pause)

As I say, I hate to bring this up on Cristtide Eve... after all, it's a holiday... and it is for the children, I've always said that...

Toby *(impatiently)* What is it, Gramps?

Ralph *(genially)* It's just that... I would just like to remind you that I am a visitor. I am a guest. In this house. And as such, I think I deserve some respect. Not just normal respect, I mean, I mean some other respect, respect which is entirely other. Some special form of respect. Indulgence, even stretching all the way to indulgence. Because I am a guest. And a guest of seventy-eight. And I tell you, I... I am not prepared to have those seventy-eight years of working myself up to being a guest here undermined by a ten year old shit whose voice hasn't even finished breaking yet.

(Short pause)

I hate to be this way on Cristtide Eve... Especially for the children...

(Short pause)

Toby Gramps, you may recall that when my IQ tests came back, I was awarded a mark higher than you or my father put together.

Ralph But I'm talking about respect...

Toby Gramps, Gramps. Believe me. So am I. You see, you must bear in mind that I am very much cleverer than you. Christ has blessed me in His infinite compassion with an intelligence which makes you seem in comparison a dullard. Which I hasten to add you are not...

Ralph Thank you very much indeed...

Toby I feel Cristtide should be a time for generosity... I have in me more potential for achievement than you could ever bring yourself to contemplate, and I swear to you, those achievements shall be mine. You may not see them, after all, you'll probably be dead even by this time next year, but I swear to you, I shall make something of my life.

Ralph With Fiona beside me, I didn't waste a single day of my life...

Toby Oh, Gramps. Really.

(Short pause)

So... I would like to ask *you*, if you could please remember... The education of little Judy is my province. I see in her kicking the Great Yid in the testicles some signs of correct thinking. Of natural bravado. Of natural bravado tempered by correct thinking. Of natural correct thinking untempered by bravado. And I approve of that. And that's what matters. So I ask you please to remember... You are only a visitor. You are only a guest. And you'll probably be dead very soon. So... when I tell you, I advise you to shut up.

*(Pause. **Ralph** backs away and sits in the armchair. **Toby** stoops by him, ruffles his hair.)*

It's been a long day, Gramps. Drunk a bit too much in the public house, hmmm? I think you should get some rest. The journey was a little too much for that old body of yours. ...Don't you think?

(Short pause. He straightens up, suddenly dismissive.)

No? Well, that's up to you. But Santa won't leave you anything if he finds you awake, Gramps. I, on the other hand, will be getting some sleep now. I am still only a little boy.

(He yawns childishly, turns to go.

*(**Ralph** stands.)*

Ralph At least I killed myself a Jew...

Toby Oh, Gramps. That old story...

Ralph And what are you going to achieve? You talk about all you're going to achieve, but what is your generation going to achieve when I'm dead? When all the Jews are already dead? We've done the hard work for you. For you, with all your IQ. No-one can tell me... no-one can make me believe that I wasted a single year of my life... With Fiona by my side, it was like a dream come true, every day, someone so full of life, of elegance – what elegance! – of patience... Every day, no waste ...

Toby Gramps. Really. I look back at your generation and I wonder... I wonder where you went wrong. And I pray to Christ that the last of you might eventually die so we can get on with it. Christ, looking down upon us, knows that the job you barely started is left for us to finish. For me to finish. I mean... When you killed the Yids, why did you leave the blacks free? Or the cripples? And especially... why did you leave the sexual perverts?

(Short pause)

Gramps. You are content to think of your wife, poor dead rotting Fiona up on the right side of Christ. In Paradise. We want to transform the world back to a Paradise. To bring Christ down to us. And I ask you... what about the sexual perverts, Gramps? He's not likely to be inspired to venture on a Second Coming, while there's still a risk of one of those ploughing Him, is there? So what about the sexual perverts?

(Short pause. Smiling, lighter:)

I'm not asking for much, Gramps. I'm just asking you to think about it. But not too much! Not now anyway! It *is* Cristtide now, after all! ... Good night, Gramps.

*(He offers him his hand. **Ralph** accepts it nervously, and they shake once, formally. **Toby** exits.*

*(**Ralph** sighs, walks around the room for a little. He picks up a photo of his wife, replaces it. At length:)*

Ralph Well, my love, another day over. Another day with you not in it. And the first Cristtide without you to kiss is upon me. Dear oh dear. But at least I know you're still there. No, I can look back at the time we spent together and say, not one day of my life was wasted while you were by my side. Well, you're by Christ's side now. But I still know you're with me still. I can feel you here.

(He taps the right side of his chest.)

Or is it... here?

(He taps the left side of his chest.)

I can never remember. But you, you are probably in both sides of my chest, you're that special. And I know that you're beside Christ looking down on me. And I say to you, my love, good night. And I only wish now that it is Cristtide we could be lovers once more. But still. Never mind. Never mind.

*(Special spotlight on **Ralph** as he clasps his hands together.)*

And I ask you, Christ, in Your infinite compassion, please do not cast my wife down into hell today. That's Fiona. Amen.

(Lighting as before. Short pause. He sighs.

*(Enter **Judy** behind him. She wears a red nightdress and carries by her side her doll, Betsy. Her hair is still tied with a red ribbon.)*

Judy ...Gramps?

*(**Ralph** does not turn round. Short pause)*

You should be in bed, Gramps. If you don't go to bed right now, Santa won't visit you.

*(Short pause. Then **Ralph** turns to face her with a smile.)*

Ralph Oh, he won't be visiting me tonight, my dear. I'm too old for that.

Judy *(concerned)* Too old? At what age does Santa stop visiting you?

Ralph I've always said, Cristtide is for the children.

Judy Why doesn't Santa visit you any more? What did you do?

(Short pause)

Ralph Are you looking forward to Cristtide, Judy?

Judy Oh yes. Thank you very much indeed, Gramps.

Ralph You enjoy Cristtide?

Judy Oh yes. And this is Betsy's first Cristtide.

Ralph Who?

Judy Betsy. It's her first Cristtide. And I'm looking forward to showing her all of it.

Ralph Yes.

(Short pause)

Judy. Betsy is a doll.

Judy Yes.

Ralph Plastic, I expect.

Judy Yes.

(Short pause)

It's her first Cristtide. I'm looking forward to showing her all of it.

(Short pause)

Why doesn't Santa visit you any more?

Ralph Do you believe in Santa, Judy?

Judy Oh yes. He has a sleigh and reindeer.

(Short pause. Suspiciously:)

Don't you?

Ralph Oh yes. Yes, I believe in Santa.

Judy And the Great Yid?

Ralph Well, we saw him, didn't we?

Judy And Christ? You believe in Christ?

Ralph ... Well, yes.

Judy Santa and Christ are best friends. And they both hate the Great Yid, I expect. Do you think Santa hates the Great Yid?

Ralph I expect so.

Judy Do you think they like me?

Ralph Oh yes, Judy. Of course they like you. They love you very much. After all, you're very lovely... loveable.

(He turns away, awkwardly. Short pause)

Judy Are you going to tell me your story, Gramps?

(Short pause)

Ralph Would you like a drink, Judy?

Judy What sort of drink?

Ralph Would you like a whisky?

Judy Oh yes, please.

Ralph You like whisky?

Judy It's very nice, thank you very much indeed.

Ralph Yes, I like whisky. We have such a lot in common, Judy.

Judy I think it's the best drink in the whole world.

Ralph A half for you, I think.

Judy Yes, please. I like halves. I think halves are the best measures in the whole world.

(He gives her her drink, having poured himself a full glass.)

Thank you very much indeed.

(She takes the glass to her lips.)

Ralph No, wait a moment.

(And he staightens her drinking hand so that he can clink his against it.)

...Cheers!

Judy Yes, cheers, Gramps. Thank you very much indeed.

(Short pause)

Ralph Look at the picture of your Gran, Judy.

Judy Which one?

Ralph Which ever one you want.

(She peers at the one on the drink trolley.

(The following dialogue is particularly fast.)

Judy Yes, Gramps.

Ralph Do you see how handsome she is?

Judy Yes, Gramps.

Ralph She's a handsome woman, isn't she?

Judy She's the best Gran in the whole world.

Ralph I hope she's happy on the right hand side of Christ.

Judy Yes, Gramps.

Ralph Do you think she is?

Judy Yes, Gramps.

Ralph You believe in Christ?

Judy Santa and He are best friends.

Ralph Look at her eyes. Hasn't she got beautiful eyes?

Judy Beautiful eyes.

Ralph Handsome eyes. Handsome all over really.

Judy Yes, Gramps.

Ralph You know, I have lots of photographs of your Gran. Of Fiona. Going back years and years. But I always prefer these ones of her when she was older, because our marriage just got better and better as the years went by. There are some compensations for old age. It's true that this old body of mine gets tired... and my urea smells of dog food... but our marriage got better and better every year.

Judy Is this part of your story, Gramps?

(Short pause)

Please tell me your story, Gramps.

Ralph You should go to bed.

Judy It'll just be our little secret. Gramps? Just our little secret.

Ralph You'll catch cold.

Judy I won't, Gramps. Toby wouldn't have let me come downstairs if he thought I'd catch cold. He's ever so nice. He's the best brother in the whole world.

(Short pause)

Ralph Toby knows you're downstairs?

Judy He sent me downstairs, Gramps. He told me that you wanted to tell me your story.

(Short pause)

What is your story, Gramps?

(Short pause)

Ralph ... Let's sit Betsy down, shall we? Betsy looks a little tired.

Judy Yes, it's long past her bedtime.

Ralph Why don't you put her over there on the armchair?

Judy That's a good idea. If she doesn't go to sleep straight away, Santa won't visit her.

(She puts Betsy on the armchair.)

There. You go to sleep, Betsy. You're the best daughter in the whole world. Go to sleep right now and Santa will visit you.

Ralph ... You're a very responsible mother.

Judy Thank you very much indeed. Betsy's fast asleep, Gramps. Tell me your story. We can stay as late as we want. I'm too old for Santa to visit now as well.

Ralph What?

Judy I've got a lovely little daughter. I've always said, Cristtide is for the children.

(Short pause)

Ralph All right. I'll tell you my story, if you help me out too.

Judy You'll tell me how you killed a Jew?

Ralph Yes, if you help me out too.

Judy How you killed a real life Jew?

Ralph It'll be our little secret.

Judy You'll describe it properly, won't you?

Ralph Put down your glass, my dear. My dear. My love. Put down your glass.

(She does so.)

Now, Judy. Please. Put down your hair. My dear. Put down your hair. Take out the ribbon.

Judy But it'll get all tangled...

Ralph Ssh. It doesn't matter. Let's play a little game. Who can talk the softest. Just our little secret.

*(**Judy** lets her hair down. **Ralph** looks at her.)*

My dear. My love. The spitting image... Do you realise, you've got just your grandmother's look? Do you know that?

Judy *(affably)* Yes, Gramps. You told me. Where shall I put the ribbon?

Ralph It doesn't matter.

Judy I'll put it on the armchair with Betsy.

Ralph Yes, yes, good idea, yes ...

Judy It'll keep her warmer.

*(**Judy** places the ribbon on the doll.)*

What's your story, Gramps?

Ralph Please, Judy. Call me Ralph.

Judy All right. What's your story, Ralph?

*(Short pause. **Ralph** takes her hand and gently kisses the palm.)*

Oh... that tickles...!

Ralph I had a job at one of the camps ... where some of the last Jews were kept. And they weren't at all well. They were put in these rooms, and every morning they would all have died.

Judy *(enthusiastically)* You mean they were gassed?

Ralph *(uncomfortably)* ...Yes. Probably, yes ... Would you mind if I...

(And he kisses her tenderly on the lips.

*(**Judy** stretches her arms behind her, as **Dennis** and **Patsy** did in the first act.)*

Fiona...

Judy My name's Judy, Gramps.

Ralph Please, call me Ralph.

Judy My name's Judy, Ralph.

Ralph Let's play a little game. Let's play that you're called Fiona.

Judy *(loudly)* ... All right. Does that mean that the game where we talk softly is over?

Ralph Sssh... No, no... Let's play both games at once... Here, could you hold this over your head...

(And he gives her the photograph from the drink trolley.)

Just cover your face with this ...

(Dutifully she does so, concealing her own features with those of her smiling grandmother's.)

Ralph ... Oh, Fiona.

Judy ... Ralph.

Ralph Yes, that's right.

Judy I remembered. Do I win anything?

*(**Ralph** puts his arms around her.)*

Ralph And one day I went to clear out one of these rooms... the chambers... and one of them wasn't dead.

Judy Oh my Christ, what did you do?

Ralph I'd never seen a living Jew before. And they don't look like us. Their skin is greener. And they don't pee like we do, this one was peeing blood. He wasn't human at all. And he... grabbed me by the leg...

Judy I'd have been so frightened...

Ralph And I brought my boot down on his head. And it passed clean through the skull. There was no resistance at all, and I tell you, even the skull was too soft to be human. It was like treading on a slug...

Judy *(excited)* Very well done, Gramps! You purified Cristtide that year for real...

Ralph Well, we didn't have Cristtide then...

(He bends down, and cautiously puts his hand up her nightie.)

Judy What are you doing, Gramps?

Ralph Ralph. Call me Ralph.

Judy What are you doing, Ralph?

Ralph Ssh. Just our little secret.

Judy No, I don't like this.

Ralph Keep the photograph up, and I'll tell you the rest of the story...

Judy But you killed the Jew, what else is there?

Ralph Ssh. You promised. You'd help me out too.

(And he explores more obviously.)

Oh, Fiona...

*(**Judy** begins to cry softly behind the photograph.)*

And at this camp, Fiona was working there. And we met there and we fell in love. And we got married. And every year our marriage just got better and better. Every year. Isn't that a good story?

*(He detaches himself from **Judy**. Gently:)*

You can put the photograph down now, Judy.

(She does so. She is shaking.)

Now, now. Just our little secret. It **is** Cristtide. Look... look, would you like a chocolate? There are some on the tree... No? How about a present?

(He picks one up from underneath the tree,.)

Any one you want... Even the biggest one if you want... Come on, you're crying...

(And he reaches out and brushes away a tear from her cheek tenderly.)

There. What is it your father calls you?

Judy *(quietly)* Judy.

Ralph No, apart from that.

Judy I don't know.

Ralph Something to do with cheeks... That's right, chubby old cheeks!

Judy ... Little chubby cheeks.

Ralph That's right, little chubby cheeks, yes.

(He strokes her cheek again.)

Do you know what Fiona used to call me? Do you?... She called me Big Chief Flabby Eyes.

(He laughs softly.)

Isn't that funny?

(Short pause)

You'll catch cold, Judy, my dear. But still. That's how I killed a Jew... Erm, maybe if you take Betsy up to bed... Santa may still come...

*(Short pause. **Judy** then walks over to Betsy and picks her up.)*

He's probably on his way now...

Judy *(softly)* Maybe... Thank you... very much indeed... Ralph.

Ralph You can call me Gramps if you want now. And please... don't thank me. Thank *you*... Thank you very much indeed...

(He laughs nervously.

(She kisses Betsy.)

Judy Come on, Betsy. Time for bed now. Santa will be here soon.

(And she exits slowly.)

Ralph Take a present with you... No? No. Oh well... Well, sleep well! Christ, in His infinite compassion, cause you to sleep well... Both of you.

(Short pause)

Thank you, Fiona. My love, my own. You're still the best. Better and better and better.

(*He kisses his finger and with it brushes the lips on the photograph.*

(*At the moment of contact, lights change. Silent Night plays. All but two of the presents are struck. A dining table set for five places is brought on.*

(*The music fades, lights rise.* **Ralph** *sits in the armchair.* **Dennis** *enters and adopts a standing position facing him.*

(*Lights rise. It is Cristtide Day, afternoon.*)

Dennis And so, sir, that's what I did.

Ralph Well, that sounds most satisfactory...

Dennis Yes, as far as it goes. But then, at half past five, the bells sounded and I had to finish right in the middle of a memo.

Ralph Oh dear.

Dennis Worse, in the middle of a sentence. That's what I find most irritating.

Ralph But you know what you are doing.

Dennis Yes.

Ralph So there should be no trouble.

Dennis Well... I thought so. But you see, sir, I return to the office tomorrow morning, and the first thing I'll see is that half-finished sentence in the half-finished memo. And I don't know. I've had two days to think about it. I now question whether the way I *intended* to finish the sentence is the way I *should* finish the sentence. And, and, you see, if I finish the sentence differently, if I change what the second half of the sentence was going to be, doesn't that automatically call into question the way I had intended to finish the second half of the whole memo itself. And if I change the second half of the memo, of the whole memo itself, doesn't that call into question what I have written in the first half of the memo, and thus the whole premise of the memo in the first place?

(*Short pause*)

Ralph Well, you could see it that way. Why not have another whisky?

Dennis Another for you too?

Ralph Thank you very much indeed.

Dennis Thank you very much indeed for your Cristtide present to me. The whisky glass.

Ralph No, son, thank you very much indeed for the whisky glass you gave me.

Dennis Well... at least I hope it'll be useful.

(He has finished pouring the drinks.)

Yes... But anyway, as I was saying, sir. I work very hard. Well, we all do. We all work very hard. Very hard indeed...

Ralph *(firmly)* Yes. Son. I think maybe you shouldn't worry so much. It is Cristtide, after all.

Dennis ... Yes.

Ralph This was always my favourite day of the year. It was the day that made all the others worthwhile, Fiona and I could be lovers again, no work to worry about, kissing, sex, free flowing saliva and sperm...

Dennis *(dubiously)* Yes.

Ralph You must be looking forward to tonight. When you can have Patsy again.

(Short pause)

Dennis Yes... father, confidentially...

Ralph Yes?

Dennis ...What if this year things *aren't* all right? What if this year I find that, when she stands naked in front of me, I no longer feel excited? No longer apprehensive... In fact, let's face it, downright sick. What if her breasts are all sagged and wrinkled this year, and I realise I'm staring at the prospect of sex with a pair of old woman's breasts?

*(Short pause. **Ralph** hesitates. Then:)*

Ralph It never happened, son. With your mother, every year it just got better and better.

Dennis *(unhappily)* Better and better?

Ralph That's the way it's meant to be. Just better and better and better.

Dennis ...Good. Good.

(And he downs his whisky.

*(Enter **Patsy**. She is dressed especially for Cristtide Day: that is, she is wearing several layers of make-up, bright pink lipstick, bright pink nail varnish, a revealing dress. The total effect is not of a woman trying to highlight her features, but of blasting those features out of existence.)*

Ralph Here is your lover now...

Patsy *(coyly)* Sorry most kindly... Am I interrupting?

Ralph No, not at all. Carry on, you youngsters.

Patsy *(to **Dennis**):* Hello, lover.

Dennis *(unhappily)*: Hello, lover.

Patsy *(voluptuously)*: Dinner's nearly ready. I'm just putting on the vegetables.

Dennis Oh good.

Patsy Before I did, I wanted a kiss with my lover.

Dennis ... Yes.

(She kisses him passionately on the mouth; he gives little response. Then she openly sticks her tongue in his ear.)

Patsy *(whispering)* Thank you very much indeed for last night...

Dennis ... Yes.

Patsy You naughty man. Thank Christ the wrapping paper held.

Dennis ... Yes.

Patsy *(louder)* I'll come back for another kiss before I start on the gravy.

Dennis ... Good-oh.

(She exits.)

(Short pause)

Ralph Well, it's nice to see the four tubs of cosmetics you gave her have come in useful.

Dennis *(to himself)* Well. Too late for regrets now. No point in that.

(He goes to pour himself another whisky.

*(Enter **Toby**.)*

Oh, hello, son.

Toby Good afternoon, sir. Good afternoon, Gramps.

Ralph Toby.

Toby I wanted to thank you both for your presents.

Ralph You're welcome.

Toby Both whisky glasses are appreciated.

Dennis Well, I hope they come in useful.

Toby *(coldly)* I'll put them with all the others you've bought me.

Ralph Well, what I say is, you can never have too many whisky glasses...

(He drains his glass.)

Dennis Another, sir?

Ralph Please.

*(**Dennis** takes **Ralph's** glass.)*

Dennis Would you care for a whisky, son?

Toby No, thank you very much indeed, sir.

Dennis You're welcome to. It is, after all, Cristtide.

Ralph Why not join us in a whisky before the meal? While the women get the food in the kitchen, all the men together, having a drink.

Toby No, thank you very much indeed, Gramps. I have no desire to become sodden and giddy and lose partial control of my urinary functions.

(Short pause)

Nevertheless, not wishing to destroy this merry Cristtide atmosphere, I will happily watch you two do so.

*(**Dennis** laughs, and gives **Ralph** his glass back.)*

Dennis He's a boy and a half, isn't he, sir?

Ralph Yes. He certainly is.

Dennis A boy and a half.

Ralph Very nearly a man now.

Dennis Exactly. A boy and a half and maybe five-sixths a man.

Ralph By the infinite compassion of Christ.

Dennis And all His little angels. Down the hatch.

(They both drink simultaneously.

*(Enter **Patsy**, who goes straight up to **Dennis** and kisses him on the mouth.)*

Patsy ... That's because the gravy's on.

Ralph Oh, that's good. It wouldn't be Cristtide if it weren't for the gravy, would it?

Dennis Patsy, how long until dinner is fully prepared?

Patsy Oh, I'd say about half an hour.

Dennis Right. Well. How about we get started? Could you and Judy bring everything in?

Patsy Give me a kiss first, lover.

Dennis *(reluctantly)* Well. I suppose that's fair.

*(They kiss. **Patsy** raises one of her legs and wraps it around **Dennis**.)*

Patsy You're ever so nice. You're the best lover in the whole world.

Ralph Looking forward to tonight, Patsy, my dear?

Patsy Oh yes, Mr Simpson. I can hardly wait.

*(She lowers her leg, and blows **Dennis** a kiss as she approaches the exit. She calls, much more harshly.)*

Judy! Get things ready! We're moving in!

*(**Patsy** exits, and re-enters with **Judy**. On **Patsy's** platter are five candles, all decorated with tinsel: on **Judy's** there are five crackers. **Judy** is wearing her pink dress and red ribbon once more – she carries with her her doll, Betsy.)*

Ralph *(appreciatively)* Ah yes. Very seasonal.

Dennis Very seasonal indeed, sir. Shall we bring our glasses to the table?

Ralph Of course.

Toby Judy, help Gramps with his chair.

*(**Judy** unsmilingly pulls out **Ralph's** chair, at the head of the table, and returns to her place next to him. Opposite to her sits **Toby**, and to her other side **Dennis**. **Patsy** sits opposite **Dennis**.)*

Judy There's no place for Betsy.

Patsy Well... no.

Judy Well, where's Betsy going to sit?

Dennis Can't she go on the floor, please, Judy? She is just a plastic doll.

Judy She can sit on the table next to me.

Patsy Oh no, she can't! I'm not having members of the family sitting on the table! Not sitting on the table during the Cristtide Miracle. Even when they *are* plastic.

Dennis Why don't you put her over there, Judy, on the armchair?

(Short pause)

Judy No.

Dennis Well, why on earth not?

*(**Judy** looks down away from everyone's eyes..)*

Toby You should be honoured, Judy. The armchair is for the most senior member of the family.

(Short pause. He rises.)

Well, I'll put the doll there then.

*(He picks her up by forefinger and thumb, holds it away from his body disdainfully. **Judy** looks up at him quickly.)*

Judy Betsy.

Toby What?

Judy Her name's Betsy.

Toby Well, I'll put Betsy there then.

(He walks to the armchair, and puts the doll on it unceremoniously. He talks to it childishly, wagging his finger at it, and finally patting it on the head with some force so that it bounces up and down on the seat.)

Right, Betsy. You just sit there. You should be honoured, Betsy. The armchair is for the senior member only.

(He walks back to his seat. Dismissively:)

Well, that's that problem solved, isn't it? We can carry on now, sir.

Dennis Yes... well. There are a couple of more presents still under the tree, I see. Let's have those opened first...

*(**Judy** sits down.)*

Judy, would you ... ?

*(**Judy** gets up again, and picks up a present. She looks at the tag.)*

Judy It's for mother.

*(She gives it to **Patsy**, and walks back to the tree.)*

Patsy Oh, thank you very much indeed, Judy. I wonder what this could be...?

(She unwraps it to discover a tub of cosmetics.)

A tub of cosmetics! Oh, how delightful! Thank you, Dennis, my lover.

Dennis   You're welcome.

Patsy   Let me play footsie with you under the table. Thank you very much indeed... Could you put some on me now, Dennis?

Dennis   What, now?

Patsy   Just a little on my cheeks.

Dennis   You don't need any more on your cheeks.

Patsy   I'm frightened they'll look too chubby...

Dennis   *(firmly)*   No. You don't need any.

Patsy   ... Oh. Oh. Sorry most kindly... Well, later maybe... But I can play footsie with you under the table...

Dennis   *(hastily)*   Who's the other present for, Judy?

*(**Judy** picks it up.)*

Judy   ...It's for me.

(Short pause)

Dennis   Well, open it then... Patsy, please stop playing with my foot, there's a lover...

*(**Judy** has unwrapped her present.)*

Well, what is it?

Judy   ... It's a red ribbon.

(She holds it up for everyone to see.)

Patsy   Oh, that's lovely, Judy. That's not red, though. That's scarlet.

Judy   A scarlet ribbon then...

Dennis   Thank your Gramps, Judy...

*(Short pause. **Toby** rises.)*

Toby   Judy...

Judy   Thank you very much indeed.

Toby   And I'm sure he'd like to see it on you. That's what you want, isn't it, Gramps?

(And he takes it and begins to replace the ribbon as the scene continues below.)

Ralph Well... Santa's done you well, hasn't he, Judy?

*(**Judy** stares at him coldly. **Ralph** looks away. Pause)*

Judy *(brightly)* And Santa... Santa hates the Jews too, doesn't he?

Patsy Well, of course!

Dennis Naturally.

Toby As Father says, naturally.

Patsy You remember the story, don't you? Of how Santa with his sleigh and all of his reindeer parked on top of a Jew?

Toby And crushed him flat.

Patsy And crushed him flat? You remember that, don't you, Judy?

Judy Oh yes.

Ralph But this was no ordinary Jew, Judy. This was a great big Giant Jew that Santa killed.

Judy *(faintly ironic)* Bigger than the one you killed, Gramps?

Ralph *(laughing)* Oh yes! Much bigger!

Dennis He had an enormous nose.

Patsy An enormous nose.

Ralph A giant Jew's nose.

Dennis Naturally.

Toby As Father says, naturally.

Ralph A giant Jew's nose, with giant Jewish nostrils and everything.

Dennis Naturally.

Toby As Father says, naturally.

Judy Well, all I can say is, I'm glad he's dead then. I wish I'd parked my sleigh on top of him!

(There is indulgent laughter from the adults for a couple of seconds.)

Patsy But, dear, you don't have a sleigh!

Judy ... Well, then, I wish that I had a sleigh so I could park on top of him.

Patsy But you wouldn't have preferred a sleigh to your little doll, would you?

Judy Betsy.

Patsy Betsy. You'ld rather have Betsy than a sleigh, wouldn't you?

(Again, simultaneous laughter.)

Judy ... No. No, well, I'd liked to have parked Betsy on top of him then. And crushed him flat.

(Everyone laughs once more.)

Patsy Let's have a look at you.

Dennis Turn around for us.

Ralph *(eagerly)* Please turn around.

(She turns round.)

Judy But what I want to know is...

Patsy You look ever so pretty, Judy.

Ralph Beautiful.

Judy But what I want to know is, what I still don't quite understand... Did Santa's reindeers hate the Jews too?

*(**Dennis** laughs.)*

Dennis Oh, Judy... You are a one. You are a girl and a half. And, I don't know, Judy... You're almost a big girl now, almost a big girl and a half now, and I feel a sense of pride, because I think that this is a girl and a half who has been taught a sense of morality. Christ, looking down in His infinite compassion, must be very proud.

Toby Thank you very much indeed, sir.

Dennis Very well done, Toby. Look at her standing there. You've taught her well.

Ralph ... Yes. Well done, Toby...

Dennis And Christ, looking down upon Toby now, must see this and recognise his excellent tutoring... Come and sit down then, Judy.

*(Short pause. **Judy** turns round.)*

Judy *(insistently)* ... Did Santa's reindeers hate the Jews too?

(Short pause)

Dennis ... Well, yes, I expect so.

Judy Has no-one ever asked them?

Patsy ... Judy, you know perfectly well that reindeer can't speak.

Toby Come and sit down, Judy.

*(Short pause. Then **Judy** moves to sit down.)*

... Good. Very well done.

Dennis And I'd like to finish by saying that this Cristtide is of course especially significant in that my father is present too. And it is, as always, good to see him and hear his advice... Thank you very much indeed, Christ...

Judy He's got flabby eyes.

(Pause. Then, outrage.)

Dennis What did you say?

Ralph Judy ... don't...

Patsy How dare you, Judy...

Judy Last night he scared Betsy...

Toby *(fiercely)* Quiet, Judy!

Judy He put his hand up my dress...

Toby Silence!

*(**Judy** falls silent. A second's pause, then with quiet fury;)*

Do you think that you have any secrets from us? We know full well how you entertained your grandfather last night. It was a Cristtide present to both of you... from your father and I. But your night of fun is over now. And no longer have you any right to call him by pet names...

Judy I was sick...

Toby *(thundering)* Quiet!

Patsy Shut her up, please shut her up...

Dennis Send her to Coventry, Toby...

Toby No. I will not send her to Coventry. Judy, for the rest of the day you are not to say another word. I am sending you to West Norwood.

Judy But it's Cristtide...

Toby Didn't you hear what I said?... I think... I think you must be very confused. I'm sending you to West Norwood where you can't speak. You must have thought I sent you to East Dulwich, where you can't hear. That's why you didn't hear what I said... But I'll say it again. Not another word from you.

(Pause)

I apologise most kindly ... for my ward.

(Short pause)

Patsy I don't like this. Dennis, can I play footsie with you under the table?

Ralph Really, I don't know what...

Patsy Merry Cristtide, everybody!

Ralph Well, thank you very much indeed for the extra present...

Patsy Dennis, I want to play footsie!

Dennis Well, play footsie if you really have to, Patsy.

Patsy But you've got to move your foot too. Merry Cristtide, everybody!

(Short pause. Brightly:)

Why don't we pull the crackers?

*(She picks up her cracker, and stands up, contriving that she still is able to rub her leg against **Dennis's**.)*

Dennis, will you pull a cracker with me?

Dennis Patsy, I'm not going to play with your foot *and* pull your cracker.

Patsy Toby...

Toby Very well, mother.

*(**Toby** stands up and reaches over to take one end of the cracker. He pulls and the cracker splits. There is nothing in the cracker, however, and it is silent.)*

Toby and **Patsy** Bang.

*(**Toby** sits back down. Short pause)*

Patsy ...Wasn't that fun? Merry Cristtide, everybody!

Dennis ... Sir, would you like to pull a cracker with me?

Ralph Certainly. It is Cristtide, after all...

*(**Dennis** stands and offers **Ralph** one end of the cracker.)*

Thank you very much indeed, son.

(They pull it.)

Dennis and **Ralph** Bang.

*(**Dennis** sits down. **Ralph** peers into the cracker end, with faint disappointment.)*

Ralph *(sadly)* ... Yes. I still always expect it to be like the old days, with crackers to have something in them...

Toby Why, what would you want to discover there?

Ralph I don't know... But it all seems a bit pointless otherwise...

(The telephone rings.)

Dennis *(surprised)* Who would telephone on Cristtide Day, for the love of Christ?

Patsy I don't know...

Dennis Patsy, stop playing with my foot and go and answer the phone.

Patsy Yes. Sorry most kindly. I'll be a minute... Yes... It's probably just... Yes.

Dennis Who?

Patsy Probably just my mother...

Dennis Jesus.

Patsy ... I'll just get rid of her. Sorry very kindly, everyone. Continue to have a merry Cristtide...

(She exits hurriedly.)

Dennis That woman has a woefully minimal imagination.

Ralph Your wife?

Dennis I was thinking principally of her mother.

Ralph Oh, I don't know. Phoning on Cristtide Day is certainly an extraordinary thing to conceive...

Toby I'm surprised they let the call through at all.

Dennis Son, you know that Christ, in His infinite compassion, still allows telephone calls on public holidays.

Toby Yes, but not at this time of the day. Not when everyone is preparing for the Miracle. In the future state, it won't be allowed.

*(Re-enter **Patsy**, somewhat dazed.)*

Dennis Well, Patsy? Was it her?

Patsy ... Yes. Yes, it was ...

Dennis Well, what the hell is she up to? Doesn't she know what day it is?

Toby She should be preparing for the Miracle.

Dennis What did she phone for?

Toby In the future state, it won't be allowed.

Patsy She was a little hysterical, actually...

Dennis What on earth for?

Patsy She said... she said she was tired of measuring her life in goldfish. That since the death of my father she has gone through dozens of them, one a week, and she's fed up with it. And yesterday she bought forty-six.

(Short pause)

Dennis Well, that's not very restrained...

Patsy *(with growing desperation)* And she couldn't think of forty-six names. She just couldn't think of that many. She said she might once have been able to, but she just couldn't think of that many now, she was too old. And the aquarium was too small, it all got too crowded. And they keep on dying, they're all floating to the surface, and she has to keep on taking them out. There's just no room for them, and they keep on dying, and she doesn't even have names for them, and every hour there are more of them blocking the surface, these unnamed goldfish, blocking the surface, and the worse part of it she says is that they don't even have names, they just keep on dying. And she says she's getting too old, and that it's no substitute, and this Cristtide she looked at her breasts and they're wrinkled and sagged, and the goldfish were no substitute, every week buying a new one, she can't help it, she still gets worried when it's quarter to six and my father isn't home from work, she still feels worried every day...

(She points suddenly to one of the balloons.)

Oh, Christ! Christ! That balloon's wrinkling...

Dennis What are you talking about?

Patsy It's shrivelling... It can't, there was a guarantee on the bag, they're not allowed to do that...

Dennis It's just a balloon.

Toby It isn't wrinkled at all, mother...

(He gets up to fetch it.)

Patsy *(softly)* And it's shrinking and getting grooved and it looks just like my breasts, and every night I feel under my blouse and can feel that it's happening and one day I'll be waiting for Dennis to come home and I'll get worried and worried and that worry will never stop...

Toby *(holding it out)* See, it's not wrinkled at all...

Patsy *(shrieking)* Give it here! Give it to me!

(And she snatches it, and, ripping open her cosmetics tub, begins spreading thick base all over the balloon.)

Dennis What are you doing?

Patsy And it's all you can do. And my mother, at home now, is counting off the goldfish as they float to the surface...

Toby There's only one thing to do with balloons which wrinkle...

(He takes the balloon off her.)

Patsy ... What are you doing?

Toby When the balloon's too wrinkled, there's no point in looking at it any more.

(And he picks up a fork and bursts the balloon with it.)

Patsy Oh no! Oh no, oh no...

Toby And that's all that over.

*(**Patsy** begins to wail.)*

Patsy No, no, you could have covered up the wrinkles... There was a guarantee on the bag. There was a guarantee on the bag.

(Savagely:)

I want the manufacturers gassed. I want the manufacturers rounded up and taken to the chambers and gassed. They can't do that, they put a guarantee on the bag, and they ruin a merry Cristtide...

Dennis Patsy, shut up this instant!

Patsy There was no need for him to destroy it!

Toby *(coolly)* You should send her to West Norwood.

*(And **Dennis** slaps **Toby** savagely across the face. **Patsy** stops wailing and everyone is silent.)*

*(Pause. **Toby** sits down impassively.)*

Dennis *(awkwardly)* Toby... Son?

(Short pause)

Sorry most kindly, sorry, son... Sorry ... But it wasn't my fault... Christ, in His infinite compassion, knows that...

(Short pause)

Son?

(Short pause)

Toby, it was Christ's fault, in His infinite compassion... Look, hit me. Please. Stand up. Take a swing at me. As hard as you like... I cede all power to you...

(Short pause)

You're much cleverer than me. The IQ tests proved that. Look, don't hit me then. The matter's in your hands... it's all up to you entirely ...

*(**Toby** stands up. Short pause. Then he takes **Dennis'** cheeks between his forefingers and thumbs, and gives them a little shake. They make a wobble sound.)*

Toby *(dispassionately)* They're getting chubby, sir. There'll be some notable wrinkles there before time... I think we should make a start on the ceremony.

Dennis *(with relief)* Yes, yes, son, whatever you say...

Patsy But that's your job, Dennis...

Toby Quiet, mother... Ralph.

Ralph Pardon?

Toby Ralph, I think you can deliver the incantation. Mother, light the candles.

*(**Patsy** rises and lights the candles nervously. **Toby** takes from the tree five little figurines of men and puts one by everyone's plate. These figurines have been on the tree all the time, legs astride the branches, with their arms raised upwards, as if in supplication. They have no faces.)*

Ralph Oh yes... right...

(He clears his throat, stands up, clears his throat again.)

Well, here we all are again. A merry Cristtide. Thank you very much indeed for welcoming me into your house. Christ, looking down on us, in His infinite compassion... and, beside him, Fiona, looking down on us too, in compassion which whilst it probably isn't infinite is still pretty much a lot, knows how welcome you have made me. If Fiona were here now, she would undoubtedly tell you herself...

Toby *(quietly)* Ralph.

Ralph ...She was the best wife I could have wished for, and every year she got better and better...

Toby Ralph.

Ralph Not a day of my life was wasted with her by my side...

Toby Hey, old man. Wake up...

Ralph *(regardless, with growing desperation)* And we would fall into each other's arms and pull crackers that made a noise and had jokes inside and paper hats...!

Toby That's enough!

(Short pause)

Patsy Toby, that is your grandfather...

Toby Shut up.

Dennis Patsy, don't interfere.

Toby Grandfather, could you kindly skip the crap? Bear in mind that this will almost certainly be your last Cristtide. Surely you would like to get your last time right?

*(**Ralph** begins to cry.)*

Eh, Gramps?... Ralph?

*(Short pause. **Ralph** pulls himself up, clears his throat. Lights dim on the scene, emphasising the candle light.)*

Ralph Christ, look down upon us now not with the eye of casual observance, but with the eye of scrutiny, and behold the dedication we make to you now.

*(The cast pick up their forks and spear the figurines. They stand up, and hold them over the flame of the candle. **Ralph** then continues.)*

We cannot offer you the blood of your enemies, only metaphors. But accept with this burning wax acknowledgement of hatred beyond the grave, beyond the camp and the chambers. We pray that no more blood need be spilt, that the camps and the chambers will one day be needed no longer. But whilst purification is still necessary, we pray we may be purged without need of the gas. And we pray that those we knew and those we loved are looking down on us by Your side, and that, by Your indulgence, You will not this day cast them into hell. Bless us with a miracle of Your grace, Lord... Happy Birthday.

All except **Judy** *(muttering)* Happy Birthday ...

Ralph ... And the annual miracle is performed. Behold, believers, a rainbow...

All except **Judy** Amen.

Ralph *(with increasing difficulty)* Feel the peace and serenity descend... Cristtide has been purified...

(He sits down heavily. The ceremony is over. Lights as before.)

Dennis Sir? Are you unwell?

Ralph Yes... yes, I'm fine... Just a little out of breath, I'm not used to... This old body of mine... Especially the soul...

*(Pause. There is an awkward silence after everyone, but **Toby**, has taken their seats.)*

Patsy *(suddenly)* Well... Merry Cristtide, everyone...

(Short pause)

Ralph I'm fine. Really, I'm fine...

Toby *(slowly, walking behind **Ralph** and putting his hands on his shoulders)* And Christ may look down upon us with infinite compassion. Indeed, it is an undisputed fact that He does look down on us with infinite compassion. But one day that compassion may falter. And when it does, we must be ready to destroy Him and replace Him.

(Short pause. All stare at him with concern.)

That is my legacy... Don't worry. I'm sure it won't happen in your lifetimes.

(He smiles broadly, picks up a cracker. He speaks brightly.)

Merry Cristtide, everybody. Merry Cristtide to you all. Now. Who wants to pull a cracker with me? ... Let's see... Judy, no. No, you're unable to do that at the moment...

*(He waves a cracker childishly at **Ralph**.)*

Grandfather. Gramps. Ralph. Gramps. Ralph. Gramps...

Ralph *(very weakly)* What?

Toby Stand up, Gramps! Don't you want to pull a cracker?... No? No, well, then...

Patsy I'll pull a cracker with you, Toby ...

Toby ... Then that leaves my father. Sir. May I interest you in a cracker? May I interest you in pulling a cracker with your son before our festive meal?

(Short pause)

Dennis Son... I cede all power to you... You take my part.

Toby Very well. Very well then.

(He moves away from the table to the centre of the room. He brandishes the cracker with aplomb, then holds it over his head with both hands – and pulls it apart.)

Bang.

(He laughs.)

Merry Cristtide, everyone.

Ralph *(quietly)* And Christ, please don't cast Fiona down into hell, not today...

Toby I said, merry Cristtide, everyone.

*(No-one reacts. **Toby** turns round, walks over to the armchair. He picks Betsy off it with forefinger and thumb, then drops it to the ground. He sits down.)*

Judy...

*(**Judy** stands up nervously.)*

Judy. Time for the meal. Go and get the pork.

(Short pause. Then the lights slowly fade, leaving only the Christmas tree lights and the candle light. Then the Christmas tree lights fade as well, and, at the moment they wink out, the cast blow out the candles into full blackout.)

White Lies

(1994)

WINNER OF THE WIMBLEDON THEATRE YOUNG
PLAYWRIGHT AWARD

OPENED AT THE STEPHEN JOSEPH THEATRE, SCARBOROUGH,
ON 12TH AUGUST 1994, WITH THE FOLLOWING CAST:
CLAIRE JILL BENEDICT
SIMON ADRIAN McLOUGHLIN
DIRECTED BY MALCOLM HEBDEN

ITS FIRST EUROPEAN PRODUCTION WAS AT THE TEATRO AGORA, ROME,
ON 18TH FEBRUARY 1997, WITH THE FOLLOWING CAST:
CLAIRE JANE GODDARD
SIMON NICK HARDY
DIRECTED BY ROBERT SHEARMAN

UNDER THE TITLE 'AFTERNOONS WITH ROGER', IT WAS FIRST BROADCAST ON
BBC RADIO FOUR ON 11TH JUNE 2003, WITH THE FOLLOWING CAST:
CLAIRE ROSALIND AYRES
SIMON CHRISTOPHER NEAME
DIRECTED BY MARTIN JARVIS

(Two stage areas, side by side. One of them is a lounge / dining room, complete with table, three chairs, and a coat stand. The other represents a squash court.
*(During the course of the play, **Simon** and **Claire** will speak to an imaginary character, 'Roger'. At times they will leave a gap for him on stage and act around him, at others they will speak directly to the audience.*

(Just as 'Roger' is imaginary, other objects and effects which are meant to be real in the context of the play cannot be seen by the audience, and are represented by mime and sound.

*(In the darkness, a man, **Simon**, suddenly imitates a doorbell.)*

Simon Bing-bong!

*(And lights up, very brightly. **Simon** is speaking directly to the audience. He is a short, fat man in his early forties, nowhere near as athletic as he likes to imagine he is.)*

Hi! Yes, come on in. Good to see you, well, it's always good to see you. Well, that's very nice of you...

(He holds out his hand, and shakes it with thin air vigorously. He backs on to the level, as 'Roger' presumably enters with him.)

Of course you're not too early, bang on time, you're always bang on time... Claire, Roger's here!

Claire *(offstage)* Coming!

Simon Claire's just coming. So, how are you? Do you like the room? Not bad, is it? Not bad at all. We've vacuumed it, especially for your visit. Well, I didn't, of course, Claire did all that. She's made a jolly good job of it.

*(Enter **Claire**. She is a woman who generally speaking does not see any need for make-up or attractive clothes. She has, however, made a little effort tonight.)*

Claire Dinner's in ten minutes, both of you...

Simon Great. Roger was just saying, Claire, he thinks you've made a jolly good job of the vacuuming... What is it, dear?

Claire *(awkwardly)* Simon ... What on earth are you doing?

Simon What?

*(**Claire** nods at the space 'Roger' is supposed to inhabit, currently just to his side, as **Simon** has his arm around him. **Simon** turns to look.)*

Claire ...Roger's coat. You haven't taken Roger's coat.

Simon ...Whoops! Silly me. Well, that's got the evening to a bad start, hasn't it? Bad start. Sorry, Roger, here let me...

(He takes the 'coat' over to the coat stand, and puts it on it.)

Claire *(laughing)* He's always forgetting things like that, don't you mind him!

Simon *(laughing)* I'd forget my own head if it wasn't screwed on, wouldn't I?

Claire *(laughing)* Probably, Simon, probably! Oh, Roger, it's non-stop laughter when you come round.

Simon Yes, the food *does* smell delicious, doesn't it?

Claire Well, I hope so.

Simon Mmm. Nothing like a traditional meal, is there, Roger? Nothing fancy, just a good old-fashioned traditional meal.

Claire I hope it's all right, I've spent all afternoon on it...

Simon And those meals are the hardest to prepare. Don't you think, Roger? Shall we all sit down?

Claire Good idea.

*(**Claire** pulls out a space for 'Roger', then **Simon** and **Claire** sit down. Short pause.)*

Claire *(hinting)* Oh, it was just something I threw on! I don't think I look pretty at all. But thank you, Roger.

Simon *(warmly)* Oh, she's more than pretty, isn't she, Roger? She's attractive. I'd even go as far to say you were attractive.

Claire *(shyly)* Oh, honestly, I'm a little dumpy really.

Simon What about you, Roger, wouldn't you go as far as to say she was attractive? There you are, Claire. Roger also would go as far as to say you were attractive.

Claire Really, I'm a little dumpy. It's just something I threw on.

Simon I bet you wish you were married to her, eh, Rog? Well, you can't, I've got her!

Claire Oh. And that's right, Roger, Simon's very attractive as well.

Simon Thank you, Claire, but I really don't think Roger finds me attractive...

Claire He does. We both do. I do. He's very strong, you know. Very athletic. Always has been athletic.

Simon *(proudly)* Well...

Claire You'd never think he was so old.

Simon ...Yes, right, thanks. You see, Roger, the body's a machine. And to make it function properly, you've got to treat it right. I still play squash, you know.

Claire That's right, he does...

Simon Difficult game, that. I'll teach you some time, Roger. It'd be fun.

Claire *(warning)* Yes. Maybe, yes.

(Short pause. Then, brightly, to overcome any awkwardness:)

You know, we do both so look forward to your visits every Wednesday, Roger. Arriving at half past six, leaving at quarter to ten...

Simon Not that we don't enjoy each other's company. Because we do.

Claire That's right.

Simon But having you here, Rog, is special. You're my friend. You're my best friend.

Claire You're my best friend too.

Simon That's right. You're both our mutual best friends!

(Short pause)

Claire I'll go and check on the baked beans.

*(Lights dim. **Simon** exits, **Claire** pulls off her dress revealing a nightgown underneath. She puts a cup of coffee, a newspaper and a pack of wrapped sandwiches on the table. She sits back down.*

*(The lights rise again, but not as brightly as before. **Simon** enters, fiddling with his tie. The energy with which **Claire** and **Simon** spoke has sapped.)*

Simon Morning, Claire.

Claire Good morning, Simon.

Simon Mmm.

Claire Did you sleep well?

Simon Is this my coffee?

Claire Yes. Black and strong, the way you like it.

Simon The way I like it. Lovely. Sleep well?

Claire It was fine. Yes, it was fine...

Simon Good. Oh, this is waking me up...

Claire Well, I say it was fine, I did have some problems actually getting off to sleep, then staying asleep once I was off...

Simon Is this my newspaper?

Claire ...Yes.

Simon *(brightly)* Good.

(He sits down, begins to read. Pause.)

Claire Would you like anything to eat?

Simon Hmm?

Claire I could do you some toast.

Simon No, thanks.

Claire Okay... Anything good in the paper?

Simon What?

Claire In the paper? Anything good?

Simon Oh, no. No. Nothing really.

(He carries on reading. Short pause)

Claire I would like to make you a breakfast some time though. A proper cooked breakfast. I am able to. I'm quite good at them...

Simon Sure, lovely.

Claire From what I remember, anyway.

Simon Not now though, Claire. The coffee's great.

Claire No. Some time.

Simon I'd rather have those few minutes extra sleep, to be honest. I need those few minutes extra sleep. I have a difficult job.

Claire Yes, I know you've got a difficult job...

Simon And a difficult drive into work. I mean, the roads out there are terrible. You've no idea.

Claire *(gently)* I do live here...

Simon Difficult drive. Difficult drive to a difficult job.

Claire That's why I thought a breakfast would give you a good start...

Simon No, no. Bad start. Bad start. You know, they say, breakfast is the most important meal of the day?

Claire Yes.

Simon Well, it's bloody nonsense, that. Absolute bollocks.

(Short pause. Brightly:)

But we had fun last night, didn't we?

Claire Oh yes. Yes!

Simon Having Roger over. All harmless fun. Harmless fun, no harm in that.

Claire Every Wednesday we've had him over. From half past six to quarter to ten. Every Wednesday for a year.

Simon Yes. But all harmless fun.

Claire I was thinking, Simon. Do you think that... That maybe we could have Roger over a little more often?

Simon More often? I don't know, it's all harmless fun, but I don't think that's a good idea, no...

Claire Perhaps twice a week? It is good fun, you said yourself.

Simon Yes, it is good fun, but I don't think we... We must stick to Wednesdays. Strictly between those times. Otherwise, you know, maybe it'll be stop being harmless. And end up being weird and bonkers.

Claire It's just that sometimes, Simon, I... When I'm on my own, I talk to him. A little.

Simon Sorry?

Claire Just a little. When I'm lonely. I'll say things like, Come on then, let's do the vacuuming, Roger. Stuff like that.

Simon *(dubiously)* ...Yes. Yes, maybe it would be best if you didn't do that. Not without me there. I mean, that was the whole point. We imagine Roger together.

Claire It's all right, Simon. I'm not really imagining Roger. I'm just pretending to imagine Roger.

Simon Well, okay then. That's not bonkers. But I wouldn't tell anyone. I wouldn't tell your friends.

Claire *(softly)* I don't have any friends. That's why I need Roger.

(Short pause)

I bet you'd have a cooked breakfast if Roger were here.

(Short pause)

Simon So, what are your plans for today?

Claire Well, it's Thursday, isn't it? On Thursday I do the shopping.

Simon Right.

Claire I get the shopping in for the weekend.

Simon I thought you did that on Saturday.

Claire That's getting the shopping for the rest of the week. No, I'll do a bit of vacuuming, do a bit of shopping, do a bit more vacuuming. That's my plan.

(He stands up.)

Simon Right. Off I go. Do I look all right?

Claire Fine.

Simon Presentable for work? ...Good.

Claire Do I look all right?

Simon Are these my sandwiches?

Claire Yes. Roger's leftovers.

Simon See you later.

(He kisses her on the head, somewhat awkwardly.)

Claire Have a good day.

Simon Okay. You too.

Claire I'll be fine.

(He exits.)

I'll be fine.

(She sits down. Short pause)

Simon, do I look all right? ...What, are you kidding? You look beautiful. You always do. You look so beautiful I hate having to go to work.

(She runs out of enthusiasm. Sighs. Brighter, feigning surprise:)

Roger? What are you doing here? I'm afraid Simon's out... Oh, you didn't want Simon? You wanted me?... Roger, would you like some breakfast? I'm very good at making breakfasts, honestly I am. Simon doesn't ever eat my breakfasts, he's missing out, isn't he, Roger? Roger, forgive me for asking, but... do I look all right? You look beautiful. You always do. You look so beautiful I hate it when I see Simon with you.

(She smiles.)

Roger. How would you like to do a bit of shopping with me?

*(Lights up on the squash court. **Simon** enters stage left, carrying a squash racquet. He is dressed in a T-shirt and shorts, both of which are a little too small for him now. Not looking at the audience, he gives a few experimental swipes with his racquet.*

*(Lights have faded on the kitchen, and **Claire** exits, striking the coffee and newspaper.*

*(**Simon** faces the audience, stares for a second in disbelief, then laughs.)*

Simon God, I'm sorry... but you look so *funny*... It's amazing what shorts will do to wreck a man's dignity...! No, I'm sorry, Roger, I'm sorry, mate. Don't you worry, we'll have a good game of squash. Once in a while I like to sneak away from work in the afternoon, a difficult job, mind you, a difficult job, but the kind of difficult job that lets you sneak away in the afternoon sometimes.

*(**Simon** is not holding a ball, but acts as if he is anyway. He bounces it on the ground a few times. Each time there is a little sound effect. A different sound effect is used when he hits the 'ball' with the racquet.)*

Like the squash court? Not bad, is it? Not bad at all. It's jolly exclusive, this place, they usually don't let member's friends in like this. Of course, it helps that you're imaginary, that makes it a lot easier. Right then. Squash.

(He hits the ball hard with his racquet, presumably into the audience.)

It's a real game, this, a man's game. Difficult. Bloody difficult, actually, but then, that's the point. The rules are simple, but in all honesty, I don't bother much, I think the point is just to knock it against the wall and get really sweaty. It lets you know you're alive. It makes you feel... *real*. Oh yes. And I tell you, when you're dripping with perspiration, you'll have never felt realer.

(He hits the ball. And again. And again. He is out of breath.)

Haven't played for a while, actually. Erm... it helps to have a partner. And I haven't found anybody to play with me... But now, we'll get that machine ticking over again! The body's a machine, you see, Rog. And a good half hour of knocking balls against a wall, and the cogs'll be turning again. Just the two of us. Away from Claire for once. In fact, policy decision here. Let's not mention Claire at all. Be completely free from her. All right? All right.

*(He throws the ball into the air to serve. As he hits it, with a loud thwack, lights out on this area and up again on the kitchen, as **Claire** enters carrying bags of shopping.)*

Claire Whew! Thank you, Roger. I don't know how I would have got all these home without your strong arms to help me. Thanks. Not bad at all. And that discount on the toilet rolls was good news. A real bargain.

(She sits down.)

We need something to pick us up. Yes.

(She produces a packet of cigarettes and some matches. She offers herself one.)

A cigarette? Oh, I don't smoke, thanks. I haven't smoked for years. Simon and I, we both gave up together. I think it would be very unkind to start again without him joining in too. ...Oh, what the hell. Just the one. Mmm, are you trying to lead me into temptation, Roger?

(She lights it with a match. She coughs.)

Oh!... That's good. Yes, you never forget how to smoke, do you? Just like riding a bicycle. Smoke goes in, smoke goes out. Whew, look, there it goes. Lovely.

(Short pause. She looks to 'Roger', and attempts to smoke seductively.)

...I feel stupid. Look, you're going to have to help me out with this. I am not, erm, a natural seducer. I do not seduce naturally. I mean, don't get me wrong, I used to seduce a bit. When I met Simon, it was me who did all the seducing. In fact, I used to seduce him so hard and, and so desperately, it used to take his breath away... It's not easy to seduce when someone's gasping all over you. I don't believe Simon even thinks of me as a woman any more. Oh, I'm sure if you asked him directly, said to him, bluntly, your wife, man or woman? – he'd come up with the right answer, he'd have to think about it for a while, but he'd get there. But lying next to him in bed, I'm just... something which stops him lying diagonally. Do you know, I haven't seen him naked for years. Not for years. Not all of it. He undresses in the bathroom. Even when we're...

You know, making love, it's so dark I can't be sure he's not got clothes on. Next time it happens, if it ever does, I'll stop in the middle and turn the light on to have a look. No. So. You're going to have to help me out. To make allowances. I'm a bit out of practice and a bit clumsy, probably, I *feel* clumsy... I'm not asking you to seduce me or anything, it *is* something I want to do myself. I'm just asking... if you could be very easily manipulated.

(Tentatively she kisses the air. Then again, longer.)

Mmm. Not too wet and no aftertaste. It's nicer than the real thing!

*(Lights back on the squash court and **Simon**. **Claire** exits.)*

Simon I do love Claire. I really do.

(And he smashes the ball viciously.)

It's just that I don't necessarily want to see her every day. You know what I mean? You know when you sometimes have things of great sentimental value, very precious, but you've no room for them. So you put them in cardboard boxes and stick them in the attic. And then, years later, you're fixing a leak up there, and you stumble across this cardboard box by accident and you get all the stuff out and it's really thrilling... That would be nice, I think. If Claire would fit in a cardboard box.

(As he continues, he reaches into the wings, takes his work clothes, gets dressed again. The trousers should go over the shorts!)

But I wouldn't want you thinking living with Claire is difficult. Because it isn't. I relish difficult things, and really, marriage is a doddle. If I want a bite to eat or my trousers pressed, she'll be there, saucepan in one hand, iron in the other. I just wonder if there should be more to it all than that. So I turn to you. Because you've always had a bit of a way with the women. You dog! And I mean that in a sensitive way. Uh, you sensitive dog... I was hoping you might be able to give me some advice. Some counselling. Teach me how to win my wife back. ...I don't mean for nothing, of course. Of course not. In return, I'll teach you how to play squash.

*(Lights change on the court – more of an external feel. **Simon** nervously prepares to enter his house. **Claire** enters the kitchen underneath the following.)*

Okay. Home again. This is going to be easy. Nothing to worry about. I'll just go indoors, and be nice to her. That's all there is to it. I'll just... make her feel wanted. Because she needs me. And when it comes to it, I need her too, when it comes to it. All we really need is each other. Yes. That sounds credible. Good.

(Brighter:)

Thanks, Roger, for everything. I'll see you tomorrow.

(He steps into the kitchen, affecting a brightness which feels somewhat forced.)

Hi, Claire! I'm home!

(He takes off his coat and holds it out.)

Claire Hello, Simon. Did you have a good day?

Simon Yes, thank you. But more importantly, did *you* have a good day?

Claire ... I'm sorry?

(She takes his coat from him.)

Simon You happy?

Claire Sure. Of course I'm happy.

Simon I've been thinking of you today. I've been thinking of you all day.

Claire Oh. Is something wrong?

Simon Not because I was concerned, as such. I was just thinking of you because I like thinking about you.

Claire Oh. Good.

Simon Yes. So.

Claire I'm glad... you, erm, enjoyed yourself...

(Short pause)

Simon Mmm. So, what did you do today?

Claire Oh, not much. Not much really. I did a bit of vacuuming. And then I went shopping. Got a great bargain on the toilet rolls, they're reduced. And I came back and did a bit more vacuuming. And I took up smoking.

Simon *(cautiously)* Oh, I don't know, that sounds like quite a full day, erm... What do you mean, smoking?

Claire Well. Everyone needs a hobby, Simon.

Simon *(dubiously)* Yes...

Claire And I did want a hobby I could do from home. You know, so I could fit it around all the vacuuming and shopping.

Simon Yes. But it's bad for you, isn't it? Isn't it? I mean, erm... isn't it? The body, Claire, you know this, the body's like a machine. You could have done what I've done. Chosen a hobby which helped that machine run more smoothly.

(*Claire* lights a cigarette under the following.)

Claire Well, yes. But I just felt this machine needed a little more oiling. You see. And my body, well, it's a little dumpy, but there's nothing much *wrong* with it. Physically. It's not great to look at, but it's in perfect working order. And I thought, well, if anyone's body can afford a filthy habit, it's probably mine. I mean, I've done without cigarettes so long my lungs are probably itching to have something to fight against. Just dying for a bit of abuse. And, besides which, it's really easy. Squash, you always tell me how difficult that is. But smoking, there's nothing to it. Just a matter of learning not to cough.

(She inhales.)

See? I've mastered that already. And if I can get that far in one day, imagine how good I'll be by the time I'm sixty.

Simon ...Yes. Yes, I... Claire. ...You know, when it comes to it... Claire, when we come to it, think about it, I think you'd have to agree that... Well, we need each other. Don't we?

Claire Yes, Simon. But I do need a hobby as well.

(Lights to half on this area. **Claire** sits down.

(**Simon** walks to the court.)

Simon Yes. A partial success. I think I can say that much. She's started smoking again. Which surprised me, actually, because she was never much of a smoker even when she gave up. She only began all those years ago when I was quitting, so we could quit together. She's like that, very accommodating. I hope she doesn't think now she's started again, I have to follow suit. I'm not prepared to wreck my body. It's a nice body. I've taken years to get it to be this nice a body. And, I'm sorry, but if our marriage *does* collapse because I won't share her hobby with her, at least I'll have my body left to console me. Yes.

(Short pause. He swishes his racquet irritably.)

...Yes, well. Only a partial failure, then. Yes. Look, are we going to play squash or not?

*(He exits. Light on **Claire**. She lights a cigarette.)*

Claire Oh, Roger. It is such a treat having you here every afternoon.
It really is, it means such a lot to me. Mind you, you're not the first
imaginary friend I've had. Oh no. And I don't mean one of those that
small children have, everyone has those. No, this was back when I was
sixteen. When everyone else at school had found a boyfriend, and I
still hadn't, and I felt very left out, you see, I'm sure you'll find this
hard to believe but I was quite dumpy back then... no, no, honestly...
All right, Roger, have it your own way, you flatterer! But whatever, one
day I invented Martin. Or Matthew, one of the two. And I made him
much more handsome than all my friends' boyfriends, perfect hair,
perfect eyes, perfect teeth, the whole works, all of which made them very
jealous, of course – and he drove a motorbike, that's right, which was
very 'in' back then, you know. And he was devoted to me, worshipped
the ground I walked on...

(She inhales.)

I became a lot more popular. People stopped treating me as if I were
dumpy. Girls at school asked me for beauty tips, because they all wanted
to attract motorcyclists... The problem was, of course, that they all kept
on asking to meet him. And I found excuses, said he had toothache,
athletes foot, whatever, but all these, ah, physical ailments hardly fitted
with my image of him as a gorgeous hunk. So eventually I decided I'd
just have to kill him off. I'd just kill him off. I gave him an accident with
that motorbike of his, he went straight into a truck. The only problem
was, you see, I was really rather attached to Matthew – or Martin
– and I chickened out at the last moment, had the truck swerve away a
fraction. I didn't make the accident quite as fatal as I should have. He
wound up in hospital, horribly disfigured, face burned off, but, still, you
know, totally alive really, still kicking. And that was all right for a while,
because everyone sympathised, and no-one wanted to meet him now he
was so scarred and deformed. But now that he was ugly I wasn't quite
sure what I saw in him any more. I mean, I created him for his looks,
not his personality. And I couldn't just *dump* him, in that condition,
that'd seem heartless. So I had to kill him again. It couldn't be a car
crash this time, that'd be too much of a coincidence. So I burned down
his hospital. Yes. Which was a mistake, of course, because there was
nothing on the news about it, everyone asked which hospital I was
talking about. And they found out I made the whole thing up. Yes. I lost
quite a lot of friends that way...

(She inhales.)

And I went back to being dumpy again for the next few years. And when Simon came along, he didn't ride a motorbike, and he wasn't all that attractive either. But he was real, he didn't run away, and being this dumpy I thought he was probably the best I could manage. Yes.

(She takes a couple of puffs in quick succession.)

Poor old Martin. Or Matthew. I can't remember his name properly, isn't that terrible, it all seems so fickle... But don't worry, Roger. My love. You mean so much more to me than he ever did. I've given you a personality too, not just looks. And I'll never leave you, I'll never abandon you. And I'll never let you abandon me. I'll never let that happen. Because that isn't the way I created you. The two of us – forever.

*(Slow fade on **Claire**. She exits stage right.*

*(Enter **Simon**, excited.)*

Simon *(to audience)* Psst! Quick, in here!... Great. Thanks for meeting me here at the house, Roger, we won't be playing squash this afternoon. Let me explain. I took your advice, tried writing her a love letter. It was crap, Rog. Really awful. The gushy bits didn't sound like me at all, and when I *tried* sounding like me, I just sounded desperate. So, here's the plan. I remember I wrote tons of love letters to Claire when we were engaged. All we have to do is dig them out, and use them!

*(Lights rise on the wardrobe. **Simon** begins to climb up the set to it, indicating 'Roger' should follow. Once in the bedroom, he opens the wardrobe and rummages inside.)*

...Right, come on upstairs, we'll try the bedroom. ...No, Rog, there's nothing *seedy* about it, they're not her private property, I wrote them, didn't I, they must be part mine... Aha! What have we got here? My old love letters!

(He holds out a file, with papers inside hole punched.)

...Well, they were surprisingly easy to find. See, they're all index filed, I told you she was efficient, isn't that romantic?...

(He leafs through.)

Right, let's see what we can get from this Valentine's card. 'To Claire. From Simon.' ...Yes, something a little earlier, I think... Ah. Right. 'Being in the same room with you is like being in a tight caress, passionate and lasting. But when you leave, you take the sunshine with you.' ...Yes. Do you think she'd really fall for that? I suppose she must do, she married me, after all... Oh yes, this is gold dust...

*(Enter **Claire**, stage right, in the kitchen.)*

Claire Right. Roger. I'm ready for this. But I want you to know something. Before we go upstairs. Before we... you know.

Simon *(laughing)* I want to run my fingers through your hair

And never pull them out from there!

Claire It's just that I've never done this sort of thing before. I'm not cheap. I'm not easy. Even when I was sixteen, with that imaginary friend I told you about. The closest I ever got to him was when I sat behind him on his imaginary motorbike, wearing an imaginary crash helmet. So. Now you know.

(She laughs nervously.)

...Sorry. Being far too serious about this! Come on.

*(She begins to walk up to the bedroom, indicating that 'Roger' should follow, in the same way that **Simon** did previously. They take the same route.)*

Simon *(alarmed)* Footsteps on the stairs! She's back early!

(He stuffs the letters he has already removed into his jacket pockets, and rushes to open the wardrobe door. He throws the file back inside, and indicates to 'Roger'.)

Quick! Roger, hide in here!

*(He slams the door shut as **Claire** enters. She is shocked to see him there.*

*(**Simon** leans against the wardrobe door with a hastily assumed air of nonchalance.)*

Hi, Claire. Good to see you.

Claire *(hissing behind her)* Roger! Out of sight! Against the wall!

(She extends her arms to help shield him.)

Simon ...Sorry?

Claire *(uneasily)* Simon. What are you doing here?

Simon Ah. Yes. Well, the truth is, I... I had a headache.

Claire A headache?

Simon Yes. So I came home. Yes. For some aspirin.

Claire Why didn't you just buy some at a chemists?

Simon Well, that seemed a little extravagant, don't you think? I mean, don't you think? When we have some here. Erm, where are they, by the way?

Claire In the bathroom.

Simon They would be, yes.

Claire Not in the bedroom.

Simon No... Right, I'll... I'll just take a look...

(*He exits left.*

(*Speedily,* **Claire** *dashes over to where she left her 'Roger', and ushers him in.*)

Claire Quick! Quick, hide in the wardrobe! I'll try to get rid of him.

(*She opens the wardrobe doors, closes them again as* **Simon** *walks in.* **Claire** *jumps.*)

Simon (*nervously*) ...You didn't open the wardrobe door, did you?

Claire (*defensively*) No. Why should I do that?

Simon (*with obvious relief*) No reason at all, good... Erm, I found them.

(*He shakes a small box.*)

It says they're soluble.

Claire Well, dissolve them then.

Simon Would you do it for me?

Claire What?

Simon You dissolve things so much better than me.

(*She's caught; there's no answer to that. She snatches the box and hurries away.*)

Claire For heaven's sake...

Simon Thank you...

(*He rushes over to the wardrobe, opens the door.*)

Right, out quick. Breathe deep, breathe deep, all right? Now, down the stairs. I'll be outside in a minute.

(*He shuts the wardrobe door as* **Claire** *enters, carrying a glass of water.*)

Claire Here you are... What are you doing by that wardrobe?

Simon Nothing. There's nothing inside anyway. I'll show you, if you like...

Claire *(anxiously)* No! ...It's okay, thank you.

Simon Okay.

(He drains the glass. Short pause. They look at each other expectantly.)

Claire So you're going then? They are quick-acting, you know.

Simon Oh. Yes. I feel much better already.

Claire Good.

Simon Wow, just look at that headache go. Yes.

Claire *(awkwardly)* You were going back to work, weren't you?

Simon *(awkwardly)* Oh... Well, I suppose I won't if you want me to stay...

Claire *(hastily)* No. No, I don't. Not unless you want to, of course...

Simon *(hastily)* No, that's fine. I should be getting back.

Claire *(relieved)* Yes.

Simon Yes.

Claire Good.

Simon Good.

(Both stand there rather awkwardly for a moment, guilty. Nodding.)

...Good.

*(And he goes down to the kitchen level. **Claire** breathes a sigh of relief, exhausted, knocks against the wardrobe door. And calls inside.)*

Claire You all right in there? Breathing okay? That was close. I'm sorry, Roger, but I've gone right off it now. All that stress... I'm getting a headache.

*(**Simon** has taken out the letters from his pocket. In his haste to put them there, they have been creased and torn.)*

Simon Oh dear, in the rush they've all got crumpled up. And she'd kept them so well all these years... Still. Never mind. I'm writing them all out again for her, aren't I?

(Cheerfully he exits left.

*(**Claire** walks down to level two, takes out a letter. Spotlight on her. She finishes reading it aloud.)*

Claire The simple truth is, I love being with you. And I think about nothing else. Which means that, when I'm not with you, it really isn't so bad. Because I can pretend. I do. Sometimes I pretend so hard it's a surprise to look around and realise I'm talking to myself. I love you. And, forgive me, that even after all this time we've known each other, I'm still too shy to say it out loud.

(She clutches the letter to her chest.)

Oh, Roger! If Simon had ever sent a letter like this... Well, I don't know, I might even have given him children! Perhaps... perhaps if I believe hard enough, perhaps if I really make an effort... perhaps you would really...

(She tries to take his hand, and grasps nothing. She concentrates harder, reaches out and appears to take something. A little shyly:)

Would you give me the pleasure of this dance?

(And slowly, but with added confidence, they begin to waltz.)

We're missing something. Ah…!

(And she clicks her fingers, and music starts to play.)

Ta-dah dah dah *dah-dah*, ta-dah dah dah *dah-dah*, that's it, you're dancing very well, *dah*, very good, ta-dah, much better than Simon would be, ta-dah, probably, *dah*, I've never actually seen him dance, ta-dah, but at least you're giving it a go... That's it... Not too fast, it isn't a race, when you finish you should look cool and calm, not sweaty...

(The music comes to an end.)

And bow... Very good. I learned that at school. It just goes to show, what the teachers say is true, some of the things they tell you *do* come in handy one day. Good...

(She hugs on to him, begins to slow dance.)

No, it's okay, we don't need music to dance. We don't need music.

(She dances with him for a few seconds silently, closes her eyes, smiles.)

I invented you, Roger. So I think it's only fair I reinvent myself for you. Stop living the fantasy of being attractive, but start being attractive. I don't want to have to always imagine. I'll spend more time on myself rather than the housework, forget the bloody housework... And I'll give you a lover who'll make heads turn in the street. I'll give you a lover who makes grown men moan. I'll make myself beautiful. Just for you.

(The dancing stops. Conspiratorial:)

Tonight, at dinner, when the three of us are together. I don't think we should seem too friendly in front of Simon. I think it would be very cruel. ...Mind you, it would be quite funny, wouldn't it?

(And she giggles.

(**Simon** *enters the kitchen as the lights become much brighter.* **Claire** *walks further downstage, and, facing the audience, takes off her earrings and puts new ones on.)*

Simon   Come on, Claire, hurry up ...

Claire   I just want to look right...

Simon   Come on. It's half past six, and I'm getting hungry.

Claire   I want to create the right effect.

Simon   What's the point?

Claire   Just a second.

Simon   Bing-bong!

Claire   What?

Simon   See? The doorbell. He's here.

Claire   That wasn't the doorbell. That was you saying bing-bong.

Simon   Come on, Claire. What's wrong? I thought you might have thanked me for the red rose I bought you. At least.

Claire   I did thank you. I said, thanks, Simon. What do you expect me to do, dance about it?

Simon   Well, you could have put it in water. It'll die if you leave it out of water.

Claire   Simon. If you were so concerned for its well-being, you should have left it where it was in the ground, rather than paying florists to pluck it out for you. Taking it away from its family like that...

Simon   Well, *I'll* put it in water then. Where is it?

Claire   Where I left it. On the kitchen floor.

Simon   What did you... Right, I'll just get it...

Claire   Bing-bong!

Simon   What?

Claire   No time. Roger's here. Get the door.

Simon But I thought I...

Claire Get the door.

*(**Simon** goes to the door, muttering.)*

Simon I don't see why you're allowed to do the bing-bongs and I'm not allowed to do the bing-bongs...

(He opens the door.)

Hello, Roger, it's...

Claire *(very enthusiastically, arms open wide)* Roger! Darling!

Simon *(conspiratorially)* Warning. She's in a very funny mood tonight. Remember what we said.

*(Behind him during this, **Claire** mouths 'Roger' a kiss.)*

Claire Roger, it's wonderful to see you! You look *fabulous!*

Simon Yeah, Roger, let me take your coat...

(He carries it over to the coat stand.)

Claire And I look fabulous too? You're too kind! Simon, what are you doing?

Simon Hanging up Roger's coat.

Claire Roger isn't wearing a coat. Don't be stupid.

Simon Oh. Right.

(Pointedly he takes the imaginary coat off the hook, and flings it to the ground.)

Claire Hey, Roger, didn't Simon look silly hanging up an imaginary coat?

(She produces from behind the table a large bunch of red roses.)

Oh, are these roses for me?

Simon What's that?

Claire And so many of them! Thank you!

Simon What are you getting flowers for?

Claire Gorgeous. I'm going to put them in a vase straight away.

Simon You were just saying you didn't like flowers, separating them from their family, that sort of thing...

Claire Simon. The whole family's right here! Maybe *you* should have thought of that. Thanks, Roger. Make yourself comfortable, and I'll fetch dinner.

*(Exit **Claire** with the flowers.)*

Simon Roger, what are you playing at? I asked you to humour her, not propose to her... And how come I didn't get any flowers?

*(Re-enter **Claire**, carrying two dinner plates. One has considerably more food on it than the other.)*

Oh, Claire! You're back! ...Look, Roger, she's back!

Claire That's right, Simon, I'm back. I hope you like this, Roger. Dinner is served.

(She puts the plates down on the table, the one with the least food furthest away from her.)

Simon Wow. God. Look at this, Roger. Wow.

Claire It's a special meal.

Simon I'll say it's special. I'll say it's special. Better than the sausage and beans we normally have.

Claire It's duck a l'orange.

Simon Well. Wow. Yes. Roger says 'wow' too.

Claire I know, Simon.

*(**Simon** sits down next to **Claire**.)*

Simon Where's yours?

Claire I'm not eating. I want to be thinner.

Simon You don't need to lose weight. Does she, Roger? You're not fat.

Claire Ah, but you see, I'm not slimming for my health. I'm slimming to get the body men moan about.

Simon Ah... Fair enough...

Claire Simon. I think you'll find you're sitting in Roger's place.

Simon ...But that plate's got less food.

Claire Yes.

Simon A lot less food.

Claire Yes.

Simon There's hardly any duck at all. It's all just... l'orange...

Claire It's what's called hospitality, Simon. Roger is our guest. And you don't give the guest less food. Move.

Simon *(muttering)* Okay, humour her, humour her...

(He gets up. Too cheerfully:)

Of course, dear. I'm overjoyed to change chairs. And eat less duck a l'orange. Roger, it's all yours.

*(**Simon** begins to eat. Deliberately:)*

Mmm. Lovely. Well done, Claire.

Claire Well, eat up. You've got three minutes.

Simon What? Why?

Claire Anything you haven't eaten by then, I'll put in tomorrow's sandwiches.

Simon What?

Claire I think that's only fair. We always use Roger's food for sandwiches.

Simon Claire. Really. I would far rather eat it now than tomorrow lunchtime stuck between two slices of bread.

Claire I'm not using it for your sandwiches. I'm using it for Roger's sandwiches.

Simon What? Roger doesn't eat sandwiches

Claire He stuffs himself on sandwiches! Both horizontally and diagonally sliced. You've got three minutes, Simon... starting now!

Simon Claire, wait...

Claire Two minutes fifty-five. You'd better get moving, Simon...

Simon What are you playing at?

Claire Two minutes fifty. Come on, get some on your bloody fork, or you're going to go hungry!

*(A couple of seconds as **Simon** considers, then he begins to eat at speed, spilling a lot of it in his haste. **Claire** laughs.)*

Come on, stuff it in, you can do it quicker than that! Try taking larger mouthfuls. What do you think, Roger? Roger thinks you'll be quicker if you take larger mouthfuls. ...Psst, Roger, now Simon's busy, let's play footsie under the table!

*(As **Simon** gorges himself, **Claire** raises her leg and gyrates it slowly.)*

Oh, yes, that's nice. Light me my cigarette? Mmm, thanks.

(She takes a cigarette and lights it.)

Simon Claire! Don't smoke at the table!

Claire You're wasting time, Simon, hurry up...

Simon That's disgusting, don't you know it's bad manners to smoke at the table?

Claire *(giggling)* Not as bad manners as bolting your food.

Simon Can't you see you're embarrassing our guest? For God's sake, Claire, Roger didn't want this! He wanted a civilised evening!

Claire In that case, why is he grinning?

Simon He's not grinning! He's grimacing! Roger, stop grimacing. It makes it look like you're grinning...

Claire *(offering the cigarette pack)* Would you like one, Roger?

Simon No, he wouldn't! Roger doesn't smoke!

Claire Roger says, oh shut up, shut up and let me have a good time. You're not my best friend anyway, Claire is.

Simon *(raging)* He didn't! Roger says, Roger says, don't put words in my mouth!

Claire *(flicking the lighter)* There you are, Roger, have a good puff on that.

Simon He doesn't smoke! The body's a machine. He thinks the body's a machine!

Claire *(suddenly serious, standing up)* No, Simon. No, he doesn't. He doesn't think the body's a machine. Because it isn't. It isn't at all. He thinks the body is soft, and, and warm, and gentle and nice to run your fingers over... particularly a body, yes, a body men moan for... because I am a beautiful woman! I am a beautiful woman after all, not a dumpy one, and, and Roger says... And I think I agree with him... That he is surprised, no, appalled, appalled at the waste, that you've been married to me for fifteen years and have forgotten that...

Simon Shut up, Roger! You just shut up! And wipe that stupid grin off your face...!

*(And **Simon** stops. He sits down, gently. Pause. Then, softly:)*

It didn't use to be like this. It didn't use to be like this.

*(Half light. The waltz music plays. **Simon** exits, striking the dishes. **Claire** puts a newspaper, cup of coffee and wrapped sandwiches on the table. She sits down in spotlight, depressed. Hold this for a few seconds. Then lights on the area again. They are duller than in the previous scene.)*

*(Enter **Simon**.)*

Simon *(warily)* Good morning.

Claire Oh, so you're finally out of the bathroom, are you? Good.

Simon I was just doing some thinking, Claire...

Claire Yes, well, next time you want to think, please do it out of the bathroom. Other people live in this house too, you know.

Simon I've reached a decision, Claire...

Claire Other people who may want to use the bathroom for what it is intended. Your coffee and newspaper are on the table. So are the sandwiches. Sorry about the colour, the l'orange soaked through. Do you want any breakfast? She asked, expecting the answer no.

Simon *(bravely)* No, I'd... I'd like something else, Claire.

Claire What?

Simon I've reached a decision. I've decided... That I'd like a kiss.

(Short pause)

Claire Pardon me?

Simon That's what I'd really like. Get a good start to the day. Good start.

Claire A kiss. You've decided that?

Simon Yes. Obviously, erm, only if you decide you want one as well, I wouldn't press you to it...

Claire This is what you spent fifteen minutes thinking of in the bathroom.

Simon Yes. Mostly. Entirely. So... Would you like a kiss?

(Short pause)

Claire Why?

Simon What?

Claire Why do you want a kiss? I think that's important.

Simon Well, erm... To begin with, you're my wife...

Claire I see.

Simon *(hastily)* Not that that's the reason in itself, God, no, I mean you're more than a wife, you're a *woman*, you know, a woman. In your own right. And, erm, a very beautiful woman.

Claire No, I'm not.

Simon You are.

Claire I'm not.

Simon You are.

Claire Simon, I know what I look like. I'm not stupid...

Simon No, that's right, you're a beautiful, intelligent woman...

Claire I know I'm not beautiful, because I haven't even washed yet. I never look beautiful until I've at least washed. I look dumpy until I've washed.

Simon No, no, beautiful anyway...

Claire And I haven't washed because you spent fifteen minutes in the bathroom thinking this morning.

Simon Yes.

Claire Honestly, Simon, what do you take me for? I'm not a beautiful woman. What I said last night, well... it was all rubbish, basically, wasn't it? I mean, wasn't it? Even if I had the bathroom for the whole morning, I wouldn't be a beautiful woman. Come on, you tell me, what parts of me are beautiful? Which bits?

Simon Well, all of it. Of you. Really, the whole thing, it's great...

Claire Beautiful women aren't like me. They're nothing like me. They end up on the covers of magazines, and married to film stars, and do advertisements for soap. That's what beauty is. That's what *defines* beauty. I'm nothing like that. I'm nothing remotely like that.

Simon *(bravely)* That's not true, you... I think you're beautiful. I think you could advertise soap.

(Short pause)

Claire Just a kiss?

Simon   Well, yes.

Claire   On the mouth? I suppose you want it on the mouth.

Simon   Well, if that's all right.

(Tentatively, they close their eyes, pucker up, and move their heads together for a kiss. They miscalculate at first, but get it right the second time. It is an abrupt, embarrassed peck.)

Claire   All right?

Simon   *(politely)* Yes. You're smoking quite a lot now, aren't you?

Claire   Thanks a lot.

Simon   I can taste it on your lips. Strong stuff. Perhaps... You should cut down...

Claire   But I've only just taken it up. It'd be silly to cut down now, just as I'm getting the hang of it.

Simon   ...Mmm.

(Short pause)

Claire   So. Off to work then?

Simon   I've just made another decision.

Claire   *(warily)* What sort of decision?

Simon   How about I take the day off? What do you say to that?

Claire   You can't take the day off. You've got to go to work.

Simon   Oh, sod them. Sod them. I've given them years, they can give me a day off. I mean, they don't own my life... okay, the morning then, I'll take the morning off.

Claire   You said all you wanted was a kiss...

Simon   Oh no, I don't mean... Nothing like that. No, I thought we could go out together. You know, I'll buy you a coffee.

Claire   You've already got a coffee. It's with your newspaper and sandwiches.

Simon   A full-blown meal, even. And it'll be just like being on a date. The two of us. On a date. What do you say? Claire? I'll give you whatever you want. To make up for last night. To make up for everything.

(Short pause)

Claire Whatever I want?

Simon Erm. Yes.

Claire Then I want Roger. Here tonight. For another meal.

Simon Ah. Don't you think that's a little...

Claire No.

Simon I mean, we've only just...

Claire No.

Simon For heaven's sake, Claire, I'm sure Roger wants to lead a life of his own!

Claire I promised he could come over. It's his birthday.

Simon Roger never said it was birthday to me.

Claire Well, it is. And I'm going to make him a special birthday cake. With chocolate and coconut and marzipan and things.

Simon I don't like marzipan.

Claire It isn't your cake. It's Roger's.

Simon Oh yes.

Claire You promised. You said I could have anything I wanted. I gave you a kiss. I let you come up to me and stick your lips all over my face...

Simon You were meant to enjoy it too...

Claire I've given you your bloody kiss. You can give me my bloody birthday cake. All right? ...All right?

Simon Yes, Claire. If you say so.

Claire So I should think. Now, if you'll excuse me, I have a lot of work to do. And the first thing I need is to get to that bathroom so I look stunning for Roger tonight.

Simon Great. Great.

Claire I'll be about fifteen minutes.

(*This last is almost a challenge.* **Simon** *hesitates, then admits defeat with a sigh, exits. Lights narrow on* **Claire**. *She sits down.*)

Claire (*dully*) Happy birthday to you
Happy birthday to you
Happy birthday dear Roger...
I've worked out how to get you, Roger. It's simple. I'll just have to get

rid of everything. My marriage, my possessions, everything. Leave it all behind, burn my bridges. Because then you'll have to come. Because if you don't, I'll be in real trouble. And you wouldn't let that happen to me. Because you love me, I know you do. I know you do because that's the way I made you... And I can make you anything I want. You'll be my best friend, you'll be my lover. Hell, you'll be my footstool if I want you to be. And you'll be prepared to die for me. You'll want to die for me. Total love. No compromises, all or nothing. Happy birthday, Roger. Because you're getting a very special present. Me. And you had better accept. Come on. We're going to bed.

*(Exit **Claire**, taking Roger's hand. Lights out on the kitchen. Enter **Simon**, in the court, dressed for squash. He swipes his racquet aggressively.)*

Simon   Do you think she's mad? I don't know, I only raise it as a possibility. I think we've tried everything, everything that is loving and kind. And she still won't break. I tell you, you know, I'm used to things being difficult, I relish difficult things. But my job, playing squash, even driving to work, it's all nothing compared to Claire. Perhaps it's a woman thing. You know? Perhaps they're all doing it deliberately, behind our backs. Look, here comes a man, quick, be completely impossible to understand! Do you think? It would make a lot of sense.

(He serves a squash ball, with sound effect, venomously.)

It's been good to have a man to talk this over with, Roger, to take advice from. But, all in all, you've been no bloody good at all. You've taught me nothing worthwhile. In the mean time, your squash has got quite good. It's embarrassing to be beaten every game by someone who's imaginary... Which I think is the point, really. I know it's your birthday, and you're coming over for dinner tonight, that's fine. But I think perhaps we should see less of each other from now on. Don't take it personally, it's just it's getting to the stage now where I really believe I need you. And you're not real, actually. Sorry about that, but it's true. And if I'm going to be reliant on somebody, I'd think I'd rather it was Claire.

(Answering an unheard person, from the audience direction:)

Look, the court will be ready soon, okay? Just be patient. Just ignore them, Roger.

(And then, angrily:)

I'm not practising! I'm playing a game! Look, what do you think he's here for? Being a bloody referee...? Look, you can see him! Right here!

Right here! For Christ's sake, I've got enough problems! My marriage is breaking up, my life is falling apart, my best friend doesn't even exist, I stand next to no chance of getting my wife back, I've no idea what to say or do, nothing works, and I love her... And I'm a bloody nice person, really worth loving, tender and gentle... So you just keep away from me, or I'll knock your bloody head off!

*(And he exits hastily. **Claire** sits in the kitchen. She is wrapped up in a duvet.)*

Claire *(weakly)* Right. So... Did the earth move for you?... Good, good. Yes, it was fine. It was fine for me. Couldn't have been finer... oh, God, look, I'd say that to Simon. I'd always say that to Simon when we, you know, because... Well. But you're not Simon, you're Roger, and I think I should be honest with you, Roger, completely honest with you, after all, that is what you're there for... I was expecting a little more. I'm not saying it wasn't fine, it was fine... but I was expecting something extra. Like any sensation whatsoever, maybe. Now, I accept that my concentration lapsed a little back there, just for a moment, but I *was* thinking of you, Roger, I was thinking of you very hard, trying to conjure you up... so much it hurt. It hurt. And, I don't know... but I was hoping, so much... I'm so lonely, and all I wanted was someone I could curl up with, bury myself in, and your arms would be around me and my arms would be around you and our bodies would... Well, *fit*... And it's got to be that way. Or it isn't worth having, you can't compromise over something this important. All or nothing. That's all I'm asking for...

(Short pause)

But you're never going to be there, are you? Not really. We're never going to fit. And I have to ask myself. Do I prefer all with Simon? Or nothing with you? I'm going to have to decide. I'll finish the birthday cake, get all the chocolate and currants and caramel and things, bung them all together, and make a final decision. Oh, God. Oh, God...

(Short pause. She sniffs. Stands up bravely.)

Still. I don't want you to get the wrong idea. I'm fine. I'm absolutely fine. And all that, you know... What we did... That was fine. Absolutely.

*(She takes off the duvet, reveals that she is wearing an evening dress. Bright lights on the kitchen. **Simon** enters, still dressed for squash, racquet in hand, in a desperate rush. He tries to recover his breath, leaning against a chair. The lights should be just a little too bright to seem natural, perhaps they are slightly coloured.)*

Claire Simon, are you all right?

Simon I've been… running… all the way… from the squash court…

Claire I see.

Simon I'm dripping. Never been so exhausted… in my life. But I had to see you. I've made a decision, Claire…

Claire *(ominously)* I've finished the birthday cake. Chocolate and chopped fruit and marzipan...

Simon Claire…

Claire And I've made my decision too.

Simon I've got to talk to you about Roger. I don't think he should visit us any more. I think tonight should be our last meal with him.

Claire *(leaving for the cutlery)* Tonight *is* going to be our last meal with him. There's no question of that.

Simon Oh. Good... That's a relief. You'll laugh at this, Claire, you'll laugh at this, but for a while I thought you were going a bit bonkers...

Claire *(offstage)* I'm leaving you, Simon. I'm running away with Roger.

(Short pause)

Simon …Erm.

Claire *(returning, setting the table)* Now, it's no use starting, Simon. I've thought it through, there's nothing you can think of to stop me I haven't thought of myself, and, yes, I know he's your best friend, I know he doesn't exist, but he loves me anyway. I feel he loves me anyway. And I feel it a lot more from him than I do from you.

Simon *(softly)* The cunning bastard... All that time he was giving advice about how to save our marriage, he was seeing you behind my back.

Claire You've been seeing him?

Simon Yes. I thought he could give a few suggestions, lend a few tips.

Claire I think that's ever so sweet of you both.

Simon Every afternoon I'd be teaching him squash, and he'd be laughing at me behind his racquet...

Claire Hang on. What do you mean, every afternoon? He's spent every afternoon with me.

Simon Well, he must... he must have slipped out...

Claire Not possible. We were very... close...

Simon *(slowly)* That doesn't make sense, unless...

Claire We've been seeing different Rogers...

Simon God! There are two of them!

Claire How the hell can there be two of them? What's going on?

Simon I suppose it could be some sort of psychic paranormal mental thing...

Claire Shut up, Simon, what the hell are you playing at, Roger? This isn't what I created you for. Not to go splitting in two and start playing squash. What are you thinking of?

Simon Claire, I think that...

Claire Shut up, Simon. It's a betrayal, that's what it is. What man can you count on if even the one you invent starts being things and doing things without your knowledge?

Simon You could count on me, Claire, I think that...

Claire Shut *up*, Simon, how can I run off with you, Roger, if I don't really know who you are, what you'll end up as, you could end up as anybody, you could end up like *Simon*!

Simon I think that I love you, Claire.

Claire And there'd be no point in you ending up like Simon, I've already got Simon, haven't I? Unless, God. Unless I'm making you end up like Simon. In which case, I suppose, God. I suppose I could have made Simon end up like Simon as well.

Simon I love you, Claire.

Claire It's my fault. I warp people.

Simon I love you.

Claire Don't shut up, Simon. Say it again.

Simon I love you?

Claire ...Yes, no, sorry, it isn't enough. It isn't good enough, it'll never sound the way Roger said it. I'm going to have to run off with him anyway.

Simon Please, Claire, please. I love you. I'm not very good at saying it, I don't know what to do with my hands, but it's true, I *do* love you, I love being with you. Even with Roger, it was you, I'd talk to you, erm, lose squash to you. I love you.

Claire You've turned red as a beetroot.

Simon *(softly)* I know. I'm so sorry.

(Then the doorbell rings.)

Claire It's Roger. He's here!

Simon But which one?

Claire The doorbell's never rung before! We've always had to say 'bing-bong'...

Simon Well, aren't you going to let him in?

Claire I don't want to let him in. Why don't you let him in?

Simon I'm not going to want to let him in, am I? Claire, I love you. We can try again, please let's just try again...

(The doorbell rings again.)

Claire Do something! It is his birthday, after all...

Simon I'm not letting your Roger in, if all he's going to do is run off with you. And if it's my Roger, well, he's a nice bloke, he'll understand.

(The doorbell rings again.)

It's your choice. It's me or him.

Claire No, it's you or *them*. It could be anyroger. At least there's only one of you.

(Pause. Softly)

I think he's gone...

Simon Perhaps we should...

Claire Sssh! He'll realise we're in!

(She reaches for an imaginary light switch. The lights fade to half light. They both get down on their knees and wait.)

I think it's all clear...

Simon I love you, Claire.

Claire Yes, yes...

Simon I love you.

Claire For God's sake, I wait fifteen years for him to start saying it, now he never stops... Would you die for me?

Simon ...Sorry?

Claire Do you love me enough to die for me? Roger would. We've been married for over fifteen years and I think we've reached that position of any normal relationship where I need to know whether you'd die for me.

Simon ...Well, I don't know, I think it depends upon what sort of death we're talking about here, I mean, what do you have in mind?

Claire It's all or nothing, Simon. I made that decision putting on the marzipan.

Simon ...Well, honestly... I'd really rather not, altogether, no. I mean, I don't know, do I? It's never likely to be an issue, is it?

(Short pause)

Look. I'm not Roger. Obviously. And I'm never going to be like him. But I'm not bad. And we've not been bad together, in the long run. We've had some good times.

Claire When?

Simon All right. Fair enough. We haven't had any good times. We can start having them. We could really try to make things better. Come on. Give me a hug.

Claire No guarantees.

Simon No guarantees.

Claire Just because I give you a hug here, doesn't mean tomorrow I don't walk out tomorrow?

Simon Okay.

Claire And you understand, if I'm right, I have warped you into being you, you may well end up even more like you? You can live with that?

Simon I'll take that chance.

(And they hug, tentatively at first, then tighter, with obvious relief.)

Simon This is fun. I'd forgotten how much fun hugging can be.

(They release each other slowly.)

Claire I could take more interest. I could come and watch you play squash.

Simon ...I don't think I'll be playing squash much more. But I'll get my exercise another way. I'll walk with you to the tobacconist's.

Claire All right.

(They kiss.)

...Come on. There's a huge cake out there, with chocolate and chopped fruit and marzipan. Would you like a slice?

Simon No, I said. I don't like marzipan.

Claire It's okay. I'll cut it off for you.

(They kiss again, longer this time. The waltz music grows louder. And then, over even that, we hear the doorbell rung again, insistently, as if someone refuses to take his finger off the button.

(The lights slowly fade to blackout as they kiss, oblivious of this. The waltz music fades out at the same time. In the darkness there is nothing left but the doorbell, which after a few seconds, fades too.)

Fool to Yourself

(1995)

WINNER OF THE INAUGURAL
SOPHIE WINTER MEMORIAL TRUST AWARD

OPENED AT THE STEPHEN JOSEPH THEATRE, SCARBOROUGH,
ON 21ST AUGUST 1997, WITH THE FOLLOWING CAST:
ROBERT RICHARD FREEMAN
BOB NICHOLAS HAVERSON
KAREN FIONA HENDLEY
CARRIE VICTORIA GAY
DOMINIC COLIN GOURLEY
BRIDGET DOROTHY ATKINSON
DIRECTED BY ALAN AYCKBOURN

Act One

(The play is set in the Royal Arms Hotel, a small, uncomfortably furnished hotel. The stage is divided into four basic areas:

(The main bedroom is composed of a double bed and small wardrobe. A telephone stands on a bedside cabinet. Connected by a door and invisible walls is an en suite bathroom. Inside it is a toilet, and bath with shower attachment. A shower curtain can be pulled around the bath.

(There is also, on the opposite side of the stage, another, smaller bedroom. We can only see part of it: indeed, the impression is that it has been cut in half, with a half-bed, half-wardrobe, etc. It is clear though that this is a single bed. The unseen part of the room is covered by one of the stage entrances.

(Both of these areas are technically upstairs: they may be slightly raised on a plinth, but the intention is that they are on the same basic level as the two downstage areas.

(The front door entrance leads into the breakfast room, which is spartanly dressed with two tables.

(The breakfast room borders on to the bar. This is more like it! – it is clear that the hotel landlord takes his bar responsibilities more seriously than any others, and the design reflects this. There are stools by the bar. Over the bar hangs a picture of the Queen. Dependent upon what time the action is taking place in, 1975 or 1995, the picture will be required to rotate between younger and older variants.

*(As the play opens, it is 1975, and the picture of the Queen is pre-jubilee. **Dominic** is cleaning glasses at the bar. Enter **Carrie**, who strides confidently over to him.)*

Carrie You don't have a swimming pool, do you?

Dominic I beg your pardon?

Carrie In your hotel. You don't have a swimming pool?

Dominic No.

Carrie You don't have a gymnasium either?

Dominic No.

Carrie You don't even have running hot water in the rooms.

Dominic Not between the hours of nine and seven, no.

Carrie I think I'm in the wrong hotel.

(Short pause)

Wait. Wait. This is the Royal Arms, isn't it?

Dominic This is the Royal Arms Hotel, miss, yes.

Carrie That's what I thought. The guide says you have a swimming pool and a gymnasium.

Dominic No, miss, that'd be the other Royal Arms Hotel. The one in the town.

Carrie There are two Royal Arms hotels?

Dominic The one in the town. And this one, the one on the hill.

Carrie Well. Is that legal?

Dominic Perfectly.

Carrie And what right have you got to call yourself the Royal Arms? They've had Princess Anne staying there. They've had the Duchess of Kent.

Dominic And we've got a portrait of Her Majesty herself hanging over the bar. That's the real thing, that is.

Carrie Yes.

Dominic None of your princesses and duchesses. We've got the genuine head of state.

Carrie It's a scheme, isn't it? You've got a scheme going with the taxi drivers.

Dominic I beg your pardon?

Carrie You trap people in your hotel by accident. When they think they're going somewhere good.

Dominic I'm sure we lose as many guests to them as they do to us.

Carrie Why? They're a five star hotel! They're a five star hotel recommended in all the tourist brochures and the 1975 Good Food Guide. They've got revolving doors and doormen all dressed in braid and tons of famous people staying there, and... And *class*, they've had royalty dunked in their swimming pool, they've had blue blood... pumping in their gymnasium. And what have you got? You haven't got any stars at all, have you? You're just a grotty little bed and breakfast.

Dominic We have the hill.

Carrie You have the what?

Dominic We're built on the famous hill. One of the most beautiful sights in Britain. People come from miles around. You see, miss, our guests are special, they don't want everything on tap. They come to look at the famous hill and enjoy the rustic scenery.

Carrie But it's raining.

Dominic *(curtly)* Try looking out of a window.

*(Enter **Bob**. He walks to the bar.)*

Carrie *(sighing)* And how am I going to get my exercise now?

Dominic Let me make a suggestion. You want a gymnasium? Then go outside and run around. And you want a swim afterwards, throw yourself in a puddle.

Bob A pint of lager, please.

Dominic Certainly, sir.

Bob Oh. I'm sorry, I interrupted you...

Carrie No, I think he'd finished...

Bob No, really. Very rude. Please, let me buy you a drink.

Carrie There's really no need...

Bob Please.

Carrie Well, all right, I'll have a drink with you. But I'll buy my own, thanks. ...A white wine, please.

*(**Dominic** takes **Bob's** money.)*

Dominic Forty pence, sir.

*(He takes **Carrie's** money. Darker.)*

And forty pence from you.

*(To **Bob**)*

Been out for a walk this morning, sir? I didn't see you at breakfast.

Bob I thought I'd take a stroll. For inspiration. Got very wet.

Dominic Right you are.

Carrie Sorry, are you saying you came here deliberately?

Dominic Of course. He came to see the hill.

Bob *(shyly)* I came to see the hill...

Dominic Mr Hunter is one of our special guests. Special guests, miss. And I never forget any of them.

Bob Cheers.

Carrie Yes.

(Dominic drifts to the other side of the bar, resumes cleaning glasses. Pause. Bob looks at Carrie nervously.)

Bob So. Erm. Do you... do you come here often?

Carrie *(surprised)* I'm sorry?

Bob Here. Often, do you come?

Carrie *(not offended)* ...Well, I must say, that's a pretty lame chat-up line. I'm sure you could do better than that.

Bob No, I...

Carrie Still. At least you didn't say, 'Haven't I seen you somewhere before?' I'm always getting that one.

Bob Really?

Carrie Yes. Embarrassing, isn't it?

(Short pause)

Bob So. Erm. Do you then?

Carrie Do I what?

Bob Come here often?

Carrie ...No.

Bob Oh.

(Short pause. Bob turns back to his drink mournfully.)

Carrie Try a bit harder, Mr Hunter... What's your first name?

Bob Robert.

Carrie I'm Karen.

(They shake hands.)

Bob Karen. That's lovely.

Carrie Yes. Now, you offered to buy me a drink, but I bought one for myself. So no luck there. You tried a terrible chat-up line, that didn't work. What next?

Bob I don't know. I'm not very good at this...

Carrie You could try asking me about myself. Find out what I do, for instance...

Bob Oh. What do you...

Carrie But then I'd tell you I'm a secretary, which is a bit of a conversation killer. So, we'll just have to keep our fingers crossed that *you* do something interesting.

Bob *(optimistically)* Yes. All right.

Carrie ...What do you do?

Bob *(shy pride)* Well. I'm a poet.

Carrie *(genuinely interested)* A poet? What, really? Would I have heard of you?

Bob *(embarrassed, pleased)* Well, you might have done...

Carrie Someone famous. How exciting. Robert Hunter. No, I haven't.

Bob That's why I came to the hill. Thought I could try some pastoral verses.

Carrie Any luck?

Bob *(looking at **Dominic**, then conspiratorially)* Well, no. The hill... Well, it's just a hill, frankly. And besides, it's raining. So my paper got too wet.

Carrie How much have you had published?

Bob Oh. I haven't had anything *published*...

Carrie So why do you think I might have heard of you?

Bob *(lamely)* I don't know... You might have done.

(Short pause)

Would you like to hear one?

Carrie Go on then. Might as well.

Bob Okay.

Carrie Sod all else to do.

Bob *(clearing his throat, then earnestly)* I wish I loved you more / But my heart can rise no higher...

*(**Carrie** chokes on her drink with laughter.)*

Carrie Oh God, no, that's just awful!

Bob Is it? I thought it was quite good.

Carrie No, no. Terrible stuff. ...I tell you, Robert, if you want to get into my bedroom, you're going to have to think of something a little more cunning than that.

*(Short pause. **Bob** stares at her, startled.)*

Bob God. Well, I... God.

*(And in his awkwardness, he knocks the glass of white wine over **Carrie's** lap.*

(Pause. She looks down at it, then at him decisively.)

Carrie Yes. That'll do. Come on.

*(And she takes him by the hand, and they get to their feet. She towers over him by several feet. She considers this, shrugs, then runs with the perplexed **Bob** offstage.*

(And as they exit, lights change. It is now 1995. The picture of the Queen over the bar slowly turns round to reveal a portrait of her twenty years older.

*(**Dominic** and **Bridget**, his wife, enter. **Bridget** stands rigid, as **Dominic** instructs her.)*

Dominic Okay. Smiling practice. Come on.

*(**Bridget** contorts her face into a smile.)*

Open a little wider. A little wider, a little wider, that's too wide. Show your teeth a little. Just the teeth, not the gums. That's good, that's great, hold it, hold it...

Bridget *(smiling fiercely)* Do we have to do this?

Dominic *(absorbed)* I should say so, yes. First guests here for a fortnight, I should say so. We want to make the right impression when they arrive. Now, that's grinning, not smiling. Don't grin, we don't want to frighten them off...

Bridget *(still smiling)* I need to ask you. About the roof.

Dominic The roof is not important, Bridget.

Bridget That builder who stayed here said it could fall apart any minute.

Dominic Builder! Probably just touting for work...

Bridget Please get someone in, Dominic, I'd feel much happier.

Dominic Do you remember the comments book we had at reception? Do you, Bridget?

Bridget Yes.

Dominic While we still had guests here to comment. Do you remember?

Bridget I said yes.

Dominic And what did they write? Loved the famous hill. Enjoyed the rustic scenery. How many people do you think wrote, 'nice roof'?

Bridget Dominic...

Dominic Go on. Take a stab. It's a nice round figure.

Bridget All right...

Dominic No-one. Because roofs, Bridget, aren't bloody important. All right? No-one has ever stayed here because of the roof. All right?

Bridget *(face falling)* I'm sorry...

Dominic Don't let the face drop! Back up, back up. And if you could try a smidgen more sincerity, that'd be a help.

*(Enter **Robert** and **Karen**. **Robert** is carrying a suitcase.)*

Robert *(cheerfully)* Well, here we are!

Karen Oh my God.

Robert You recognise it? Are you surprised?

Karen Shocked.

Dominic *(expansively)* Mr and Mrs Hunter, welcome to the Royal Arms Hotel! I hope while you're here you have a wonderful time, looking at the famous hill, enjoying the rustic scenery...

Karen It hasn't changed at all. It's exactly the same. It's like my worst nightmare.

Dominic My name is Dominic Bradshaw, proprietor of this establishment. And this is Bridget, my wife... smile!

Bridget *(shyly)* Hello.

Dominic Any service we can...

Karen *(angrily)* Robert! Why the hell have you brought me back here?

Robert It's romantic. I thought it'd be a surprise.

Karen I hate surprises!

Robert Not always you don't.

Dominic Any service we can provide, don't hesitate...

Karen Go on then. Tell me. When have I ever enjoyed one of your surprises?

Robert ...When I proposed?

Karen *(gritted teeth)* More recently.

Dominic *(giving up)* Yeah, anyway, have a really great time here. Whatever.

Robert Oh. Yes. Sorry. Thanks.

Dominic I hope while you're here you'll be able to visit the famous hill. Great historical importance.

Karen Seen it. Been here before.

Dominic *(smiling)* Have you? Yes, of course, I thought I recognised you! I never forget special guests! And you were special guests, weren't you?

Robert *(pleased)* Well, it's nice to be remembered...

Dominic Mr and Mrs Hunter. Yes, about a year ago, wasn't it?

Bridget *(eagerly)* The couple who got food poisoning?

Dominic Shut up, Bridget...

Robert No, twenty years ago, November 197...

Dominic Don't tell me, it'll come back! Never forget a face...

Karen *(coolly)* I doubt you saw much of our faces at all. We spent our entire stay here twenty years ago banging each other in one of your uncomfortably cramped bedrooms.

(Short pause. We hear distantly the break of thunder.)

Dominic Yes, well, anyway. Bridget, would you take the suitcase and show them to their room.

Bridget Certainly.

(She tries to pick up the case, but it is far too heavy. She practically falls over trying to manage it.)

Robert Perhaps I can take that...

Dominic No need, sir. Bridget is fully qualified. ...Keep smiling!

Robert No, really, it might be quicker...

*(And he rescues **Bridget**.)*

Bridget I'm sorry.

*(To **Dominic**)*

Sorry.

*(**Dominic** gives her a filthy look.)*

This way.

*(**Robert** and **Karen** head in the direction indicated by **Bridget**. **Bridget** makes to follow, but is held back by **Dominic**.)*

Dominic If you ruin this for us, Bridget...

*(And, unnerved, she runs off after **Robert** and **Karen**.)*

(Lights on the main bedroom as they near it. We hear another clap of thunder, closer this time.)

Bridget I do hope you enjoy the room. It's my favourite. En suite bathroom, very airy.

Karen How many other people are staying here at the moment?

Bridget Well, there's me and my husband.

Karen Christ, Robert, we're the only ones here. This is embarrassing...

Bridget *(softly, producing a key to unlock the door)* It's off peak...

Karen *(to **Robert**)* How did you find this place after so long?

Robert It wasn't easy. Even directory enquiries wouldn't help. They kept giving me the Royal Arms in the town. You don't want to stay in that other one, they said, it's horrible. I had to get very insistent.

Karen *(dryly)* Good going, Robert.

(They all step into the room.)

Bridget *(cheerfully)* Here we are...

Karen Wait. I think there's been a mistake. This is a double bed.

Bridget Nice and well-springed...

Karen My husband would have booked a twin room, not a double. Or even two singles. We don't sleep together any more, do we, Robert?

Bridget I think it was a double...

Robert Karen...

Karen You did, didn't you? You booked a double room!

Bridget Very well-springed...

Robert I thought you wouldn't notice...

Karen Two years sleeping apart, you thought I wouldn't notice...

Robert I thought it would be a surprise for you...

Karen *(more softly)* Robert. If you wanted to sleep with me again, you needn't have gone to all this bother. You should have just asked me.

Robert I'm sorry.

Karen I'd have said no, but it would have saved a bit of money.

Robert *(slight outburst)* It isn't natural! No-one has a headache for two years!

Karen Well, I don't like it! It's slimy and sweaty and sticky!

Bridget *(awkwardly)* Erm. And through here's the bathroom.

(She demonstrates; opens the door, waves her hand back and forth over the threshold.)

Like that.

Karen Sorry. Thank you very much, Mrs...

Bridget Bridget. Anything you want, just give me a call.

Robert Thank you.

Bridget *(eagerly)* Pick up the phone and dial nought. Or, if you prefer, reception's right beneath you, just bang on the floor if you like.

Karen Right.

Bridget ...You know how to use the phone, don't you? Just pick up the receiver...

Karen Yes.

Robert Yes.

Bridget Yes. Right. Well... I'd better be going then. But do call. If you want a chat or something.

Robert I think we'll be all right.

Bridget *(slight desperation)* If you get lonely or anything, and want to hear a friendly voice.

(Short pause)

I'll be going then.

Dominic *(raising his head and shouting upwards)* Bridget? Are you still up there?

Bridget Oh, please! Don't tell him I'm here!

Robert But you...

Bridget He hates it if I hog the guests! I'll just hide in the bathroom.

(She runs into the bathroom, closes the door.

*(**Dominic** enters the bedroom.)*

Dominic Sorry to disturb you. Have you seen my wife?

Robert Well, I...

Karen No.

*(**Dominic** hesitates, then walks across the room and pushes open the bathroom door.)*

Bridget *(bravely)* Hello, dear. Just checking the bathroom. It seems fine.

*(**Dominic** looks back at **Karen** coldly.)*

Karen *(coolly)* I forgot.

Bridget *(nervously)* She forgot, Dominic. Easily done. You're always telling me how forgettable I am...

*(But **Dominic** doesn't break eye contact with **Karen**. Then he exits, **Bridget** following fast behind.)*

Remember, anything you want, the slightest thing, you know where I am...

(She points downwards.)

Just thump.

*(And she leaves the bedroom. Outside it **Dominic** is waiting for her.)*

Dominic *(sighing, calm)* Bridget, Bridget, Bridget. You must stop doing this. The guests don't want to speak to you. They want to speak to each other.

Bridget I get so lonely, Dom.

Dominic Well, that's what I'm for, isn't it?

Bridget Dominic. Just an idea. In the future... rather than having a double room... could *we* have a twin? Or two singles?

*(Short pause. **Dominic** stares at her.)*

Dominic *(slowly)* Have you ever asked yourself why I married you, Bridget?

Bridget Frequently, actually...

Dominic And what's the answer you come up with?

Bridget I don't know...

Dominic Well. Was it for the conversation? Do you think it was for the conversation? No. Or the company, maybe?

Bridget I do good cooked breakfasts, I do them well...

Dominic It was for the sex, Bridget. For sex. I made that quite clear when I proposed to you.

Bridget *(faintly)* Oh yes, I remember.

Dominic So don't think you can wheedle out of it now.

*(They exit. Lights solely on the bedroom. Rain is pouring outside. Both **Karen** and **Robert** evidently haven't been speaking for a while. **Karen** talks dispassionately as she unpacks the suitcase.)*

Karen Tonight you sleep in the bath. And tomorrow we're leaving.

Robert Why are you unpacking then?

Karen It's just the way I am, Robert, I can't sleep with a packed suitcase. Sorry, I'm just not that spontaneous... Why have you brought me back here? Where we first met? I don't want to be reminded of that, do I?

(Pause.)

Robert I'm sorry. I just thought it would be romantic.

Karen It was smug, Robert. That's what it was. You in the car, driving. Me not having a bloody clue where we're going. Smug.

Robert So. I've failed again.

Karen *(not unkindly)* Yep. 'Fraid so.

(She sighs, takes out a nightie, unfolds it. She looks at it thoughtfully.)

I'm a failure. Basically. If you look at it.

Robert What? Oh. Erm, rubbish.

Karen I'm forty-five years old. And I can't think of one thing I've done which I can feel proud of. Not one thing I can actually call an achievement, say, look, that's an achievement, that is.

Robert You're just being silly, Karen.

Karen Don't call me silly. Not one thing, Robert. And do you know why that is? Do you know why my life's a failure?

Robert I wish you'd stop unpacking for a moment...

Karen Because I married you. That's why.

(Short pause)

Nothing personal.

Robert ...I wish you'd leave the clothes alone. Why did you pack a bikini, for God's sake? It's November.

Karen We're failures, Robert. Both of us, failures.

Robert I'm not a failure.

Karen You are.

Robert I'm not. I'm very happy as a poetry teacher.

Karen You're miserable.

Robert I'm not.

Karen You don't get on with the children, you don't get on with the staff...

Robert Some of them are all right...

Karen They all hate you and you hate them.

Robert They don't know me very well...

Karen Face it, Robert. We've taken our lives and done absolutely nothing with them. And I'm forty-five, Robert. With medical technology and a good diet, I could reach ninety, I might only be half way. And, God, I hope I do more in the second half than I did with the first. More than getting married and pregnant. God, I hope so. Because I had ambitions, Robert, before you got in the way. I wasn't going to be a secretary for ever, I know that.

Robert What ambitions?

Karen I don't know what ambitions, I've forgotten, it was a long time ago! And friends, God, yes, I used to have tons of friends. When I was at school, everyone wanted to be my friend, I had to turn lots down, I kept a very select group. I haven't got any friends at all now, not a single one.

Robert You've got me.

Karen You're not a friend, you're a husband.

Robert Oh.

Karen And I only started losing them when I met you. And that's because we're a ridiculous couple. We look awful together. When we go out shopping, everyone in the supermarket stops and points.

Robert (*overlapping*) Not all of them...

Karen You're a homonculus, and I'm Godzilla.

Robert You're angry at me because I'm short?

Karen No.

Robert Stop hanging things up for a minute, please. You used to laugh at our size difference.

Karen (*coldly*) I never laughed. It's no laughing matter.

Robert Stop hanging things up.

(*She does, looks at him directly. Short pause*)

I love you, Karen.

(*Short pause. Then she turns back to the unpacking.*

(*In the breakfast room, enter **Bridget** in a night dress. Dim light on her as she sits down on one of the chairs and stares into the distance unhappily.*)

Karen Things have changed. Okay, fair enough. Got to expect change in twenty years. Except for the fact that the type of person you've changed into is precisely the type of person the type of person I've changed into can't stand. You're not the man I married.

(*Pause; thunder. A flash of lightning plays across the stage.*)

Robert (*boldly, cruelly*) Well, you're not the woman I married either!

Karen Of course I'm not the woman you married! I had friends then, and ambitions! Being married to you has warped me!

(*In the breakfast room, enter **Dominic** in a dressing gown. Slightly brighter light on this area. He stands awkwardly, some feet from her.*)

Dominic Are you all right, Bridget? Are you all right, love?

*(**Bridget** does not react. Short pause.*

*(**Robert** sighs, sits down on the bed. **Karen** returns to her unpacking. Neither look at the other.)*

What are you doing down here in the dark? Love? Did the storm wake you? Love?

(Short pause)

It's gone one in the morning, love. Don't you think you'd rather be in bed? Rather be in bed than sitting down here in the dark? And the cold? Come on. Busy day tomorrow. You've got to make breakfast first thing. You can't make breakfast if you're tired.

(Short pause)

Bridget?

Bridget What?

Dominic You'll catch cold. You can't make breakfast if you catch cold. You'll start coughing, get germs all over the food. Did the storm wake you, love? The storm woke me. And I rolled closer to you, to get warm, you know how I do. Sleep against your warm skin. And there wasn't any warm skin there, it was very disconcerting. I just kept rolling and rolling, Bridget. I fell out of bed.

(Short pause)

Could have broken my back, Bridget. You wouldn't want that, would you? Did the storm wake you, love? Did the... the storm... Look. Look, could you bloody well say something, please? I mean, I'm standing here in the dark and the cold trying to be nice, and it's gone one in the morning...

Bridget The storm didn't wake me.

Dominic Good. Come back to bed.

Bridget No.

Robert *(sitting on bed, still not looking at **Karen**, softly)* You're right, of course. I'm not liked at school. All the boys call me 'prat'. Which wouldn't be so bad, there are worse things they could call me, you should hear what they call some of the PE teachers! But it's right to my face. Calling out the register: Abercrombie? Yes, prat. Bywater? Yes, prat. Even the headmaster gets up to it. 'Morning, headmaster'. 'Morning, prat'.

(He looks at her. Short pause)

I had ambitions too, remember. I wanted to be a poet. And you laughed at it.

Karen That's because it was drivel.

Robert Yes. I know it was. But I might have got better. Perhaps. If I hadn't stopped. If I hadn't taken your advice.

Karen Yes, well, don't worry about that. I don't give advice to anyone any more, haven't for years. Being this much of a failure, I don't think I'm in any position to.

Robert And what about Douglas?

Karen What about him?

Robert Well, what's he going to say? It'll be a bit of a shock to him. Finding out his parents don't love each other any more.

Karen God, Robert, he already knows. Douglas has all the sensitivity of a bucket, but even he must have worked it out by now.

Dominic This is about earlier, isn't it? Is this about earlier? I hope this isn't about earlier, because that would be really stupid. Really stupid, Bridget. Is this about earlier?

Bridget Why do you do those things?

Dominic Oh come on. That's just me joking.

Bridget It's humiliating.

Dominic I'm a kidder. You know that. I'm always kidding.

Bridget You're not always kidding. Sometimes you're not kidding.

Dominic Well, no, okay, sometimes I'm not kidding, no. I can't kid all the time, I'm only human.

Bridget I don't want you kidding at all. I can't tell when you're kidding and you're not kidding any more.

Dominic You should be able to tell the difference. You're my wife. What's a wife for, if she can't tell the difference...?

Bridget And in front of strangers too. They can't tell you're kidding. If I can't tell you're kidding, what chance have they got?

Dominic They're only guests. Who cares what they think? Sod them.

Bridget If you could just make it more obvious when you're kidding.

Dominic Obvious? In what way?

Bridget I don't know. You put me down, insult me, whatever. But at the end you give a little laugh. Something like that.

Dominic A little laugh?

Bridget Or a chuckle.

Dominic Rather spoil the joke, don't you think?

Karen Getting any reaction from Douglas at all would be a miracle. Slumped in front of his computer games, headphones jammed over his ears. It's all I ever hear from him these days. Thumping bass music and the occasional blip.

Robert No, he's a good lad...

Karen And if I ever do confront him, you know, get actual words out of him rather than sound effects, it's always the same. Are you all right, Douglas? What would you like for tea, Douglas? He'll just grunt, 'You're not my real mother', and go back to his bedroom to blow up aliens.

Robert Well...

Karen Which I am, actually. It was a very uncomfortable process, I'm not likely to forget it.

Robert It's just a phase he's going through. Kids always go through phases.

Karen Yes, but how long is this bloody phase going to last? He's fifteen. He's been like this since he was eight.

Robert Well, he's a good lad, really.

Karen I don't like him, Robert. I don't like him at all. He wasn't worth the morning sickness and the labour pains and the pushing. If I'd known it was going to end up like this, a fat bulk who grunts, I wouldn't have bothered. I'm telling you. If he weren't my son, and I saw him walking towards me on the pavement, I'd cross the road. I would.

Robert *(gently)* You did cross the road.

Karen Just the once. Typical. The one time I do it, and that's the time he bothers to give me a second look.

Robert We've got to solve these problems between us, Karen. For his sake.

Karen You're out of touch, Robert. All of his schoolfriends... They're all from broken families. We're the abnormal ones. The ones who haven't been divorced yet, we get stared at in supermarkets. And I am not, I cannot wait until my son has evolved from neanderthal state before I leave you.

(Short pause)

Robert So you are leaving me then? Karen?

(Short pause)

I wish you'd stop hanging things up.

(Short pause)

I'm going for a little walk.

(He exits.

*(Underneath the following, **Karen** takes a bottle of vodka out of the suitcase. She looks at it for a while, then decisively swigs from it. She puts it under the bed.)*

Bridget It's just that sometimes I really think things are closing in, they're just closing in and going to crush me. Sometimes, quite often in fact. And everything's getting darker and colder, Dominic, and your kidding isn't making me laugh, I really feel I'm going to get lost in it all, it's just making it even more dark and cold.

(Short pause)

Dominic Well, you shouldn't sit down here in the cold then, should you? And the dark.

(Short pause)

God, I don't know, Bridget. I wish I could make you understand. You keep on thinking there's something wrong, you're always doing this. But there isn't. Everything's all right between us. We're very happy. Both of us, very happy. If I could only drum that into you...

Bridget I'm sorry.

Dominic *(genially)* You know what it is, don't you? It's that overactive imagination of yours again. Thinking things are wrong when they aren't. And it's silly, because most of the time you don't think at all, do you? You walk around without a thought in that pretty little head of yours. And then, suddenly, whoosh! Too many thoughts at once.

Bridget But it does feel that there's something very wrong, Dominic. It does really.

Dominic Take it from me, Bridget. With thinking. Little and often, that's the way.

Bridget I'll try to remember.

Dominic That's what I do.

(Short pause)

But I'm sorry. If I've... You know.

Bridget You hurt me.

Dominic You said.

Bridget It actually hurt.

Dominic Well, I'm sorry. If it did.

Bridget ...Say what you say sometimes.

Dominic What?

Bridget What you say. You know.

(Short pause)

Dominic You're my world. You're my everything.

Bridget ...But how do I know you're not kidding now? Do you see?

Dominic I didn't stick a chuckle at the end.

*(Re-enter **Robert**, a little shamefaced.)*

Karen You're back then.

Robert Well, there wasn't really anywhere to go...

Dominic Really. I don't know what I'd do without you. You're everything to me.

*(He offers **Bridget** his hand. She takes it, gets up. He gives her a hug. She gratefully accepts.)*

I love you.

Bridget Oh, Dominic. Why can't you be like this all the time?

Dominic *(a little embarrassed)* Well. You'd find it boring, wouldn't you?

Bridget No. No, it'd be wonderful. It'd be wonderful if you were always like this.

Dominic *(a little firmer, letting her go)* No. It'd be boring.

Bridget ...Yes. If you say so.

Karen *(kindly)* God, I was naive back then. I believed that when you poured that wine over me, it was an elaborate come-on. I thought, aha, now here's a lover of real cunning.

Robert No, sorry.

Karen No. It took me years to realise you were just very clumsy.

Dominic *(gently)* Come on. Are you coming to bed now?

Bridget Yes.

Karen For years I kept on wondering, well, where's he gone? This Casanova? The man who cuts a dash with the Chardonnay?

Dominic And no more silly little thoughts? Thinking all done?

Bridget Yes.

Dominic Come on then. I love you. Give me a smile.

(She smiles happily.)

No. A little wider. And don't show your teeth so much. That's it.

(He puts his arm around her shoulder. As the exit together.)

Remember, you've got to do the breakfast tomorrow.

(Lights fade on this area.)

Robert *(smiling)* I seduced you really well, didn't I?

Karen *(smiling)* You were very good.

Robert It was a fun holiday, wasn't it? Breakfast in bed...

Karen Practically everything in bed.

Robert It was fun.

Karen And I remember, we went up to my bedroom. My skirt was still wet, of course, though it wasn't that bad really. And in the doorway you picked me up in your arms and carried me over the threshold.

Robert I'd heard that's what you were meant to do. I didn't realise you were supposed to be married.

Karen It was so unnecessary. It was lovely.

Robert I don't really have to sleep in the bath tonight, do I?

Karen *(softly)* No.

Robert *(a thought)* ...You're not sleeping in the bath either?

Karen No. We'll both sleep in the bed.

Robert In the bed. Together. Great.

(Gently he kisses her.)

Karen *(softly)* No, Robert. I don't want that.

Robert I still love you, Karen.

(He kisses her again, on the cheek.)

Karen ...No, I'm sorry. I'm sorry, but... It's too late, you... You're a different person. I'm a different person. Both of us, we're different people, and I... it's too late. I'm sorry.

*(**Robert** moves away. **Karen** hesitates, then she turns and kisses him passionately.*

*(Lights fade and music plays as **Robert** and **Karen** exit. We hear thunder and rain behind the music.*

*(Lights rise on the breakfast room, the next morning. **Bridget** sits at one of the tables. As **Robert** enters, she gets up and stands to attention. The music fades, leaving the sound of rain.)*

Robert *(cheerfully)* Good morning!

*(**Bridget** nervously pulls out a chair for him.)*

Bridget Good morning, sir. I'm sorry there's no hot water. It just doesn't seem to want to come out...

Robert Oh, don't worry about the hot water! There's more to life than hot water, isn't there?

Bridget I expect so. Did you sleep well?

Robert Off and on.

Bridget Would you like a cooked breakfast?

Robert Yes, please, a cooked breakfast with everything, I'm starving. And one for my wife too, she'll be down in a minute.

Bridget Very well.

(She exits.)

Karen There's no hot water! Can you believe it, there's no hot water!

Robert *(cheerfully)* Good morning!

Karen Not too much to expect, a bit of hot water, is it? Thought I'd take a nice warm shower, the nozzle started spitting little ice cubes at me.

Robert Don't worry about the hot water! There's more to life than hot water!

Karen Shut up.

(*Dominic* *enters the bar area, dressed as at the beginning of the play. He starts cleaning glasses.*)

Robert You're not in a very good mood, are you?

Karen No.

Robert That's a pity. Because I am. I'm in a great mood. Couldn't be greater, my mood.

Karen I'd forgotten how you always take all the covers.

Robert (*chuckling*) Did I really? I'd forgotten how I used to do that too.

Karen Robert, this is not one of those endearing husband-wife things, it's bloody annoying. I was freezing last night.

Robert (*warmly*) Just like old times, eh?

Karen Until I stepped in the shower and actually froze.

(*Enter **Bridget**, with two cooked breakfasts.*)

Bridget Good morning. Did you sleep well?

Karen What's this? This is a cooked breakfast. I never eat cooked breakfasts.

Bridget Oh. Your husband said...

Karen Oh well, if my husband said, then that explains it.

Bridget Would you like some cereal? Or some toast?

Karen Could I just have a coffee, please? Strong and black.

Bridget A black coffee.

Karen Very strong, very black.

Robert I didn't know you didn't like cooked breakfasts.

Karen When have you ever seen me eating a cooked breakfast?

Robert Well, never. But then you never see me eat a cooked breakfast. And I love a cooked breakfast.

Karen The reason you never eat cooked breakfasts is because I don't cook you cooked breakfasts. Because I don't like cooked breakfasts.

(*Carrie* *enters the breakfast room. She is dressed as at the beginning of the play.*

*(During the argument between **Karen** and **Robert**, **Bridget** has been slowly backing away, not wanting to intrude, but uncertain that it would be exactly polite to leave either. **Carrie's** entrance gives her an excuse, and she walks to **Carrie's** table with relief.)*

Robert ...You really are in a bad mood, aren't you?

Bridget Good morning. Did you sleep well?

Robert Well, I'm just glad that everything's sorted out between us.

Karen Are you?

Robert Mmm, sausage!

Karen I still don't love you, Robert.

Robert ...Oh. But I thought after...

Karen We made love. Doesn't mean I'm in love.

Bridget Would you like a cooked breakfast?

Carrie No, thank you. I never eat cooked breakfasts.

Robert But you suggested we made love. It was your idea.

Karen Only because you were sighing and grunting and sulking and I wanted to get some sleep.

Robert ...You've put me right off this sausage.

Karen And even then you took the covers.

Bridget Would you like some cereal then? Or some toast?

Carrie No, thank you.

Bridget Some orange juice? A coffee?

Carrie Do you have a swimming pool?

Karen Stop sulking.

Robert *(destroyed)* I'm not, I... I just can't think of anything to say...

Karen Eat your sausage then.

Bridget This is a breakfast room.

Carrie I know this is a breakfast room. But do you have a swimming pool?

Bridget ...Start again.

Robert I just can't believe... After the fun we had last night, the first time in years...

Karen Just because we made love once, Robert, it doesn't solve anything.

Robert We didn't make love once! It was three times! Three bloody times!

Karen Well, it all blurred into one for me.

Carrie Never mind.

*(**Bridget** nods, confused, and exits. **Carrie** drums her fingers on the table, thoughtfully.)*

Robert I don't love you either then. So there.

Karen What?

Robert If you're not going to love me, I'm not going to love you either.

Karen This is pathetic.

(She gets up and exits.

*(Decisively **Carrie** gets up and walks to the bar.*

(The picture of the Queen slowly turns to that of 1975.)

Robert That's right, you just run away! Just because you can't argue against the logic of it! *(He bites into his sausage sulkily.)* This is awful.

Carrie *(to **Dominic**)* You don't have a swimming pool, do you?

Dominic I beg your pardon?

Carrie In your hotel. You don't have a swimming pool?

Dominic No.

Carrie You don't have a gymnasium either?

*(**Bridget** walks to **Robert's** table with the coffee.)*

Bridget Here you are. One very strong, very black coffee.

Robert She's gone.

Bridget Oh. Doesn't she want the coffee?

Robert I wouldn't have thought so.

Bridget But I've made it now! Would you like it?

Robert No. I think I need something stronger.

Bridget This is very strong. Very black.

Robert I think I'll go to the bar.

(He gets up. Helpfully:)

You can have the coffee, if you like.

*(Underneath the following, **Karen** enters the bedroom, begins packing the suitcase again with determination.)*

*(**Robert** walks to the bar.)*

Dominic No, miss, that'd be the other Royal Arms Hotel. The one in the town.

Carrie There are two Royal Arms hotels?

Dominic The one in the town. And this one, the one on the hill.

Carrie Well. Is that legal?

Robert A pint of lager, please.

Dominic *(gratefully)* Certainly, sir.

(The picture slowly turns to 1995, and until specified, continues turning, as if unsure which year to plump for.)

Robert Sorry, did I interrupt you...?

Carrie Yes, as it happens.

Robert Sorry... Can I buy you a drink? To apologise?

Carrie It's all right. I'll buy my own, thanks. ...A white wine, please.

Dominic Forty pence from you.

*(To **Robert**)*

And one pound eighty from you.

Carrie *(shocked)* How much?

Robert Forty pence for a glass of wine? That's incredible.... All right, why not, I'll have a glass of wine then!

*(He smiles at **Carrie**.)*

Can't be bad, eh?

Dominic That's one pound ninety then, sir.

Robert What?

Dominic One pound ninety.

Carrie *(in disbelief)* One pound ninety for a glass of wine?

Dominic No, miss. It's forty pence for a glass of wine.

Carrie *(relieved)* That's what I'd have thought! I mean, for one pound ninety...

Dominic *(laughing)* You could practically buy an entire off licence!

Robert *(laughing as well)* Well, here's forty pence then!

Dominic *(the laughter stopping)* What's that for, sir? A bag of peanuts?

Robert For a glass of wine.

Dominic *(irritated)* I told you. It's one pound ninety.

Robert Well, how come it's forty pence for her?

Dominic *(confused)* It just is. A glass of wine... for her is forty pence. For you... it's one pound ninety. No, hang on...

Carrie That doesn't make sense.

Robert I call it blatant favouritism.

Dominic Surely, that can't be...

(And he shakes his head decisively, as if trying to shake something.)

Well, that's just the way it is. Do you want a glass of white wine or not?

Robert Yes.

Dominic Right then. So stop being silly, both of you.

Carrie Don't call me silly.

*(And slowly **Robert** turns to stare at her.)*

One pound ninety. I'd complain if I were you... Are you all right?

Robert Yes, I... I'm sorry, but haven't I seen you somewhere before?

*(As before, enter **Bob**. He walks to the bar, to sit down next to **Robert**, but behind his back.)*

Carrie *(laughing)* Well, I must say, that's a pretty lame chat-up line. I'm sure you could do better than that.

Robert No, I really mean it, I know you from somewhere...

Carrie Still. At least you didn't say, 'Do you come here often?' I'm always getting that one.

Robert Really?

Carrie Yes. Embarrassing, isn't it?

Bob A pint of lager, please.

Dominic Certainly, sir.

Carrie Try a bit harder... What's your name?

Robert Robert.

Carrie I'm Karen.

(They shake hands.)

Robert Karen. That's a nice name.

Dominic *(to **Bob**)* Forty pence from you, sir.

Robert My wife. Her name's Karen too.

Carrie Your wife? ...Yes. ...I tell you, Robert, if you want to get into my bedroom, you're going to have to think of something a little more tactful than that.

Robert *(softly)* My God. You're...

*(And he turns round slowly, eyes wide, to face **Bob**.)*

Dominic Been out for a walk this morning, sir? I didn't see you at breakfast.

Bob I thought I'd take a stroll. For inspiration. Got very wet.

*(And in his shock, **Robert**, staring at **Bob**, clumsily knocks the glass of wine over **Carrie's** skirt. He winces, turns back to look at her slowly.)*

Carrie Yes. That'll do. Come on.

*(And she pulls the still stunned **Robert** to his feet. Again, she towers over him. Then she runs with him offstage.*

(The picture settles on 1975.)

Bob Excuse me.

Dominic Mr Hunter?

Bob Could I have some writing paper, please?

Dominic Writing paper? No, sir. This is a bar.

Bob *(lamely)* I thought I might write some poetry... And my paper got a bit wet... No, it's okay.

Dominic Writing paper. Absurd. My special guests don't get up to a lot of writing. They prefer looking at the famous hill. Or enjoying the rustic scenery.

Bob Fine. *(And he takes his pint over to a breakfast table. He waves some water off his sheet of paper, drapes it over the table.)* Now then. ...Yes. I think I'll write an ode.

*(**Robert** and **Carrie** enter **Carrie's** half-bedroom. **Carrie** almost immediately disappears from view.)*

Robert Look, I'm sorry about that, I hope you don't think I was...

*(From offstage **Carrie** throws her dress to him; he catches it inexpertly.)*

God, you're taking your clothes off...

Carrie I've got to change. I'm sure I'm not showing you anything you haven't seen before...

Robert No, well, you're certainly right there...

Carrie It doesn't matter, I've brought lots of clothes with me.

Robert Yes, you always overpacked your suitcase...

(Another article of clothing is caught.)

Excuse me for asking. You say your name is Karen?

Carrie That's right.

Robert Karen Brewer. It wouldn't be Karen Brewer, would it?

*(Short pause. Re-enter **Carrie**, barely dressed. She stares at him.)*

Carrie ...How did you know that?

Robert Your name's Karen Brewer. Second name's Priscilla, but you don't like people to know that, don't know why. Born on 26th January 1950... somewhere in Kent? Or near Kent? What else. You don't like dogs because you find them too dependent, if you had a pet, it'd be a cat, but they make you sneeze. You don't like cooked breakfasts. Your favourite meal is spaghetti bolognaise, but not the way I'd cook it, because you say the pasta's too stringy. There's a mole on your thigh, you call it a beauty spot, but actually it's a mole. Though it is still very beautiful. Just checking. You're that Karen Brewer?

(Short pause.

*(In the main bedroom, **Karen** sits down on the bed with despair. She fishes under the bed for the bottle of vodka.)*

Carrie That's incredible. How do you... Well. That's amazing. Do you do that for a living?

Robert Oh. Yes. Well, obviously there's a lot of money to be made out of telling people their name and how they have pasta.

Carrie *(missing the irony)* I bet there is. I bet there is. That's genius, that is. Are you famous? Would I have heard of you?

Robert *(slowly)* Let's just say I'm sure you'll hear a lot of me in the future.

Carrie I've always wanted to meet someone famous. Are you going to get undressed?

(Short pause)

Robert Don't you find me a little short?

Carrie Well, you are a little short, yes...

Robert Don't you think that I'm a homonculus, and you're, well...

Carrie I think it's quite funny.

Robert Godzilla. What?

Carrie Me tall, you short. Don't you think it's funny?

Robert I knew you found it funny...!

(She undoes his flies.)

No, no, wait. Karen. Tell me. The year. What year is this?

Carrie *(blankly)* 1975, of course.

Robert Yes. Right.

Carrie You know so much about me, but you don't know the year. Still. I suppose that's what geniuses are like, isn't it? Brain works differently. Can't expect them to be normal. Not when you're abnormally gifted.

(She puts her hand through his flies.)

What other areas are you gifted in?

Robert *(jumping back, pulling flies up)* 1975, is that the time? I really must be going.

Carrie Oh. But I will see you later, won't I?

Robert Oh yes. I think I can guarantee that.

(He exits.

*(**Carrie** sighs, retreats to the other side of the bedroom, presumably to get dressed.*

(*Bridget* enters the main bedroom, carrying a cup of coffee.)

Bridget I hope I'm not disturbing you, I brought your black coffee.

Karen What?

Bridget The very strong, very black. That you wanted.

(*Karen* looks at her levelly, takes a swig from her vodka bottle, resumes packing.)

You're not leaving, are you?

Karen Yes.

Bridget Oh God. What was it? Was it the cooked breakfast? Was it anything I've done?

Karen I no longer love my husband. My marriage is over.

Bridget ...Oh, I'm relieved to hear you say that!

Karen Great.

Bridget Dominic gets so angry when I drive the guests away. Yes. Very angry... ...Erm, so how's he taking it? Your husband?

Karen He doesn't know yet.

Bridget Crikey. That's clever. But don't you think you should? I mean, mightn't that give him psychological problems?

(*Karen* stares at her.)

...If you don't want the coffee, can I have it?

Karen Do what you like.

Bridget *(eagerly)* So I can stay here with you?

Bob *(staring at the paper)* Ode.

(*He sucks his pen.*)

 Ode ode ode ode ode.

(*Robert* enters the bar, walks to *Dominic*.

(*The picture changes to 1995.*)

Robert I'd like some writing paper, please.

Dominic *(brightly)* Certainly, sir. I've got plenty of that. Specially designed.

(*He fishes under the bar.*) Would you be wanting a pen as well, sir?

Robert No, no, that's fine...

Dominic Because I haven't got one of those.

(He gives him a sheet of thick, cardboard-like paper.)

There you are.

*(**Robert** flexes it in his hands.)*

Good quality paper that, sir. What you write on that will outlive both of us.

Robert *(reading)* The Royal Arms Hotel. Established 1974.

Dominic *(proudly)* Dominic Bradshaw. Proprietor. That's me, that is. And here you see, underneath, are the 1995 hotel prices.

Robert *(reading)* Welcome to the hotel, and we hope that you return soon...

(He turns over.)

...To look at the famous hill and enjoy the rustic scenery.

Dominic That's it. Friendly.

Robert ...Doesn't leave much room for writing on, does it?

Dominic It's all right, I'll give you two sheets.

*(**Robert** accepts the second sheet, makes to move away.)*

While you're here, sir, I did want a word with you about Bridget...

Robert Oh. Look, I really had no idea she was in there...

Dominic Oh, no, don't you worry about that, sir. I don't hold you responsible.

Robert Oh. Good.

Dominic I blame your wife.

Robert Ah.

Dominic It's women, you see, sir. They're not like us. Very devious little creatures, women. Wouldn't you agree?

Robert Well, probably not, actually...

Dominic I mean, I like women. I like women a lot. Fatally attracted to them, I might say. Couldn't do without them, could we, sir? Though it might be better if we tried, got a pet or something...

Robert Erm, I don't know...

Dominic Nice shapes, obviously. And that little look they give you sometimes, butter wouldn't melt in their mouths. But can you really say, sir, that you know what they're thinking? What's going on in those pretty little heads of theirs?

Robert I think Karen and I really quite connect...

Dominic No, of course you can't. Off they go, hiding in bathrooms, or hiding other people in bathrooms. Though butter wouldn't melt in their mouths. And you know why. It's anatomy. Different appendages to us. Turns their heads, I shouldn't wonder.

(Short pause)

Still, got to love them, haven't you?

Robert *(gently humouring)* ...Yes. Well, look, thanks for the paper. Both sheets, really smashing. Better rush off now, make sure the wife hasn't got into any mischief. Okay?

Dominic No, wait, sir, I've got something I think you'll find interesting...

Robert Yes, well, probably not, eh?

Dominic But I've got it here. I've got it right here. I only share this with my special guests.

Robert What makes me a special guest?

Dominic *(momentarily thrown)* Oh. Well. You asked for some writing paper, didn't you? That's kind of special.

(He produces:)

Robert A photo album?

Dominic That's right.

Robert You want to show me... No, look, I really...

Dominic *(firmly)* It'll only take a minute. And you really *are* very privileged. They're of my wife, Bridget.

(Lights fade on this area a little, rise on the bedroom.)

Bridget No, I don't think my husband would like that at all.

Karen *(still packing)* Well, I don't think it's any of his business.

Bridget No, I mean if I left him.

Karen Oh, I see.

Bridget *(laughing awkwardly)* I mean, I don't think he'd care you were going. Don't think he'd give a stuff!

Karen Yes, well.

Bridget I mean, he's not in love with you, is he? He's in love with me.

Karen I expect you're right.

Bridget I know I'm right. So if I just, I don't know, stuck all my things in a suitcase and went, I don't think he'd like it. At all. That's all I'm saying.

Karen Well, don't do it then.

Bridget Okay.

Karen Just don't do it.

Bridget No, I won't.

Karen Good.

Bridget Yes.

Karen Problem solved then.

Bridget No problem at all.

Karen *(holding up some clothes)* Perhaps I should pack these at the bottom. I don't want them to get crumpled. Or perhaps they'd get more crumpled at the bottom. Perhaps they'd get less crumpled at the top.

(Short pause)

I'll pack them in the middle. Yes.

Bridget I couldn't leave Dominic. For a start, he loves me. We love each other. That's the first point. And the second point, well, I'm sure he'd get very lonely. We don't get many guests, so there'd be no-one for him to talk to. Three. And we've been married for twenty-five years. You don't just up and go after twenty-five years. Give him psychological problems. Twenty-five and a half years. In fact, just over. Round it up, say twenty-six. And... point four, erm... Well. He needs me. Don't you think? Yes. He needs me to make the breakfasts. I don't think he's ever made a breakfast in his life, poor love, wouldn't know where to start. He needs me. Twenty-six years... It's a very long time.

Karen I hope they'll be all right in the middle.

Bridget I'm sure there's a fifth reason but I can't think of it at the moment.

*(Emphasise lighting on the bar. **Dominic** is still showing **Robert** the photo album. **Robert** is trying very hard to seem politely interested.)*

Dominic And here, you see, is a picture of Bridget smiling in August 1982.

Robert Goodness.

Dominic Hardly credit it, would you? Looks younger there.

Robert A good thirteen years younger, yes...

Dominic And this one's her smiling in July 1982. Even younger still.

Robert Are all of these pictures of your wife smiling?

Dominic That's right, yes. I think she's at her best when she's smiling.

Robert Yes, I'm sure...

Dominic Squints her eyes up a bit, eyes not her best feature. And here, look! June 1982. Picture of Bridget smiling.

Robert You've got one for every month?

Dominic Every month we're married, yes. Twenty-three years, seven months.

Robert God.

Dominic Two hundred and eighty-three photographs.

Robert All of her smiling?

Dominic All of her smiling.

Robert Well. Well done.

(Short pause)

Why?

Dominic That's love, that is, isn't it? I mean, that's love. Two hundred and eighty-three pictures of your wife grinning.

Robert I suppose so...

Dominic How many photos have you got of your wife grinning?

Robert I honestly don't know the precise number...

Dominic Not as many though, I'll bet.

Robert Well, they're really smashing. I mean that. Yes. I don't know why you don't display one. Have a picture of your wife over the bar, instead of the Queen.

Dominic *(firmly)* Her Majesty can be enjoyed by everyone. My wife is to be enjoyed by me alone.

Robert ...Well, I think that minute's up, so I'll be going now. But really, very beautiful.

Dominic *(laughing)* Beautiful? They're not beautiful!

Robert Oh. But I thought...

Dominic Bridget's not exactly pig ugly, but I do think she's abnormally plain. Don't you think? She never was a pretty girl, even when I married her. But I took a good look, and I thought, well, fifty-fifty chance here. She could get better, she could get worse. Time would tell, my photographs, they'd tell. And they have told. She got worse.

Robert Oh, I...

Dominic See this at the beginning of the album? Compare that to October 1995. Which wasn't one of her better months, not even for her.

Robert I don't think...

Dominic I wake up next to that. Look at it. Every morning, I find that next to me on the pillow. And not even smiling. Snoring, but not smiling. And so I come downstairs. And I get out this album, this wonderful photo album. And I look at the most recent photo, hold the book up, and flip the pages to the front, like this...!

(And he flips the pages.)

And look, there she goes! Getting younger, and all the wrinkles falling off. And the smile looking more sincere.

Robert Just like a cartoon?

Dominic And whenever I want to, I can make Bridget the wife she used to be. Everyone should have one of these. I tell you, it's this book here that has made our marriage so successful.

(Pause)

Robert Look, I hope you don't take this the wrong way, Mr Bradshaw...

Dominic Dominic.

Robert Dominic. No, actually, I think I'd better stick with Mr Bradshaw... I'm sure there are many people who would find these pictures of your wife rivetting. Some of the people I work with, the PE department would, I know. But not me. Actually, in fact.

Dominic Don't trust any of them, sir. Women, they're different from us.

Robert And the same with your marital, ah, eccentricities. I'm afraid. Not really my area. And so, if you don't mind, I'm off to find my wife. Because I know a way I can get her back. The way things used to be. With just these two bits of paper. You'll see. And I'm sure that doesn't interest you, but, hell, you bored me too. So there you are. Sorry.

(Short pause. A little embarrassed:)

I hope things work out. Cheer up.

(He exits.)

Dominic *(muttering to himself)* Don't trust any of them. The bitches.

(He resumes cleaning glasses; lights fade on this area.)

Bridget And so that's what it all boils down to. That's why I have problems with men.

Karen Yes, I'm sure...

Bridget They don't like me very much.

Karen *(still only half listening)* Bit of an obstacle.

Bridget That's right! And trouble was, I kept on falling in love with men who wouldn't give me the time of day. Dozens of them, one after the other, sometimes overlapping. This was years ago, before I met Dominic. I used to follow them everywhere, phone them up each night, I'd make them little presents and send them through the post. And they'd tell me to get lost, but I'd never take the hint. I'd just stay with them for hours and hours and hours.

Karen *(sighing)* Yes.

Bridget 'Piss off, you stupid cow', they'd say. 'We'll call the police.' One of them went abroad, never came back. I just thought he was playing hard to get. But then, you see, I've never been very perceptive... I think you're wonderful, Karen.

Karen Oh yes?

Bridget Packing your bags and leaving, I admire it, I really do.

*(**Karen** looks at the now packed suitcase, the vodka bottle resting on the top.)*

Karen ...I'm not going to be able to get this bloody case shut...

*(And underneath **Bridget's** speech, **Karen** removes the vodka bottle, drains it, flings the empty bottle on to the bed. She tries to close the suitcase again, but still without success.)*

Bridget And I'll tell you another interesting thing about our marriage...

Karen No, no, listen, I can't get the bloody case shut. This is important. It makes no bloody sense, I mean, it all fitted in before, I've not added anything else.

Bridget Maybe it was putting those clothes in the middle.

Karen *(thoughtfully)* Maybe.

Bridget But now Dominic, years later. I don't even like looking at his face any more. What can I do?

Karen You could try sitting on it.

Bridget I'm sorry?

Karen The suitcase.

Bridget Oh yes.

*(She obliges. **Karen** pulls at the zip.*

*(During the following, **Bridget** unthinkingly does as **Karen** asks, leaving her at one point with her legs sticking out practically at a right angle to her body.)*

Karen I'll see if I can get the zip round...

Bridget And obviously at times we've come close to loving each other properly...

Karen Shift a bit, one end's sticking up...

Bridget 1977 and bits of the early eighties were quite good...

Karen Raise your legs so I can pull the zip round...

Bridget But overall I just feel he humiliates me...

Karen Higher than that, I can't get under...

Bridget Putting me into very difficult positions...

Karen Nearly there...

Bridget It hurts me. It causes me actual pain.

Karen Lower them now.

*(She pulls the zip to. She offers **Bridget** her hand.)*

Well done.

Bridget *(intensely)* You'd say Dominic was an attractive man?

Karen *(surprised, lowering her hand)* Well, I...

Bridget You'd say that, wouldn't you?

Karen I suppose so...

Bridget Good. I don't find him attractive, but so long as I know I've done all right.

Bob *(still staring at the paper)* Ode, ode. Ode to... Ode to Something or Other.

(He starts scribbling happily.)

Oh, let's just write it, I'm sure a subject will spring to mind halfway through...

*(**Bridget** gets off the suitcase.)*

Bridget Ready to go, are you?

Karen Nothing can stop me.

(She pulls up the case – it is too heavy.)

I'll need Robert to give me a hand carrying it.

Bridget God, I admire you. But I don't think I *will* leave Dominic, thanks. Not now. No-one else'd have me. And I think the loneliness would drive me quite mad.

*(Enter **Robert**.)*

Robert *(excitedly)* Great news!

Bridget *(to **Karen**)* I think you're very brave.

*(To **Robert**, solemnly:)*

I'm so sorry.

*(**Bridget** exits. **Robert** looks at **Karen** quizzically, who shrugs.)*

Karen I'm glad you're here, Robert. I've got something very important to say to you.

Robert *(cheerfully)* And I've got something very important to say to you!

Karen Yes, well, yours can wait. Because I doubt very much whether it's as important as what I've got to say to you.

Robert Much more important, Karen, believe me, miles more important!

Karen *(irritated)* Shut up, Robert, there's no bloody way what you've got to say is more important than what I have to say, because what I have to say isn't just very important, it's very very important, okay? Of extreme import.

Robert Mine's still more important.

Karen Not a chance.

Robert Try me.

Karen *(angrily)* Because what I'm going to say is that I'm leaving you. Completely. We're finished. The marriage, everything. Because I can't stand the thought of wasting any more of my life on you. Because I can hardly believe I've wasted all the time I already have. I'm going, and I'm never going to see you again. Important enough for you, you bastard? *(Short pause)* Only I was going to say it more tactfully than that.

Robert ...No, mine's still more important.

Karen *(coldly)* Is it?

Robert Oh yes.

Karen Well, hurrah. Bully for you.

Robert Don't you want to hear what's so important?

Karen No, I don't think so.

Robert Oh, go on.

Karen No. If what you've got to say is *so* much more important than that your wife's leaving you after nineteen years of marriage, then I'll probably catch it on the news later.

Robert What if I were to tell you that I've found a way to save our marriage? Now, wouldn't that be more important?

Karen No, I'm sorry, Robert, I've thought it through long and hard, and the whole thing's completely irreconcileable. Of course, I'll always be very fond of you...

Robert Karen...

Karen Though that fondness is being sorely tested at the moment...

Robert Listen. Our lives don't have to be like this...

Karen Because the only way our marriage will get better is if we both work very hard at it. And I think I've worked hard enough already to get it as bad as this.

Robert ...Look! Two bits of paper!

(Short pause)

Well go on then, take them. Now, what I want you to do is write on these bits of paper. Write down everything you can think of that has gone wrong in our marriage. Everything that has annoyed you, irked you, every single incident you would blame for things being as bad as they are.

Karen I think I might need more paper.

Robert Because I'm sure it can all be traced back. Somewhere, somehow, it all went wrong, somewhere, back along the line, something happened which changed us. And if we can just work out what that was – and it can't be difficult, because it must have been pretty important to have done all that damage – then everything can be fine. So, when you're scribbling away, Karen, if you can be as specific as possible, and try to remember dates and locations.

Karen What the hell are you talking about?

Robert For example. You remember that holiday we took in Wolverhampton six years ago?

Karen The one where it rained all the time?

Robert Yes.

Karen And we did nothing but argue?

Robert That's the one.

Karen Just like this holiday.

Robert Now. Would you say that fortnight in Wolverhampton in 1989 was a contributory factor to the breakdown of our marriage?

Karen Probably more a symptom.

Robert Okay, but say it was responsible, you'd just jot it down, then I'd go away and deal with it. Nothing to worry about any more, it need never have happened. We wouldn't have gone to Wolverhampton. We'd have gone somewhere else. Like Southend. Because I'd do anything for you, anything at all.

(Short pause)

Karen Would you really?

Robert You know I would.

Karen Then you'll give me a hand with the suitcase?

Robert Yes, of course.

(Together they lift it up.)

What do you want the suitcase for?

Karen Because I'm leaving you, you idiot.

Robert *(laughing)* No, Karen! Silly! You've missed the point!

*(And he drops his end of the suitcase. It falls to the ground, and **Karen** goes with it.)*

Karen *(gritted teeth)* Don't call me silly. Just explain to me what is going on.

Robert I can't.

Karen *(barely patient)* Why not?

Robert It's a surprise.

Karen I don't want a surprise! Now, you tell me what's going on, right now, or I'll... take the... Take the bag and...

(She gives up trying to drag the case.)

I'll just leave without it.

Robert *(sighing)* All right. We're here.

Karen Yes?

Robert In the hotel. Or rather, we're downstairs.

Karen I see.

Robert I'm downstairs, and I'm pretty sure you're downstairs as well.

Karen We're upstairs, Robert.

Robert Yes, but we're also downstairs. Not now, of course. I mean, twenty years ago. But twenty years ago, now. There's something odd going on, do you think it's something to do with the storm?

Karen *(lost, struggling)* You think it's something to do with the storm?

Robert Well, I don't know, I'm no expert, this has never happened to me before. Anyway, so I can take this paper, when you've written on it, and I can give it to me. I can give it to you too, if you like. I can give it to both of us. And we can read what you've written, and we needn't ever do it. There. Simple, really.

(Short pause)

Karen My leaving you has come as quite a shock, hasn't it?

Robert What?

Karen It's what that silly woman was saying. Psychological problems. Why don't you lie down?

Robert No, I'm going downstairs. I've got to find me.

Karen Well, you do that then. Do you want me to come and find you as well?

Robert No, you stay here. Don't want to complicate things further. You stay here and write our problems down.

Karen All right.

Robert You see, there's a slight difficulty. We haven't met yet.

Karen Haven't we?

Robert No. I would have met you, but I got in the way.

Karen Oh dear.

Robert Quite. So I better go and deal with that. Go and find me, and introduce me to you. Then everything'll be all right.

Karen So long as you're happy.

Robert *(cheerfully)* After all, how difficult can it be to get us together? We're destined for each other, I know it!

*(He gives **Karen** a quick peck, hurries away.)*

Karen Oh my God. I've cracked his brain.

(She walks into the bathroom, screws up the writing paper, drops it into the toilet bowl.

*(**Robert** enters the breakfast room, walks straight over to where **Bob** is writing his poem.)*

Robert Excuse me. You're single, aren't you?

*(**Bob** looks at him with faint horror. Short pause)*

Bob *(softly)* Oh my God, it's that obvious, isn't it?

Robert No, not at all...

Bob *(miserably)* It must be written all over my face. 'Do not date here.'

Robert Well, all that's going to change! How would you like to meet someone who'll love you forever?

(*Bob stares at Robert – looks away, looks back. Eventually:*)

Bob Erm. Look, don't think I'm not flattered, but just because I'm a poet it doesn't mean...

Robert No, no, a girl. A girl.

Bob Oh. A girl. Yes, well. Thanks anyway. But I'll tell you. Actually, I'm quite good with girls.

Robert What are you talking about? You're completely hopeless with them.

Bob You'd be surprised. Actually, I'm quite a goer. Very experienced. Oh yes.

Robert Listen. Jennifer Collins letting you touch her breast on the school bus doesn't make you experienced, all right? It does not constitute a mature relationship.

Bob How did you know that...?

Robert The only thing it makes you is any member of the fourth form with half a crown to spend. All right?

Bob My God. If you know that, then you...

Robert Yes.

Bob You must be...

Robert Yes!

Bob Jennifer Collins' dad!

Robert Yes! No. Yes, whatever, yes, it doesn't really matter...

Bob How did you track me down? You don't want me to marry her, do you?

Robert I didn't track you down, just listen...

Bob How is Jennifer? What's she doing nowadays?

Robert *(fiercely)* She became a nun.

Bob ...Did she?

Robert Yes. Now, can we move on?

Bob God.

Robert There's a girl here who's just right for you. Wonderful person, lovely personality. And I know precisely how you can win her. No school buses, no half crowns, just a foolproof plan. All right?

Bob ...All right, Mr Collins, I'm with you.

Robert Great. Just do everything I say.

(*He walks to the bar.* **Bob** *follows.*)

Two pints of lager, please.

Dominic That'll be three pounds sixty, sir.

Robert (*to* **Bob**) ...Tell you what, you get the drinks. And a glass of white wine too.

Dominic That'll be one pound twenty.

Bob I don't drink white wine.

Robert Oh, it isn't for drinking.

(**Bridget** *enters the breakfast room, calls to* **Dominic***. She is quite distraught, but trying not to show it.*)

Bridget Dominic. Dominic, I need a word.

Dominic Not now, love. I'm working.

Bridget No, now. I need you now, I really... I'm not happy again.

(**Dominic** *puts down his cloth with irritation, walks over to her.*

(**Robert** *and* **Bob** *talk quietly at the bar.*)

Dominic You've been crying, haven't you?

Bridget I'm sorry, Dominic, but I'm really *not* happy, I'm trying to, but it's not working...

Dominic Your eyes are all puffy. I thought we agreed you wouldn't be unhappy again?

Bridget Please don't be angry, Dominic. I don't mean to be unhappy...

Dominic You do pick your moments.

Bob All sounds a bit strange to me. You mean, I take the white wine and...

Robert Trust me, never fails.

Dominic Tell you what. Something that'll cheer you up...

Bridget (*anxiously*) I don't want to go to bed...

Dominic Not that. I'll take a photo of you. You like me taking photos of you, don't you?

Bridget That isn't due for another week yet...

Dominic *(sternly)* You like me taking photos of you.

Bridget I like you taking photos of me.

Dominic Well, that's settled then. I'll go and get the camera. You make yourself look nice.

Bridget Yes.

Dominic Try and do something with your eyes, they're all puffy.

(They exit.)

Karen I never realised he was so fragile. Still. Proves me wrong about one thing. I don't know him as well as I thought.

Bob But what do I say to her?

Robert Look, it doesn't matter. Just do what I've told you, she'll love you, you'll love her, we can all go home.

Bob I've got to say something though. Perhaps I could recite her one of my poems...

Robert *(hastily)* No! ...No, let's just keep this simple. Here she comes now. I'll just hide under the bar. Remember what I said.

*(He hides under the bar. As **Bob** continues to talk to him, **Carrie** stops, watches from a distance with some bemusement, then shrugs and walks to the bar.)*

Bob What, that girl?

Robert *(impatiently)* Yes! All right?

Bob Isn't there another one I could have instead? She's very tall.

Robert Is that a problem?

Bob I just find tall girls a bit intimidating, that's all...

Carrie Excuse me...

*(**Bob** jumps back with a cry.)*

Bob Don't do that...

Carrie I'm sorry. Have you seen a man? About your height, but twenty years older?

Bob You mean, Mr Collins?

Robert *(hissing, anxiously)* No, you haven't!

Bob What?

Carrie *(to Bob)* What?

Robert No!

Bob No... I don't think I've ever met him.

Robert *(muttering)* My God...

Carrie ...Ah.

(She drifts away.)

Karen *(decisively)* He needs me.

(And she exits. Lights off in the main bedroom.)

Bob It isn't working! She doesn't want me at all!

Robert Just go and say hello to her.

Bob But you said...

Robert Go on!

(Bob approaches Carrie nervously. He stands behind her, psyching himself up for the deed. He opens his mouth a couple of times.)

Just do it!

Carrie *(turning round, startled)* ...Yes?

Bob *(bravely)* Hello.

Carrie Yes. Hello.

(Bob grins at her, looks down. He looks up again.)

...Was there something else?

Bob Erm... Will you excuse me for a moment?

(And he dashes back behind the bar.

(Enter Karen, who watches from the doorway with bemusement.)

Robert What are you doing here?

Bob This is more difficult than you suggested...

Robert Give her the white wine!

Bob Oh yes.

Robert And spill it over her!

Bob Are you sure about that part?

Robert Just do it!

(*Bob re-emerges, attempts to be suave.*)

Bob Sorry to keep you waiting. Would you like some white wine?

Carrie Oh. Well, I...

(*And **Bob** throws the wine in her face.*)

Robert Not in her face!

Carrie What are you doing?

Bob What?

Robert Not the face! The dress!

Bob (*calling*) Sorry!

(*To **Carrie***)

Sorry.

(*And he takes his lager and throws a good portion of it over her dress.*)

Carrie Stop doing that! Why are you doing that?

Bob It isn't working!

Robert It will!

Carrie Do you always do this to complete strangers?

Bob (*desperately*) Let me tell you a poem!

Robert No, not the poem!

Bob Shut up!

Carrie What?

Bob No, not you shut up, just listen. I've written you a poem, listen. I wish I loved you more / But my heart can rise no higher. / By nature I am not / A wooer nor a sigher...

(*And in spite of herself, **Carrie** bursts into laughter.*)

Carrie You're probably insane, but I do find that quite sweet...

Bob What are you laughing at?

Carrie The poem, it's very funny...

Bob No, it isn't. It's very serious and heartfelt.

Robert Change the subject!

Carrie It doesn't make any sense even. What's a sigher?

Bob *(annoyed)* What do you think? It's someone who sighs.

Carrie There's no such word!

Bob There bloody is!

Robert For God's sake, try harder!

Bob What?

Robert You're losing her! Improvise!

*(**Bob** hesitates for a second, then in desperation throws the rest of his lager over her face.*

(Short pause.)

Carrie *(almost in tears)* I wish I knew why you keep doing that to me. I don't think I've done anything to you.

*(And she rushes off, passing the still stunned **Karen**.)*

Excuse me.

Karen *(watching her go)* My God.

Bob That didn't go as well as expected...

Robert It was a complete bloody shambles! What did you start on about the poem for? It was going fine until you brought in the poem!

Bob I'm sorry...

Robert I better get after her. If you've ruined anything... I tell you, her falling in love with you is far too important for you to screw it up!

*(He makes to exit, sees **Karen**. He speaks to her confidentially.)*

I think this could be more difficult than I thought.

*(He exits. **Karen** watches him dazedly. She looks across to **Bob**, who sits at the bar miserably.)*

Karen Maybe my brain's cracked as well.

*(Slowly she walks over and sits down by **Bob**. She looks at him curiously. Eventually **Bob** swings to face her.)*

Bob *(upset)* ...What?

*(**Karen** shakes her head hastily, looks away.*

*(Enter **Dominic**, with camera. He goes behind the bar.)*

Dominic Camera. For the wife.

Karen *(faintly)* Oh yes?

Dominic Get you a drink?

Karen A vodka. Large.

*(She looks across at **Bob**.)*

...No, wait a moment. Make it a white wine.

Dominic That'll be one pound ninety.

Karen *(to **Bob**)* Excuse me... You're single, aren't you?

Bob Oh God, not you as well, I've had enough of this...!

Karen I only say, you must be single. Because you look the sort who'd be faithful to your girlfriend. That's all I'm saying.

Bob What?

Karen If you already had a girlfriend, you wouldn't want another.

Bob Well, no, of course not.

Karen So if you already had a partner, you'd leave that other girl alone. And you wouldn't have to marry her. And she wouldn't get pregnant, she'd still have ambitions and friends. If you had someone else.

Bob What?

Karen *(smiling)* Come up to my room. And get out of those wet clothes.

Bob I don't have wet clothes.

(And she picks up the white wine and pours it into his lap. He looks up at her, incredulous. She winks at him. Faintly:)

Oh my God.

(Blackout.)

Act Two

*(Fade to darkness. Out of it **Dominic** speaks, clear and confident.)*

Dominic Okay, you can start smiling again.

*(And there is a camera flash. Lights up, revealing **Dominic** taking photographs of **Bridget** in the breakfast room. She sits on a table, smiling furiously.)*

Hold it.

(Another flash from his camera; the sound is slightly echoed.)

*(And lights up on the main bedroom. **Karen** and **Bob** enter.)*

Karen Well, this is it.

Bob No, wait...

Karen What?

(He offers his arms.)

There's really no need...

Bob Please...

*(And she lets him pick her up and carry her in his arms. **Bob** had not quite anticipated how big **Karen** actually is.)*

Karen All right?

Bob For the moment.

Karen Try and move towards the bed...

Bob I can't see...

Karen What?

Bob There's too much of you, you'll have to steer...

Karen Forward, forward, gently...!

(And they collapse on the bed.)

Bob There. That was romantic, wasn't it?

*(**Karen** gets up.)*

Karen Romantic?

Bob *(ashen)* Oh my God, I've made a mistake, haven't I? I thought when you invited me up...

Karen Take your clothes off.

Bob *(doing so)* You see, I'm not very used to this sort of thing, not at all, actually, and I'm always misreading signals...

Karen All of them. Now. And get into bed.

Bob Oh. Okay.

(He backs into the shower, takes off his clothes down to his underpants, as the scene in the breakfast room continues.)

Dominic And wider. Wider than that.

Bridget *(smiling)* I can't. It hurts.

Dominic Oh, everything hurts with you...

Bridget The corners of my mouth'll bleed...

Dominic Come on, Bridget! For God's sake, you can smile better than that!

Bridget I can't...

Dominic *(displaying the album)* There! April 1972. That's the smile I want.

Bridget I can't smile like that...

Dominic Of course you can! Look, you're doing it here! Try harder!

*(And **Bridget** gets up and runs away, upset.)*

Bridget! Come back here and smile! Bridget! ...You can't hide from me, Bridget. I'll find you eventually.

(And he exits determinedly. Lights fade on this area.)

*(**Bob** is now standing in nothing but his underpants. He is very self-conscious about this. He looks down at his body with dismay.)*

Bob Oh my God, this isn't going to work.

Karen What?

Bob I'm repulsive. I'm completely repulsive.

Karen *(idly)* Yes, but it doesn't matter...

Bob *(nervously, babbling)* It's all the wrong size, and it's all in the wrong place. Look, you can call this off. Really. I wouldn't blame you. Not with a belly like this. I wouldn't want to sleep with a belly like this, mind you, of course, I have to...

*(And **Karen** kisses him abruptly on the mouth to silence him. It works.)*

Karen Robert. Do understand. I don't care what you look like.

Bob Ah. A spiritual thing, is it?

Karen Listen. I don't want to be your girlfriend. This is a one-off. We are here to avert destiny.

Bob Oh yes?

Karen Something is going to happen to me here. Something that will change my life forever. And we have to prevent it.

Bob *(blankly)* ...We could always use precautions...

Karen ...Yes.

(Short pause. She turns and unzips the suitcase. She throws the clothes out, searching.)

Bob What are you doing?

Karen Looking for my nightie. I think I packed it at the bottom.

(Short pause)

Bob Can I help?

Karen No.

(Short pause. **Bob** *looks around the room, unsure of what to do. He gets into bed.)*

Bob *(brightly)* Would you like me to recite you a poem?

Karen Whatever.

Bob Okay. I wish I loved you more / But my heart can rise no higher. / By nature I am not / A wooer nor a sigher. / I want you so, I want to weep. / So kiss the tears from off my cheek / To make my face stay drier.

(As he recites, **Karen** *looks up and stares at him intently. Short pause)*

It's not specific. I call it 'Ode to Whoever Would Like It, Really.'

Karen *(softly)* Absolutely incredible.

Bob Oh. Do you like it?

Karen *(still absorbed)* God, no, it's awful...

Bob *(sighing)* Yes. Everyone says that...

Karen It doesn't matter... When you said the poem... I don't know, your whole face lit up. You really believe in this,don't you?

Bob I think I'll give up writing, actually...

Karen No!

Bob I think so. For years I've been doing this, a dozen a day. I'd have thought that with all that practice I'd have done something good by now. But it's all drivel, really, isn't it?

Karen *(earnestly)* Robert, listen. Don't stop. Whatever happens, don't stop. Trust me.

Bob *(a little surprised)* Oh. All right then.

Karen I don't remember you *believing* in anything. And having fire in your eyes...

(And she approaches him, and kisses him more tenderly.)

*(**Robert** and **Carrie** approach the closed door of the bedroom. **Carrie** has dressed again.)*

Robert All I'm saying is, give the boy another chance...

Carrie I'll discuss this in your room or not at all.

*(He puts the key in the lock. **Karen** starts.)*

Karen Oh my God, it's my husband!

Bob You've got a husband? You didn't tell me you had a husband!

Karen Hide in the bathroom!

Bob I don't do this with single women, let alone married ones!

Karen In the bathroom!

*(He closes the bathroom door. **Karen** notices **Bob's** clothes on the floor, and rushes over to them. She stoops behind the bed, starts hiding the clothes underneath.*

*(**Robert** enters cautiously with **Carrie**. He does not see **Karen**, obscured by the bed. Similarly she cannot yet see him. **Carrie** strides confidently into the room.*

*(Upon hearing him enter, **Bob** nervously stands in the bath and, as an afterthought, pulls the shower curtain around.)*

Karen *(frantically)* With you in a minute, Robert!

Robert *(hissing)* Quick, hide in the bathroom!

*(He holds the door for **Carrie** and pushes her inside.*

*(**Karen** looks up, just missing her. She is appalled to see **Robert** opening her hiding place.)*

Karen What are you doing with that bathroom door?

(*Robert hesitates, then pulls it to, with affected nonchalance.*)

Robert ...Nothing.

Karen (*warily*) I just think... I just think that neither of us should use the bathroom. For a while.

Robert (*warily*) Yes. I think that's a good idea.

(*Carrie backs into the bath. Bob undoes the shower curtain and taps her on the shoulder.*)

Bob (*gently*) Excuse me...

(*Carrie gives a little scream, which she remembers in time to muffle with her hand.*)

Carrie Oh my God, it's you again!

Bob Hello. Robert Hunter.

Carrie I don't care what your name is! Why do you keep following me?

(*Robert starts to sing loudly.*)

Bob I was in the bath first...

Carrie And why do you keep wetting me?

Bob I'm sorry, I...

(*And he fumbles awkwardly in a gesture of apology. It turns on the shower.*)

Carrie Turn it off!

Bob I'm trying, it's stiff...

(*Karen starts to sing too, to cover Bob's voice.*)

Bob There!

(*And he turns the handle tightly. The wrong way, of course. More water gushes out, much louder.*)

Carrie It's freezing!

Bob I'm sorry!

Carrie Why are you doing this to me?

(*Karen and Robert sing louder over the water, both trying to ignore it, both surprised the other is. Carrie and Bob continue to scream.*)

*(And **Dominic** enters.)*

Dominic   Excuse me, I seem to have mislaid my wife again...

Karen   We haven't seen her...

*(And **Dominic** looks at the bathroom door suspiciously, from behind which there is now an incredible noise.)*

Dominic   ...Wouldn't be hiding in the bathroom again, would she?

Robert   Well, I...

*(And, in some mild hysteria, **Robert** and **Karen** laugh at him.*

*(**Dominic** pushes the bathroom door open. **Bob** and **Carrie** freeze, then laugh at him as well.)*

Dominic   You're very strange people, do you know that?

*(He goes in to turn off the shower. **Robert** and **Karen** are both anxious to leave.)*

Robert   *(brightly)* Well, I think I'll be going for a walk.

Karen   So will I.

Robert   Right.

(And they both exit briskly.)

Dominic   Something's blocking the toilet. What have you been up to?

(He puts his hand down the toilet.)

I don't normally stick my hand down U-bends. That's the wife's job.

(And he pulls out the writing paper.)

Who's been flushing paper down the toilet? ...Right. Well, you're all going to be charged extra for this. You'll see.

(And he exits, carrying the cardboard.)

Bob   Are you all right?

*(**Carrie** nods.)*

I'm sorry. It's Mr Collins. He's trying to get me to go out with you.

Carrie   He's trying to get me to go out with you too.

Bob   I've an idea. Let's just not.

Carrie   Shake on it.

(They do.

*(**Dominic** re-enters the bar, looks at the wet paper in his hands, reading with growing confusion.)*

There's something very funny going on here. I must find out what.

*(She smiles, and exits. **Bob** looks after her, sighs, perhaps regretfully.)*

Bob ...Now where did she put my clothes?

(He fishes under the bed and gets dressed again during the following.)

Dominic The Royal Arms Hotel. Dominic Bradshaw, proprietor. What is this? 1995 prices... 1995?

(And he stares at it in confusion.

(Lights dim on the area. During the next scene, he walks to the breakfast room, and sits there, reading and rereading the writing paper.

*(**Bob** has almost finished redressing. **Karen** re-enters the bedroom.)*

Karen Has he gone? I backtracked.

Bob I'm just heading off. I'm going to have to think about this. Write a poem about it, maybe...

Karen I love you.

Bob Ah. I'm... surprised.

Karen *(happily)* So am I! Very surprised, very nice feeling. I never thought I'd fall in love with you again. I just bargained on some quick, unpleasant sex. Slimy, sweaty and sticky.

Bob Aha?

Karen But I love you. Do you know how many years it's been since I said those words?

Bob Quite a few, I'll bet.

*(**Carrie** re-enters her bedroom, disappears to get changed.)*

Karen We're going to be so happy together! This time round it's going to work.

Bob *(slight outburst)* I wish you'd stop talking about me as if you knew who I was!

Karen *(happily)* But I do.

Bob Not just write a poem, I think. Perhaps a whole anthology.

(He exits, taking whatever clothes he hasn't yet put on with him.

(*Karen* sits down on the bed happily.)

Karen This time it's going to work. Who would have thought it?

(*And happily, she begins to repack her suitcase from all the clothes she's left strewn over the bed.*

(*Robert* enters *Carrie's* bedroom.)

Robert Excuse me... oh my God, she's stripping off again...

Carrie (*emerging*) Please. Come in. I just got a bit wet.

Robert Yes.

Carrie Again.

Robert I've been thinking very hard. And I need to ask you. Please. Consider going out with that young man you met earlier. Robert Hunter.

Carrie (*sighing*) And is that all you've come for?

Robert The one who threw those drinks over you.

Carrie I haven't forgotten.

Robert You see. Let me say this. I think he'd make you a perfect husband. And let me give you the reasons why. Yes. Okay. Well, for a start, he's gentle, he's kind...

Carrie You're gentle and kind...

Robert I know he's a little awkward and everything, but he'll grow out of it. Sort of. And I know he's a little short, but, well, it's a nice short...

Carrie You're a nice short.

Robert And the acne, that'll definitely go...

Carrie Robert. I don't want him. I want you.

Robert Which is very nice of you. But I really wouldn't write off young Robert, you know, he's got great potential...

Carrie And you want me too, don't you?

Robert Look, frankly, it's pretty irrelevant whether I want you or not.

Carrie Kiss me.

Robert No, no, that's not a great idea. Take my tip. Kiss Robert. The nervous, gawky one downstairs somewhere.

Carrie Is it the age gap? Is that what's worrying you?

Robert Well, it's a start. Isn't it? I mean, you're what...

Carrie Twenty-five.

Robert Which would make me...

Carrie About twenty years older.

Robert Precisely. So when you're my age, I'll be...

Carrie Dead.

Robert ...No, I won't be dead...

Carrie Dying then.

Robert *(irritated)* No, God, I hope not, I'll still have years left in me...

Carrie So what's your point?

Robert Karen, you don't want to go out with me. There's no point in going out with me, I'm... I'm nothing, I've done nothing. I'm unfit, I've got a paunch. I'm very dull, I've got no interests at all.

Carrie I always wanted to go out with someone famous.

Robert Well, there you go. I'm not really famous. I'm the least famous person I know.

Carrie Because I wanted to be with someone who'd done more than me. You know? Actually lived a little.

Robert Absolutely. And young Robert, I'd recommend him in that category...

Carrie But I'm never going to meet anyone famous, am I? Not as a boring secretary. So if I can't find experience through achievement, I'll settle for experience through age.

(Pause)

Don't you want me?

Robert Oh, God, yes. Yes, I want you. When I look at you... And all the memories come flooding back. How Karen was before the years went by. How she was before the coldness and the silence, before I did whatever it was I did to her. And I remember you... so fresh...

Carrie If you want me, take me...

Robert *(thoughtfully)* And, yes, that's right, you were so much more sexually direct then...

(She grabs and kisses him on the mouth.)

No, we can't make love! We're married! Listen. My name's Hunter.

Carrie Hunter?

Robert Yes.

Carrie Robert Hunter? Like that other one?

Robert Yes. Now do you see?

Carrie That's very odd. That you're pimping for your relatives. I hope you're doing it for family loyalty rather than money. But I'm prepared to overlook that now.

(She kisses him again.)

Robert I suppose I could always *get* fitter. Take up jogging or something.

(She kisses him again.)

And I could find some hobbies. To make myself more interesting.

(And again.)

You're so fresh! I love you! ... I can't wait to tell Karen!

(And he exits excitedly.

***Karen** stops short in her packing.)*

Karen Douglas!

(And she resumes packing more thoughtfully.

Carrie *(following **Robert)*** Robert!

*(**Dominic** is still rereading the writing paper. At times he puts it away, shaking his head – but he always takes it out again, frowning.)*

*(Enter **Bridget**. She walks up to him nervously. He doesn't look up, or listen to what she says.)*

Bridget Dominic? ...I just wanted to say sorry. For hiding from you. It was silly, and it was childish. I shouldn't do it, it only makes you angry. Dominic? You're not angry, are you?

Dominic Bridget... I need to ask you... I need to ask someone.

Bridget *(happily)* That's beautiful. You never ask for my advice...

Dominic *(impatiently)* It isn't advice, I don't want your advice. Just... how would you feel... How would you feel, if you had evidence... real evidence, that your life is never going to change?

(Short pause)

Bridget You should chuckle. If you're kidding, you should put a chuckle at the end.

Dominic *(dead)* I thought running a hotel would be a bit of a laugh. You know, something to do until I thought of something better. But I'm never going to think of something better.

Bridget But you love the hotel. The rustic scenery, erm... The famous hill...

Dominic Oh, for God's sake, it's only a hill, isn't it? I wouldn't give my life for it...

(Short pause. He looks at the paper again, despairingly.)

Bridget *(softly)* And how would you feel... not with evidence, but just because you *knew*... That nothing was ever going to change? That this was it. And your advice never *would* be asked, not ever...

*(Short pause. **Dominic** doesn't look up. **Bridget** sighs.*

(Thunder, lightning flash. The picture over the bar turns to 1995.)

Dominic *(softly)* To think. I'll still be here in 1995.

Bridget But it is 1995.

Dominic ...Is it?

(He turns round, looks at the picture. Confused, he gets up, and walks over to it.

*(**Bridget** makes to exit. **Dominic** calls after her, half-heartedly.)*

Where are you going?

Bridget To pack.

Dominic *(not listening)* Okay.

*(**Bridget** exits.*

*(**Dominic** reaches out and touches the picture cautiously. He laughs nervously to himself.)*

Stupid.

(He sits at the bar.

*(**Robert** enters the main bedroom. **Karen** is still packing, nearly finished.)*

Robert Karen, I need to speak to you...

Karen No, I'm sorry, I can't listen to you, I won't listen to you...

Robert Sorry?

Karen You'll only talk me out of it. But this time I'm really leaving you. Because there's no fire in your eyes, Robert, there used to be but it's gone now, there's no fire there at all, and I can't live any longer with a man with dead eyes.

Robert *(beaming)* I'm relieved to hear you say that!

Karen Oh. You are?

Robert Now you won't mind! I've fallen in love with your younger self! God, she's wonderful, Karen! I'd forgotten how wonderful you used to be. She's just like you!

Karen She would be.

Robert Only better!

Karen ...Yes, well, then you won't object to my running off with your younger self then.

Robert *(only half listening)* No, no, that's fine, do what you want, he's a nice enough kid...

Karen Yes.

Robert *(shaking her hand)* Goodbye. It's been great.

Karen Yes. Just one thing.

Robert Yes?

Karen Douglas.

*(Short pause. **Robert** re-enters the room slowly.)*

Robert Oh my God. Douglas.

Karen We won't have got married. I wouldn't have got pregnant. He won't have existed.

Robert But that's... I can't just kill our son!

Karen I can.

Robert ...Yes, well, I suppose I can too when I come to think of it. ...Don't you think we ought to tell him?

Karen It's not going to do him an awful lot of good, is it?

Robert He is our son. I think we owe him an explanation.

(*Karen* picks up the phone.)

Karen Go on then.

Robert ...I think we should both do it. Mother and father.

Karen (*sighing*) All right. I suppose that's fair...

Robert You go first.

(*Karen* dials. As she does so, **Bob** enters the bar. **Dominic** is still in thought.)

Bob Can I have some writing paper, please?

Dominic Sod off.

(And **Bob** retreats to a table.)

Karen What do I... 'There's no easy way to say this, but...'

Robert There's no easy way to say this, I like that.

Karen Hello, Douglas. Hello. Now, listen. There's no easy way to say this, but I... Your mother. Mother. Remember her?

Robert (*calling, bravely cheerful*) Hi, son!

Karen No, I haven't phoned to check up on you... No, I... Listen, I don't care if you burn the house down, it isn't going to make any difference in the long run. Right. There's no easy way to say this... Douglas, have you got your headphones on?

Robert Let me talk to him...

Karen You've got your bloody headphones on, haven't you?

(*Robert* takes the receiver.)

Robert Hi, son, it's Dad! ...Yes, that's the one. How are you, son, are you all right? ...Well, we just phoned to say, well, how are you, really, check you were, erm, all right...

Karen (*warning*) Robert...

Robert Well, no, there was something else, actually. Yes. Now, erm, there's no easy way to say this, but... Yes, it's hard to concentrate with the, could you turn the music down, son? ...Yes, I'm sure it's bitching, but it doesn't sound so good second hand. Third hand. Third ear...

Karen Give me that... Take your bloody headphones off! ...I *am* your mother! Don't say that! How can you say that, how can you be so cruel? I fed you, I reared you, I changed your nappies, you... He's put the phone down on me. He's put the bloody phone down on me!

(*Robert takes the phone and dials again.*)

Robert Here, let me try.

Karen You better tell him, Robert, you better tell him straight, because I don't think I...

Robert (*impatiently*) Yes, yes.

(*There is silence as **Robert** waits by the phone; there is nothing to say. **Robert** smiles encouragingly at **Karen**. She turns away.*)

It's ringing.

Karen Yes.

Robert Oh, hello, it's... It's the answering machine.

Karen Now the little sod's putting us on the answering machine!

Robert Ssh, here's the beep... Hello, son. Me again. Dad. Son, that wasn't very nice of you, you know.

Karen Tell him straight!

Robert Son, you're going to die. Well, not actually die. Not as such. You're never going to have been born.

(*To **Karen***)

Too straight?

Karen Just a tad.

Robert Perhaps I can start again. Can you do that?

Karen I don't think so. We've found a way of rewinding our lives, but I think we're beaten with the answering machine.

Robert I'm starting again, son. All right? Just ignore that bit. Now.

(*He clears his throat.*)

There's no easy way to say this, but...

(*able**Karen** gestures for the telephone. **Robert** hesitates, hands it to her.*)

Karen We have been given a chance. A chance to make our lives better, to wipe out past mistakes. I think we'd be stupid to reject it, not now we know so much more. For example, I don't think we'd ever invest in an answering machine again...

Robert Good point.

Karen And I'm sorry, Douglas, but you're one of those mistakes.
You really are. No doubt you're off playing on your computer at the
moment, and think that killing aliens is more important than what I
have to say, but, hell, I'm going to say it anyway, because it *is* important,
it is, and it may not benefit you, after all, you won't even exist shortly,
but it might just help me. I don't love you. I've never liked children
anyway, I never understand how your father surrounds himself with
them at school. But I was always told you love your own. And I don't.
Because I think that love has to be earned. I do, Douglas. And you have
done nothing in your fifteen wasted years to inspire love, nothing. It
doesn't matter that you're family, I don't have to love you, I don't, so
there. And all the guilt you've made me feel over the years for it... Well,
you'll be deleted soon, and good riddance. And there'll be no pain, so
don't worry, you'll never have even felt pain. But I'll still feel it. Because
I'll still remember the things you said and the contempt you've shown
me. Goodbye.

(She flings the phone down, and exits, angrily.)

Robert ...Well, it was a long message, so perhaps the tape ran out...

*(And, somewhat awkwardly, as if handling a corpse, he puts the phone
gently back on its cradle. He then exits, towards **Carrie**'s room.*

*(**Karen** enters the bar at speed.)*

Karen You're not interested in computer games or strapping
headphones on, are you, Robert?

Bob I don't know what you're talking about...

Karen The seventies were so civilised, weren't they? I think we're going
to have a great time there together, I've been thinking of nothing else.

Bob Ah. I'd sort of rather hoped you hadn't...

Karen What do you mean?

Bob There's no easy way to say this, but... Thank you. For the attention
and, interest and, and things. But well, I don't actually like you very
much. And I'd just as soon never see you again.

Karen ...Is it the age?

Bob *(soothingly)* Oh no. It's you. So don't worry about that.

Karen Oh.

Bob I tell you, even if you were twenty years younger, I couldn't
imagine liking you.

Karen You're wrong.

Bob I think I know what I feel...

Karen If I were twenty years younger, you'd be besotted by me. One rainy weekend's sex in a dingy hotel and you'd think you were in love. Chocolates, flowers, even bits of poetry, you'd never leave me alone.

Bob ...Yes, well, who can say, but I think I'd better be going...

Karen Please! Let me be your secretary!

Bob What?

Karen When you're a poet, you'll need a secretary, won't you?

Bob I don't think that...

Karen Give me an interview now! Ask me if I can type! Go on!

Bob ...Can you type?

Karen Yes! Ask me something else!

Bob I don't know what else secretaries do. I'm going.

Karen They sort papers. Can I sort papers? Yes, I can sort papers. See, I'd be perfect!

Bob Goodbye, Karen...

Karen I've got to get out of here. Now, more than ever. You've got to take me with you. Back to 1975. I was happy then. Don't you see, it's the last chance I've got?

*(She grabs hold of **Bob**. He shakes her off, exits.*

*(**Carrie** and **Robert** re-enter her bedroom. **Robert** is exhausted, **Carrie** polite but faintly bored.)*

Robert Well, that took me back. I'd forgotten how fun sex was against smooth skin.

Carrie Yes. It was fun.

Robert It *was* fun, wasn't it?

Carrie Yes.

Robert Up against the wardrobe, jammed behind the bath. Very athletic.

Carrie ...Just tell me. Is all that wheezing normal?

Robert Wheezing? I wheezed?

Carrie You wheezed a bit.

Robert I didn't know I wheezed. At which point did I wheeze?

Carrie Oh, no specific moment. Just a general wheezing.

Robert Well, I'm sorry if it was off-putting...

Carrie No, no, it didn't break my concentration once...

Robert Good.

Carrie I wish there *were* a gymnasium here. Or a swimming pool.

(Short pause.)

Robert It's been a long time. That's all.

Carrie I was just worried...

Robert I'll get better.

Carrie I just wasn't sure it was normal.

Robert You'll see, I'll get better.

Carrie If it's normal, I'll get used to it.

Robert So... You still want us to...

Carrie Yes.

Robert Good. I'll go and...

Carrie Okay.

Robert You'll still be here and...

Carrie Mmm.

Robert ...Right.

(He exits.

*(**Carrie** sighs, looks around the room without enthusiasm. In time, she leaves too.*

*(**Karen** is sitting, shocked and still, in the bar.)*

Dominic Hey, you. You. I want to ask you something. Okay, listen. Imagine that you knew your future. And your future... Well. It was the same as your present. Exactly the same. How would you feel about that? Would you feel trapped? I mean, here you are, you're so *ordinary*, that twenty years time, nothing has changed at all? Or do you think you'd feel? You see, I've been thinking about this. And if things are going to be the same in twenty years, well, you're home free, aren't you? You'll be all right. You can do anything. But if I can do anything I want... And I do it, I do anything I want... but it doesn't alter my future... Then what I want can't be very important. Can it?

*(But **Karen** doesn't react at all.*

*(**Robert** enters the main bedroom. **Bob** is following him.)*

Bob Now, I don't want to seem rude or abrupt or impolite or anything, but there's something I have to ask. What the bloody hell's going on, Mr Collins? Sorry.

Robert God, Robert. Haven't you worked it out yet?

Bob What out?

Robert I'm you. I'm your older self. Hello.

*(Short pause while **Bob** takes this in.)*

Bob You're me?

Robert Yes.

Bob ...You're not Mr Collins?

Robert No.

Bob Not Jennifer Collins' dad?

Robert No.

Bob *(lost)* So she didn't become a nun?

*(And, stunned, looks **Robert** over with increasing dismay.)*

What the hell have you been doing with myself?

(Short pause)

Robert Look, this is obviously a bit of a shock to you...

Bob You're what I become? Are you the best you could do? Don't I ever lose that paunch?

Robert I muddled through...

Bob No. You don't just 'muddle through' with my life. Have you got that? Because my life's special. Christ, my poetry. What about my poetry?

Robert I gave it up.

Bob You did what?

Robert *(angry)* Don't shout at me. We couldn't write our ways out of a paper bag.

Bob I might have got better. I would have got better. You bastard! That's the only thing I'd got...

Robert We're no bloody good at it!

(*And* **Bob** *stares at him, resentful. Then they both sit heavily on the bed.*)

(**Carrie** *enters the bar with her suitcase. She sees* **Karen** *sitting there, then approaches her, nervously.*)

Carrie I think we need to talk.

(*Short pause*)

Look, I know what you're going to say... I'm sorry. I mean, I know that, bluntly, I am stealing your husband. But... You're me, aren't you?

(*She sits opposite her older self.* **Karen** *looks up, surprised, but not willing yet to commit herself to speech.*)

It seemed so ludicrous, but... Carrie. Whatever happened to you?

(*Short pause. Then* **Karen** *sobs quietly.*)

Karen Nothing. Nothing ever happened to me.

(*Short pause.* **Carrie** *reaches out for her awkwardly.* **Karen** *pulls away, not unkindly. Bravely:*)

You look like you want a drink. Do you want a drink?

Carrie No, not really...

Karen I want a drink. We'll have vodka.

(*She walks behind the bar.*)

Carrie I don't drink vodka.

Karen Well, let me tell you. One particular New Year's Eve... 1991, I think... When you've never felt so low, and you don't want another year, not yet... You'll get very well acquainted with the stuff. Sod it, this thing's set for measures. Well, that's no good to me...

(*And with sudden strength, she pulls the bottle violently from the rack.*)

I don't suppose they'll mind.

Carrie I think they will.

Karen Yes, you're probably right.

(*She picks up two glasses, and sets them down on a breakfast table. She pours two glasses of vodka.* **Carrie** *sips at hers, winces.)*

It gets better.

(And she ignores her glass, and swigs from the bottle.)

Bob *(quietly)* And Karen? Is that what you did to Karen?

Robert You don't know what you're talking about...

Bob First you ruin my life, then you ruin hers as well. No wonder she's so ghastly.

Robert Karen is not ghastly! She's a wonderful woman!

Bob She's dreadful! Why did you ever make me marry her?

Robert I love Karen very much! I'm warning you, don't insult our wife again!

Bob And what the bloody hell have you grown over your upper lip? Whoever gave you permission to grow a bloody moustache?

Robert It keeps my face warm in the winter...

*(During the following speech, **Bob** gets more and more angry. As he does so, leaks appear in the bedroom roof.)*

Bob You've made me look ridiculous! ...Look, I had dreams, I had hopes. Lots of them, you know what they are, we had lots of them. Have you achieved any of them? What exactly have you done in my name? You've grown a sodding moustache! Which is too small and, and too bristly and makes your face look fat! That's what you've done! You've given me a fat face!

Robert Shut up, you little bastard. I've been embarrassed just watching you. I'm not keeping this body safe for you. It's mine. I know it's not great, it's not much to be proud of, but I've been through hell and back with this body, all right?

Bob You listen...

Robert No, you listen. My life's fine. It's not the greatest in the world, but it's very far from being the worst either, and I'm very happy most of the time. Well, not very happy, but pretty content. And pretty content's pretty good for 1995. And I've muddled through, and that's been harder than it sounds, and so I think I have earned the right to grow whatever facial hair I want! Do you understand? I might grow a beard next!

(And more water gushes in.)

Bob Don't you bloody try it!

Robert I will if I want to, right down to the floor if I want to! You try and stop me!

Bob All right! All right, I will! ...Put your fists up!

Robert *(suddenly calm with surprise)* ...I beg your pardon?

Bob I'm going to knock your block off.

(And evidently, a new leak hits the lights, because there is a loud fizzing noise, and they are plunged into blackness.

(Downstairs in the breakfast room and bar, more leaks appear, but without the ferocity of those in the bedroom.)

Karen *(looking at **Carrie** intently)* I used to be so pretty. Not beautiful exactly, not that. But pretty.

Carrie Well. Oh.

Karen *(with sudden exasperation)* You've only known him a day!

Carrie *(cheerfully)* Well, we're spontaneous, aren't we?

Karen No. Why are you doing this?

Carrie I'm lonely, Carrie.

Karen Oh, my poor girl... Being with Robert won't make it go away... It'll never go away.

Carrie I'm just a secretary, I'm nothing really, I don't want to be a secretary forever...

Karen If you go off with Robert... Then that's it. We've sacrificed everything. For a husband I can't be sure I ever loved and a son who won't speak to me... And our ambitions will never be realised.

Carrie *(blankly)* Ambitions?

Karen Ambitions. Our ambitions. Whatever they were.

Carrie I don't have any ambitions.

Karen What?

Carrie I don't want to be a secretary forever. I think all I want is to get married. And have children, maybe.

Karen *(broken)* Was that it? Is that all it ever was? ...Was I always so empty?

Carrie Carrie. I'm lonely. And I like him. What else should there be?

Karen Look, I don't know much. I'm not the sort of person who would usually offer advice. But you are me, after all, and I do have twenty years experience on you, so I think maybe this time you're stupid enough for me to get away with it.

Carrie *(not offended)* Yes, that sounds reasonable...

Karen I'm middle-aged. And the thing about middle age is that it sounds fine, you know, you're only in the middle, you're still halfway, that sounds okay mathematically. But you see, Carrie, it's all a big lie. Because you're not halfway at all, you've nearly finished. You aren't going to change your life suddenly, because it's all too hard, much too hard. And every year that year seems shorter. And you look back over it on New Year's Eve and you can't remember one thing that you did in it to make it any different from the others. And you realise that those years that might have counted, when the changes might have mattered, you frittered away because you thought you'd wait till later. Carrie. Please. Don't wait till later. Please. Get some ambitions now.

Carrie What ambitions?

Karen I don't know what ambitions, it doesn't matter what ambitions, you'll never achieve them anyway! You'll have to give them up sooner or later, everybody does. But at least, when you're middle-aged, you can look back and say you had some. At least you can look back and regret something worthwhile.

(Short pause)

Do you want another drink?

Carrie I really don't drink very often...

*(**Karen** laughs dryly.*

(The lights in the main bedroom fizz on again, only this time they continue to flicker, and they have turned more reddish-brown. Water is now pouring all around the room.

*(**Bob** has his fists up, dances on the bed around the more reluctant **Robert**.)*

Bob Come on then!

Robert Robert, this is stupid.

Bob Come on! I'm going to bloody kill you!

Robert You can't fight. You know you can't. Remember when we were at school? The sheer number of times we got our heads flushed down toilets...

Bob *(jabbing him with a rather ineffectual punch)* Defend yourself, you bastard!

Robert Oh, for God's sake.

*(And he knocks **Bob** to the ground.)*

Bob ...Ow.

Robert Sorry. Are you all right? Let me help you up...

Bob *(refusing his hand)* Tell me, Robert. Tell me. How many compromises did you make?

Robert Come on, give me your hand...

Bob *(insistent)* How many? Two? Three?

Robert It's not as simple as that...

Bob How many?

Robert *(earnestly)* I don't know! Every day I make compromises! Every morning when I wake up alone, that's a compromise. Only getting a peck on the cheek before I go to work, and not one on the lips, there's another. Never having cooked breakfasts – and I like cooked breakfasts...

Robert & Bob Sausages...

Robert It's all there is. Compromise. You'll see. You'll understand.

Bob Not for me.

Robert Well. Okay.

Bob I'm never going to be you.

Robert Fair enough.

Bob Just to spite you. You understand? I shan't be you, to spite you.

Robert Well, best of luck to you. Really. Come on, take my hand, it's getting very wet in here...

*(**Bob** accepts his hand, and **Robert** pulls him up. **Bob** knees him in the groin; **Robert** falls down, winded.)*

Bob Muddle through that...

(And he makes to exit.)

Robert Robert! Wait! ...You're not really going off with Karen, are you?

Bob Hurt you, would it?

(He exits.

*(Underneath the following, **Robert**, still winded, pulls himself up into a sitting position by the bed.*

*(**Karen** and **Carrie** have been drinking.)*

Carrie That wonderful smile he has. Don't you think he has a wonderful smile?

Karen *(smiling)* Oh yes. It can be lovely.

Carrie The way it slowly creeps across his face, teeth beginning to show. As if he were embarrassed by it, love him...

Karen Like he can't help himself. And the way he'll look at the ground as it happens...

Carrie That's right! He does that!

Karen No, that never stopped. I always wondered if it would...

Carrie And he's so gentle. So patient...

Karen That reminds me. There was a time a few years ago, when he... Well, it was very special. I won't spoil it for you.

Carrie No, don't. I love surprises!

Karen ...Yes. I suppose I *did* once.

Robert *(sadly)* Oh, Karen...

(And, decisively, he takes the suitcase out of the room.

*(In the bar, **Karen** gets up.)*

Karen Carrie, listen. However much you like surprises. Your spontaneity... I don't know when I lost all that. But I think it must have been Robert's fault. ..

Carrie *(overlapping)* You know I can't... I can't listen to you, Carrie.

Karen What I used to be. You're great. Don't ever make yourself second best.

Carrie You know I have to ignore this.

Karen Yes. I know.

(Short pause)

Carrie But overall, you would say... That our life *is* a happy one? Overall. You would say.

(Short pause)

Karen A word of advice. Just a word.

Carrie What?

Karen He's got a very ticklish stomach. You tickle him there, he'll let you do anything.

Carrie Really?

Karen Just above the navel. And if he ever suggests a holiday in Wolverhampton... say no.

(She holds out her arms. They hug.

*(Underneath, **Bridget** enters with two small suitcases and coat, watches them awkwardly.)*

Carrie Funny feeling hugging yourself, isn't it?

Karen Sort of tingly. Carrie. You take care of yourself.

Carrie You too, Carrie.

Karen *(softly)* I always wanted to be called Carrie...

Carrie But no-one ever would.

Bridget Excuse me... I hope I'm not interrupting...

*(**Karen** and **Carrie** disentangle.)*

I just wanted to say thank you.

Karen Thank you? What for?

Bridget Because I'm doing it. I'm leaving him. I'm actually leaving him. And I don't think I'd have been brave enough without your example.

Karen Oh, please, I hope I didn't give advice, I never give advice...

Bridget Because it is brave, isn't it? Just walking out after all these years. Looking on your whole life, saying, no, don't like it, and throwing it all away.

Karen *(warily)* Yes. Thanks.

Bridget *(unhappily)* And there being nothing outside to grasp on to, nothing to look forward to, you'll be alone, completely alone... Oh God, what am I going to do? ...Still, anyway, thanks. Goodbye.

*(She puts both cases in one hand, shakes **Karen's** hand.)*

And goodbye.

*(She transfers the cases to the other hand, shakes **Carrie's** hand. And she walks to the exit.)*

*(Burst of thunder, flash of lightning. **Dominic** appears. More rainfall.)*

Dominic Bridget! What are you doing?

*(**Bridget** turns around slowly.)*

Bridget *(nervously)* Oh, hello, Dominic. I'm leaving you.

(Short pause. Another burst of thunder.)

Just something I decided. Didn't take long. Thought about it, said yes. Packed my cases. Didn't take long either. Don't have very much, don't want most of that. And that was it. Walking out. For good. If... That's all right with you...

(Short pause)

Of course, if it isn't... All right with you, I... I could just go back upstairs. Unpack the suitcases. Won't take long, don't have very much. And not leave you. If you'd prefer.

(Short pause)

Dominic?

Dominic *(quietly)* Since when did you get so articulate?

Bridget I'm sorry?

Dominic You're not the woman I married. The woman I married wasn't articulate. Put the bags down.

(She does. Only then does he walk across the stage to her, unhurriedly. He grips her arm.)

Did you really think I'd just let you leave? After all these years? If I'm trapped here, if this is all my life is going to be, then I don't see why you should get anything better.

Bridget Dominic, you're hurting me. Chuckle, why aren't you chuckling?...

Dominic Shut up. I love you and need you, Bridget. I told you that last time 'you packed your bags'.

Bridget I'll just go upstairs and we'll say no more about it...

Dominic We'll say plenty more about it. If you wanted to leave me, Bridget, you should have done it years ago. When I still took you seriously.

(He lets her go.)

Go upstairs. I'll join you in a minute.

Bridget *(faintly)* Yes. All right.

Dominic *(calling to her as she walks towards the exit)* And smile.

(She stops. Short pause)

Bridget No. ...I'm not going to smile.

Dominic I said smile.

Bridget I'll go upstairs. And I'll get unpacked. And I'll stay here forever. But I'm not going to smile. Because there's nothing to smile about.

Dominic *(temper lost for the first time)* Smile, you stupid bitch!

(And he lunges for her, grabs her by both arms. She drops the cases, gives a cry.)

Carrie *(bravely, nervously)* Any time you feel like stopping this... Would be okay with me.

Dominic ...And who the hell do you think you are?

Carrie I'm Karen Brewer!

Karen *(less confidently)* Yes. And I'm... Karen Brewer too...

Dominic Is she your wife? I don't think she is. Do you have two hundred and eighty-three photos of her grinning? I don't think you do. So you Karen Brewers can shut up and mind your own business...

*(And he pulls **Bridget** roughly across the stage.*

*(With a cry, **Carrie** leaps over and grabs his arm.)*

Get off!

Carrie Carrie! Help me!

Dominic Now you're just being silly...

Karen Don't you dare call her silly!

*(And furiously **Karen** jumps on him. **Dominic** releases **Bridget**, flings off **Karen** and **Carrie**.)*

Dominic Right, now you're for it...

Karen Bridget! Help!

Carrie Bridget!

Dominic Interfering bloody bitches. Can't trust any of them...

Bridget What do you want me to do?

Karen For God's sake, anything!

(*Bridget hesitates, then jumps on top of picks up the bucket and rams it on Dominic. He finds this unexpected sign of resistance unexpectedly funny. He laughs as Karen and Carrie grab hold of him as well – and in the struggle smash his head on to the bar. The bell rings merrily as his head connects.*)

Dominic ...What did you... You actually...

(*He staggers towards them, then falls to the ground. A shocked silence.*)

Carrie Now, Bridget! Get out of here while you've got the chance!

Bridget I can't. He's right. I've nowhere to go, I've nothing to do...

Karen Wait. Bridget. Would you have left him in 1975?

Bridget Well, I didn't.

Karen Listen. There's a path out there, back to 1975. I don't know why, all I know is that it's there and I'm going to take it. If I went back and found you, would you listen to me?

Bridget (*thinking hard*) I doubt it. Lots of my friends told me to leave Dominic. I stopped talking to them... The photographs! Show me the photographs!

Carrie Photographs?

(*Bridget finds the album at the bar.*)

Bridget All these pictures of me smiling! Both of you... Take these. And which ever one of you makes it back to the past... show me how much he made my smiles hurt in the future. And make me dump the bastard.

(*Thunder. The picture of the Queen spins round even quicker. A lightning flash, and with a small explosion, it flies off the wall.*

(*It should be noted that the spinning photograph and the overflowing toilet are elements which can be removed if they prove too diffficult.*

(*Enter Bob, with suitcase. He has dried himself.*)

Bob (*abruptly*) Right. I'm leaving. You. Still want to be my secretary?

Karen Just a moment, Robert...

Bob No, not just a moment! I resent the way that you and your stupid husband have pushed me around. Well, never again. I'm leaving now, and if you want to join me, it's now or never.

Carrie Where's the other Robert?

Bob I'm not prepared to discuss it. ...What's been going on here?

(*Karen* hesitates, kisses *Carrie*.)

Karen Goodbye, Carrie. Take care of yourself.

Carrie Won't I ever see you again?

Karen I don't know. Another thunderstorm, some time, maybe.

(*Enter* **Robert**, *struggling with the suitcase. He is still in some pain.*)

Robert Karen! Wait!

Carrie Robert?

Robert Not you. Karen. Listen. We don't have to do this.

Karen We're all ready to go, Robert...

Robert No, no, we don't have to do this. It's a mistake. I know it, it's a big mistake... You've got to help me find it, Karen, whatever will make you want me again.

Karen I don't think anything will...

Robert Just give me a little more time.

Bridget The storm's right above us. I think you should go.

Karen I've got to go.

Robert Another hour...

Carrie Robert, love. Let them go. You've got me.

Robert What?

Carrie It's what you said. That I'm just like her, but younger, erm, cleaner...

Robert I said fresher, not cleaner, fresher, and you're not, so shut up.

(*Carrie* moves away, upset.)

Karen (*gently*) Robert. This is ridiculous.

Robert No. This is what's ridiculous. That you prefer him to me. You can't prefer him to me? Look at him...!

Karen I'm sorry. I do.

Bob Come on!

Karen Wait!

*(To **Robert**, soothingly:)*

It's not that I'm losing you. Not really. Every day, as Robert gets older, I'll see him turning into you...

Robert *(miserably)* Bloody hell...

Bob That isn't going to happen.

Robert *(fighting back tears, fiercely)* I just thought... God, I still do love you. And I had hoped... you loved me too, because you did, you know you did. After all we've been through together. Not good things, I admit, but we muddled through, didn't we?

Karen Robert, please...

Robert No, please, please don't say anything until I've finished...

(Short pause. He looks around, sits down, defeated.)

I've finished.

Bob God, he's crying now. This is embarrassing.

Karen *(gently)* Robert...

Bob Karen, either you're with me or you're not. But I'm leaving now.

Bridget Well, made up your mind? I'm dying to know. Who's it going to be?

Robert *(pleading)* Karen...

Bob *(sternly)* Karen.

*(**Karen** sighs. She kisses **Robert** on the top of the head. He sighs with relief. Then she hurries towards **Bob**. They leave, **Bob** crowing at **Robert** in a victory tempered by the fact he is left to struggle with the suitcase.)*

Carrie Robert... I'm so sorry...

Robert *(dead)* Hello, Karen.

Carrie Hurry out after them. You could still catch them...

Robert No. It really is too late.

(He sighs heavily, then puts his face in his hands.

*(**Carrie** stoops, hugs him.)*

Carrie It's all right...

Robert This is so humiliating...

Carrie Sssh. I don't mind. I don't mind being second best.

Robert Yes. Sorry. I was a little... erm, tactless there...

Carrie Tactless. Yes.

(And she rocks him back and forth gently in her arms. Gratefully he gets to his feet, and they hug properly, all the time **Carrie** *cradling him.* **Robert** *breaks off at last.)*

Robert Why on earth would you love me?

(And **Carrie** *kisses him.* **Robert** *hardly responds, but does not resist. She looks at him, he back at her. Silence.)*

Bridget *(quietly)* You'd best be going. If you're going.

*(***Carrie** *offers* **Robert** *her hand. He takes it. They exit.*

*(***Bridget** *sighs.*

(And then the storm stops. The sound of the rain fades away, and the leaking water abruptly dribbles to a halt. Lights on the stage become perceptively brighter.

*(***Bridget** *smiles sadly, then turns to walk away. As an afterthought, she turns back, looks at* **Dominic,** *groaning as he recovers on the floor. She stands over him.)*

And from now on, you sleep alone.

(And she exits dismissively.)

(Music plays. **Dominic** *gets to his feet, straightens the bucket. He goes behind the bar, hangs up a new picture over the bar. It is of* **Bridget***, power dressed, unsmiling.*

(He takes a mop, and begins to clean the floor.

(Lights become much brighter over the entire set. There is something faintly fluorescent and artificial about them.

(A clap of thunder. Enter **Robert** *and* **Carrie** *from outside. They are now ten years older.* **Robert** *no longer has a moustache.)*

Carrie God, it's terrible out there...

Robert Well, that was the idea, wasn't it?

(He approaches **Dominic***.)*

Excuse me...

(*Dominic* nervously stops working.)

Could we see the manager, please?

Dominic It isn't a complaint, is it, sir? Because we don't have to involve her, really...

Robert No.

Carrie We're old friends.

Dominic I'll go and tell her.

(*He exits.*)

Carrie It's strange that the place has changed so much. I didn't think it would.

Robert Practically all the hotels in Britain have been converted into motorway service stations. Why should this one be any different?

Carrie I don't know, after what we went through here...

(*Robert* shrugs.)

Robert, I need to talk to you.

Robert Can't imagine why.

Carrie I just thought that being back here again... Where we first met... You know, romantic...

(*Robert* stares at her. She trails off. He resumes looking around the room.)

(*Enter **Bridget**, dressed as in the picture. **Dominic** trails shyly.*)

Bridget So, it is you.

Carrie (*warmly*) Hello, Bridget.

(*Bridget* marches up to her and kisses her on both cheeks. *Carrie* is slightly surprised.)

Bridget Every time it rains, I expect you to show up...

Robert (*abruptly*) Any sign of Karen yet?

Bridget No.

Robert What's keeping her? She must have had a storm some time since 1975...

Carrie (*laughing nervously*) He's so keen to see my older self! Don't know why! I'd have thought one of me was enough to handle!

*(**Robert** glares at her, walks off testily.)*

Dominic *(awkwardly)* If that's all, can I get back to my cleaning now?

Bridget Give me a smile first. Wider than that. Good, off you go.

(He exits.)

Robert You mean that's...

Bridget Yes.

Robert My God.

Carrie Carrie gave you the photograph then?

Bridget Back in 1975, yes. Thirty years ago now. I told Dominic I wanted a divorce. I expected him to be angry or something, but instead he just burst into tears. Just cried for hours, took me by surprise, I can tell you. Begged that I wouldn't leave him, got down on his knees. I can still make him get down on his knees, shall I show you?

Carrie No, it's all right...

Bridget Said he'd do anything to stay. We wouldn't have to be married, he just needed to be with me. So I gave him a job, he does the cleaning and cooks the breakfasts. ...You know, I always thought he'd just get bored and leave eventually, but it's 2005 and he's still here...

Carrie And it works? You're happy?

Bridget Perfectly. I haven't smiled for years.

Carrie *(awkwardly)* Look, I hope this isn't... The photograph you gave me. I brought it back.

*(She gives it to **Bridget**, who looks at it for a moment.)*

I don't know, it just seemed more yours than mine...

*(Abruptly **Bridget** puts it away.)*

Bridget Thank you.

*(Enter **Bob** and **Karen**. They too, are ten years older. **Karen** looks much the same, but noticeably more tired. **Bob**, however, wears sunglasses and boasts a pony tail. If boasts is the word. Heeled shoes make him noticeably taller than his elder counterpart. He carries a mobile phone.)*

Karen Robert, I wish you'd take off those sunglasses.

Bob It's the fame. I don't want people recognising me.

Karen But it's November. There's nothing more conspicuous than wearing sunglasses in November.

Bridget *(expansively, rushing towards **Bob**)* Mr Hunter! Robert Hunter! A celebrity in my hotel.

Bob No autographs.

Karen He doesn't do autographs.

Bridget I'll be honest with you, Mr Hunter...

Bob *(into his mobile)* Hello?

Bridget I never used to like poetry.

Bob Hello?

Bridget Found it a bit difficult. But I have a book of yours by my bed each night.

Bob *(distant)* That's nice.

Bridget *(without irony)* In case I can't sleep.

Bob *Hello?*

Bridget Incredible stuff. They say that because of you poetry's more popular than it's been for centuries.

Karen *(dryly)* Poetry is the new rock 'n' roll.

Bridget Perhaps later a picture of the two of us outside the hotel?

Bob No autographs, no photographs.

Karen He doesn't do graphs of any kind.

Bridget Fine. Well, don't decide now. In your own time.

*(She exits. Awkward silence. **Robert** and **Bob** stand far apart. **Karen** and **Carrie** smile at each other nervously.)*

Karen Well.

Carrie Well!

(Short pause. Then:)

Karen It *is* good to see you again!

(And they come forward and hug gratefully.)

Bob Ah. Robert. Yes.

Robert You look a right prat in those sunglasses.

Carrie *(walking back to **Robert**)* Come on, Robert. Try and be polite.

Robert I'll be polite.

Carrie Remember... This is Robert Hunter!

*(**Robert** gives her a filthy look.)*

Karen *(gently)* Please. For me.

Robert How are you, Robert?

Bob I can't complain, Robert.

*(**Carrie** and **Karen** drift off, talk together quietly.)*

Robert I'm sure you can't. What year have you come from?

Bob 1985.

Robert No, I don't think you could complain. Not in the year of your greatest triumph.

Bob *(wanting to go)* Well, I haven't done much writing recently, you know? No time. Not with all the celebrity luncheons and television retrospectives...

Robert *(doggedly)* You write a poem in 1985. It's called 'Ode to Love'.

Bob Yeah, well, snappy title. Any good, is it?

Robert Well, they've stuck it all over the London Underground.

Bob *(pleased)* Well, you can't argue with that, can you?

Robert *(cold anger)* I can. You see, I know you. I know you too well, I know the sort of person we are. And I know that all those feelings... it's just bullshit. I know you, it's all just words, it's just fake.

Bob But you follow my career anyway?

Robert Follow it? I teach it.

Bob Good for you.

Robert Robert Hunter teaching Robert Hunter, they all find that funny. Except now they say I'm teaching it wrong. What you've written... What I've written, it's rubbish, it's all rubbish.

Bob This 'Ode to Love'? You haven't got a copy, have you?

Robert Not the sort of thing I carry around.

Bob *(amiably)* Pity. I thought if I copied it down, I could save myself some effort later on...

Robert Don't worry. I'll write it all right. Every year, it's on the bloody syllabus.

Bob *(with sudden menace, dropping the affability)* Fine. But listen, sunshine. Stop saying you wrote my poems. I wrote my poems. You understand?

Robert ...Do you really never take off your sunglasses? Don't you keep walking into things?

*(Short pause. Then **Bob** turns and walks away abruptly.)*

*(**Karen** walks hesitantly to **Robert**; **Bob** stares at **Robert** across the room.)*

Buggered if I'm going to tell the little shit that next year they'll make us poet laureate.

Karen Hello.

Robert ...Hello.

Carrie *(to **Bob**)* I just had to say. I'm a huge fan.

Robert Excuse me.

*(And he drifts away from **Karen**.)*

Carrie I adore your poetry. Particularly 'Ode to Love'.

Bob *(still looking at **Robert**)* You know, I think of him every day. It's like he haunts me. I could end up like that...

Carrie Oh, he's not you at all! Not remotely. I mean, you're *famous*, aren't you?

Bob Very.

Carrie *(fast, nervous)* I've got goosebumps all over me, just being this close to you. Robert gives me goosebumps too, but in a bad way. A flesh crawling sort of way. He's so negative, he's just... given up. And I've tried, really tried with him. He doesn't seem to notice, he hardly ever speaks to me. I've taken lovers, had to, he doesn't mind, sometimes he suggests future candidates for me. From the school, PE teachers he thinks I'd like. And even that was fine for a while, but I've really gone off sex now. When that's all it is. It's just all slimy and sweaty and sticky. Don't you think?

*(Short pause. **Bob** slowly turns to look at her.)*

Bob Come on. Let's go for a walk.

Carrie Where? It's raining.

Bob Let's walk around the hotel. So how well do you know 'Ode to

Love'?

*(He takes a room key. They exit, leaving **Karen** and **Robert**, apart. At last:)*

Karen I didn't want to see you. I knew it would be awkward. I only came because I knew it was impossible. I knew this time thing couldn't happen twice.

Robert Yes. It is awkward. I'm sorry.

Karen Silly. Don't be silly.

(A moment, then they both smile at this.)

Are you all right, have you... been all right?

Robert Oh. Well. You know. Ups and downs.

Karen Yes.

Robert Mostly downs, actually.

Karen At least you now know what a great talent you had. You know it for sure. That must count for something. Surely.

Robert *(smiling)* You know, it's funny. Everyone has regrets. The feeling that if they'd made a different decision their lives would be better. But only I have proof. Only I have it rubbed in my face every morning when I drive to school to teach poems I've written, which I never got round to writing. When I go into bookshops, when I watch chat shows even, God, I'm always on chat shows. And I tell you, even in twenty years time, Karen, he won't have taken off his sunglasses...

Karen At least you know you had it in you. You may not have used it, but you had it in you. I don't even have that.

(Short pause)

Robert Karen... Are you all right?

Karen No.

Robert You look awful... Erm, I mean that nicely...

Karen I just never understand. If he can write poetry of such beauty, why he always has to speak such rubbish.

Robert Why on earth don't you leave him?

Karen Oh, he usually leaves me. Sacks me. Quite often. His usual chat-up line to girls is, 'Can you type?'

Robert I'm sorry.

Karen But they can never stand him for long. So he always comes back to me. You know, I used to say there was fire in his eyes. And there still is sometimes, when he's writing, always. But I don't know. Perhaps it isn't enough. Flammable eyes, a bit overrated.

Robert I know this sounds terrible, but... I'm so relieved you're unhappy! All these years, it's not just been the poetry, it's been you, it's the thought that he's got you! But he *hasn't* got you, has he? You don't sleep with him, just as I don't sleep with Karen...

Karen We've had a son. Called Douglas.

(Short pause)

Robert Oh. ...Oh.

Karen What can I say? I made the same mistake twice. Some rainy weekend in Wolverhampton.

Robert God, I miss you.

Karen I better go and find Robert.

Robert You've no idea how much. Every day I think of you. I've thought of going to see you... but you'd be in your seventies, it wouldn't be the same...

Karen Please. Don't. I must go and see if Robert's all right...

Robert I just need to know. Do *you* miss *me*?

Karen *(softly)* Yes.

Robert You do? And, and you think of me? You do think of me?

Karen All the time. ...I've got to go...

Robert *(eagerly)* Well, why? If you feel that way, and I feel that way, then surely...

Karen *(angrily)* Because we've already done it, Robert. You and me together, we know what it's like. And it isn't going to get any better. And it wasn't that great to begin with.

Robert Oh, Karen...

Karen Robert. I did love you. I did love you once. And I've never loved anyone as much as I loved you. Once.

*(Pause. They look at each other. Then as **Karen** turns to go, **Robert** reaches out and kisses her.)*

Please, there's no point...

Robert I love you.

(He kisses her again, gently. Lets her go. She looks at him for a moment, then with far more passion grabs his head and kisses him on the mouth.

*(He rings the reception bell. **Dominic** enters.)*

Now. Take us to the room now.

Dominic Right now, sir?

Robert Right now.

*(**Dominic** exits, **Robert** takes the hand of the quizzical **Karen**.)*

Karen You booked a room?

Robert It's a surprise. Just in case. I know you don't like surprises, but...

Karen *(delighted)* I love surprises!

*(And they chase out after **Dominic**.)*

*(Re-enter **Bridget**. She sits down in the breakfast room, takes out the photograph with mild curiosity. She looks at it and frowns, stares at it. Silence.*

*(**Carrie** and **Bob** enter her former bedroom.)*

Bob Tell me. Can you type?

Carrie I'm a secretary.

Bob That's useful. ...I think you can help me with an important new poem I have to write.

*(**Robert** and **Karen** enter the main bedroom. He offers his arms.)*

Robert May I?

(And he picks her up. He carries her to the bed, staggering, and they collapse on to it with laughter.)

Bob Kiss me. So I can check.

*(**Carrie** and **Bob** kiss.*

*(Re-enter **Dominic** in the bar. He returns to his cleaning.)*

Carrie Is that all right?

Bob Oh yes. I think I can crank a few verses out of that.

Robert I love you.

Karen I love you too.

*(**Bridget** looks up from the photograph thoughtfully.)*

Bridget Dominic! Come here a minute.

*(**Dominic** approaches. **Bridget** rises, looks at the photo again for a second, then kisses him on the mouth. A few seconds of passion, then she pulls away.)*

No, I'm not missing anything. You can go back to work.

Dominic Bridget... please...

Bridget Smile.

*(**Dominic** smiles bravely, teeth clenched, as if to stop himself from crying.)*

And back to work.

(He returns to the other side of the stage, and stares at her mournfully. She sits down again, looks back at the photograph.)

Carrie To think... someone famous wants me!

Bob But listen. You'll always come second to my poetry. You understand?

Carrie *(happily)* Of course. That's what geniuses are like, isn't it? Brain works differently.

Bob Kiss me again. For research.

(They kiss; freeze.)

Robert And what about tomorrow? Are we going to stay together tomorrow?

Karen Let's sleep on it.

*(They kiss; freeze. Spotlight on them. Then spotlight on **Carrie** and **Bob**. Then two solo spotlights on **Dominic** and **Bridget**, **Dominic** still looking at her, **Bridget** still looking down at the photo.*

*(Slowly **Bridget** tears up the photograph.*

(Blackout.)

Binary Dreamers

(1996)

WINNER OF THE GUINNESS AWARD FOR INGENUITY,
IN ASSOCIATION WITH THE ROYAL NATIONAL THEATRE

OPENED AT THE MAN IN THE MOON THEATRE, LONDON, PRESENTED BY NEXUS THEATRE
COMPANY IN ASSOCIATION WITH THE ROYAL NATIONAL THEATRE,
ON 2ND APRIL 1996, WITH THE FOLLOWING CAST:

BARBIE MARIANNE O'CONNOR
ALASTAIR WAYNE FORESTER
BARBARA JACQUELINE QUELLA
BERNARD ROBERT WOODALL
SIOBHAN LUCY CAMPBELL
VOICE OF THE COMPUTER PETER JONES
VOICE OF JENNY CLAIRE WELLER
VOICE OF JEREMY WAYNE FORESTER
JENNY ROSY MADDISON
JEREMY JACK MADDISON
DIRECTED BY DAVID CRAIK

Act One

(In the darkness, we hear music – light, pastoral and innocent. It quietens, replaced by a low hum. This hum plays throughout most of the drama, so shouldn't be too noticeable.

(Lights rise on what would appear to be an almost empty stage. There is no furniture, the only solid object being an enormous computer screen built against the wall. The floor is polished smooth, and looks almost comfortable.

*(**Barbie** paces, muttering to herself. She is a not unattractive woman in her thirties. At the moment she is wearing her hair down. She carries a small file within a ring binder, to which she nervously refers from time to time.)*

Barbie *(dully)* I don't care about any of that. Have you brought my bloody gin?

(And she looks down to the file. She is quite pleased to find that is what is written there, though this evidently is not completely reassuring.)

Okay. That's okay. I think I've got it now, okay.

(She lightly drops the file to the floor. A couple of deep breaths. She steps towards centre stage awkwardly.)

So. It's you again. So. It's you again. More cheerful. So! It's you again! Brighter. So, it's *you* again! Too bright. So! It's you again. Yes. Now. So!

(She takes a step forward, and shakes an imaginary hand.)

It's you again. Or maybe I should... So, it's *you* again...

(And she shakes on the 'you'.)

Or maybe I shouldn't shake his hand. Would that be too formal? Shaking his hand? Formal? Or, well, I am touching him. Would that be too informal? I think it would be too informal, the shaking. Of the hand. Or too formal. So. So! It's you again. But I've got to be welcoming. He's been at work all day. All day, poor love! That's it, what if... So, it's you again, poor love. No, no, so, it's you again, dear. I'm not his mother. So, it's you again... darling. Darling? 'So, it's you again, darling', well, why not? So long as I don't emphasise it too much. So, it's you *again*, darling. Still too strong. Emphasise everything else, everything but the darling. *So it's you again*, darling. Yes. Yes.

(Short pause)

And then maybe a little handshake at the end. If it feels right. I'll play it by ear.

(The noise downstairs of a large door being opened. It creaks slowly, then bangs shut as if it is the heavy portal to a dungeon. The sound of a man coming up the stairs.)

Oh God. Here he comes! Relax, you know it. So, it's you again, darling, possible shake, so, it's you again, darling, possible shake. It's okay, he loves you. He'll do his part!

(A couple of seconds pause. Then, with panic:)

Oh God, I'm not meant to greet him at the door!

(And she rushes out. A couple of seconds later, she rushes back on, scoops up the ring binder, and runs off again.)

*(Save the hum, a few seconds silence. Then enter **Alastair** – a plain, tired man in his thirties. He carries a work bag, and is dressed in work overalls. He crosses over to the computer terminal, takes from his breast pocket a card, and holds it in front of the screen base so it can be scanned.)*

(A beep. Then the screen displays a cheerful logo, pronouncing it to be HOMEWORLD TM, and the words, LOGGING ON. Bright, fanfare muzak plays loudly.)

Alastair *(irritated)* Volume down. Do you hear me? I said, volume down.

(And the volume dips. Muttering:)

I hate that bloody music.

*(The screen fills with data. There is a voiceover. The names are prerecorded by **Alastair** himself, the rest a slightly Americanised computer voice.)*

Computer Your name is...

Alastair voice Alastair Payne.

Computer Welcome.

Alastair voice *(exactly as before)* Alastair Payne.

Computer You are Repairs Worker Second Class, Serial Number 74B38CD/3...

Alastair *(speaking with it)* 74B38CD/3, yes, yes...

Computer Your wife is called...

Alastair voice Barbara.

Computer Your son is called...

Alastair voice Jimmy.

Computer Your daughter is called...

Alastair voice Jenny.

Computer Your cat is called...

Alastair voice Tiddles.

Computer Would you like to change any of these names? If so, say 'yes' after the tone.

*(There is a long tone. Testily, **Alastair** remains silent.)*

You have made no changes. Welcome to your homeworld...

Alastair voice Alastair Payne.

(And the screen shows him his lounge. It is reasonably well furnished – a sofa, chairs, fireplace, flowers on a bookshelf. But there is still something relatively cold about it, as if all these objects are simply components rather than anything truly decorative or homely.)

Alastair Show me Tiddles. Dial Tiddles.

(With a little blip a cat appears on the screen. Or at least, a very good computer simulation of a cat.)

Ah, hello, Tiddles. How are you?

(More sternly:)

Put on mew mode.

(The cat mews.)

That's good. There's a good cat. There's a good cat.

(He strokes the screen gently, and sighs.)

Put on purr mode. Oh, Tiddles. I wish it was just you and me. That'd be fun, that'd be all right, I wouldn't need a wife. But they do insist, don't they? They do insist. Oh well. Better get it over and done with, eh?

(The cat mews.)

Barbara! Barbara, I'm home!

*(As **Alastair** turns his attention from the cat, the cat remains on screen, as if frozen, staring out at the room. It looks like some overelaborate, barely moving screen saver, and it is this which makes it just a little disquieting.*

*(And **Barbie** enters – very nervous, very stiff. She walks towards him, and beams suddenly with a wide smile.*

*(**Alastair** looks at her, stunned, open mouthed. **Barbie** is too nervous to appreciate this.)*

Barbie So! It's you again! Darling!

*(And, impulsively, she holds out her hand. Dazedly **Alastair** offers her his in return, and she shakes it.)*

Alastair *(croaking)* I beg your pardon?

Barbie *(thrown a bit by this)* What?

Alastair ...What?

Barbie Didn't I do it right? This is my first time. Shit, I'm not meant to say that. Bugger, I'm not meant to swear.

Alastair Barbara? Are you...

Barbie You want me to say it again? Right, erm. So! It's you again! ...Darling.

*(And she offers her hand. **Alastair** takes it, beginning to articulate.)*

Alastair Who exactly are... Barbara? Is it actually you?

*(Short pause. **Barbie** looks around a little nervously.)*

Barbie Look, I'm very sorry, but this is definitely... This is my first time. I shouldn't have said that, but I did, and it is, and I don't know, maybe I'm wrong, but this is definitely *not* what it says in the report...

Alastair No, I'm sorry...

Barbie You're meant to be all tired and bored. Not agog and gaping.

Alastair No, you're absolutely right...

Barbie I wouldn't mind, but this is my first time, and I'm a little nervous.

Alastair I can see that. I'm sorry.

(Short pause)

Barbie Sorry, I lost it a bit there, I would never normally...

Alastair *(more to himself, staring at her)* It's just that, well... it's remarkable.

Barbie What is?

Alastair *(indicating her body)* The whole thing, all of it, I... No, don't worry about it. Let's start again.

Barbie What, all over? Are we allowed to do that?

Alastair None of this happened.

Barbie It doesn't count.

Alastair Exactly.

Barbie *(smiling naturally for the first time)* Great. Thank you. Thank... I won't let you down. I'm a little, well, I've never met a real repairman before! In your overalls and everything, I've seen a few fake ones, but you can always tell the difference. And you're all so wonderfully *purposeful*, aren't you? I can see it in your face now, I'm a little, well.

Alastair *(rather coldly)* Shall we be getting on with it?

Barbie Which is exactly what I mean! You're breathtaking.

(And she exits.

*(**Alastair** is still rather stunned. He looks at the frozen Tiddles.)*

Alastair *(mildly)* Well, it's hardly my fault.

Barbie *(offstage)* Shall we do it from my entrance, or will you give me a cue?

Alastair Barbara! Barbara, I'm home!

Barbie *(offstage)* From there then, okay.

(And she marches on, much quicker than before.)

So! It's you again, darling.

Alastair ...No handshake this time?

Barbie I've got this far, let's not push my luck.

Alastair Fair enough.

Barbie Your line.

*(Though most of her lines should be quite withering or bitter, **Barbie** tries to interpret them in as upbeat a fashion as she can.)*

Alastair So, how are you, love?

Barbie Same as ever. What do you think?

Alastair Well, you seem okay...

Barbie Do I look worse or something?

Alastair No, no, you look fine.

Barbie Well, thank you so much for your enthusiasm.

Alastair It's been a long day, love, please...

Barbie You look the same as usual too. So no surprises there.

*(**Alastair** can't resist, as the conversation goes on, looking **Barbie** over, taking a look behind her, even prodding her curiously. **Barbie** gamely tries to ignore this.)*

Alastair Did you have a nice day?

Barbie Oh, sure. While you've been out at work, having fun, I've just been stuck here. Stuck here all day. I've been bored out of my skull.

Alastair Sorry to hear that...

Barbie Bored, bored, bored. Erm, is everything all right?

Alastair It's uncanny, the whole thing. You look just like her. Down to the last blemish. There's just one thing I can't put my finger on...

Barbie Should I go on?

Alastair *(absorbed)* Yes, yes...

Barbie *(cheerfully)* I'm doing quite well, aren't I?

(She counts off on her fingers, resumes.)

Bored, bored.

Alastair Well, you haven't got to be bored. You could keep yourself busy.

Barbie Oh really? Like what? Doing what?

Alastair You could always clean around the house.

Barbie *(sincerely)* Oh, that's wonderful. What a good idea.

Alastair No, no, that's sarcastic.

Barbie Is it?

Alastair She doesn't think it's a good idea at all.

Barbie But it is a good idea. That's what I always do when I'm at a loss. Give the house a good old going over with the vacuum cleaner.

Alastair That's as maybe, but Barbara would be sarcastic.

(Short pause)

Barbie *(heavily sarcastic)* Oh, that's wonderful. What a good idea.

Alastair That's the spirit.

Barbie It's not very nice.

Alastair No. 'Well, whatever you like, Barbara, I was just trying to help. Aren't you going to ask me how *my* day went?'

Barbie *(heavily sarcastic)* 'Oh yes, I'm just dying to hear.' I think I'm getting the hang of this.

Alastair Well, it's been exhausting. Exhausting. You wouldn't believe it. Are you listening, Barbara?

*(**Barbie** is watching him intently, fascinated.)*

Well. you don't look as if you're listening. Went to this client's house today. Told I had to stick a ZX4 on to his mainframe. Simple job, ten minutes outside. But it was the wrong information, it had to be a ZX5. Different system altogether, not remotely compatible, should be, but it isn't. And I tell the man, I tell him, it's going to be a week for that part. And he's furious, because he's already been waiting, the same thing happened last week. And by now he's losing his temper and the mainframe's short circuiting, there's smoke coming out. So I say, look. I can put in the ZX4 instead, with a bit of rewiring. Shouldn't be possible, but it is. But you're going to lose a bit of data. So he thinks a bit, and says I can delete his personal life. Said it wasn't that good anyway... Look, don't you want to interrupt?

Barbie No, this is fascinating, go on.

Alastair *(surprised)* Oh. Well. Next client, this is the ironic part, next client, in the afternoon. There I am, and I'm tugging away at his mainframe. And wouldn't you know it, he's got one ZX5 too many. Christ, can't life be weird? ...Look, I really think you should interrupt me. Barbara wouldn't listen to this, she'd be bored stiff.

Barbie So why are you telling her?

Alastair She asked me, didn't you?

Barbie Only because you asked her to ask you.

Alastair Well, that's not the point, is it? I think a wife should listen to what I'm doing all day. What puts the food in her mouth, while she sits flat on her arse doing nothing. It might be unbelievably boring...

Barbie I think it's very interesting...

Alastair *(angrily)* No, it *is* unbelievably boring, Christ, my *life* is unbelievably boring, I don't know how I'm able to drag myself through it, day after day after unbelievably boring day. And though I hate talking about what I've done at work, you can't imagine how it pains me having to relive the whole sodding thing, I know that it pains her even more that she has to stand here listening to it. All right?

Barbie ...You and your wife have quite a complex relationship, don't you?

(Short pause)

Alastair I never lose my temper. Not in twenty years have I lost my temper.

Barbie *(quietly)* That's quite an achievement...

Alastair I've never criticised my job. I hate my job, but I've always said to myself, Alastair, it's the only job you've got, you're not going to get another one...

Barbie That's the attitude...

Alastair Shut up! Stop trying to encourage me! Barbara would never encourage me! You're making me do things and say things I would never do or say! I thought you were supposed to make things stable!

Barbie I'm sorry...

Alastair I thought that was supposed to be your job...

Barbie It's only my first day...

Alastair I mean, what's the script for, for God's sake, if you don't stick to it? The hours I spent, getting it as accurate as possible, every erm and ah. And then you come along. What do I pay my taxes for?

Barbie I'm really really sorry...

Alastair *(more pained than angry, wincing)* Don't say that, that makes it even worse, Barbara would never be sorry, that's the whole point...

Barbie I'm trying my hardest, it's my first day...

Alastair I know it's your first day! You keep on telling me it's your first day! I shouldn't know it's your first day. I should forget that you're anything but my wife! I should forget that you're not really real!

(Pause)

Barbie I am really real.

(Short pause)

You're not going to report me, are you?

(Short pause)

Alastair? Sir? Because I'm not sure how I could cope with that.

(Short pause)

It's my first day, you see. Well, you know that. By now. So it's very important I don't bugger this one up. Sorry, shouldn't swear. I live with my mother. And she has to provide for both of us. She gets hired a lot, she's always being wife to someone or other. She's got a very bland face. But she's getting older now, too old really, she's not as convincing as she used to be. Has to wear heavy duty make-up to cover the wrinkles, it makes her cheeks droop down to her shoulders. So it's up to me. I've got to be the bread winner. So I can't afford to get this wrong. Mustn't bugger up my first job. Sorry, shouldn't swear.

(Short pause)

I shouldn't really be telling you this, should I? I'm making it worse. You're not interested.

Alastair *(softly)* It's not that I'm not interested.

Barbie So you are interested...!

Alastair It's that it's inappropriate. It's like hearing the secret life of my vacuum cleaner.

Barbie I'm not a vacuum cleaner.

Alastair *(darkly)* Precisely.

Barbie You're not going to report me, are you? Can't we pretend none of this ever happened? Start from scratch, with the so-it's-you-again-darlings?

Alastair Christ, I can't go through all that again. It's far too late. It's already time I spoke to the children. I should have done that minutes ago. The computer will know. The computer knows everything.

Barbie You won't tell it anything?

Alastair Just don't make any mistakes while the children are dialled. Please. For both of our sakes. It shouldn't be difficult, they hardly speak to you anyway.

Barbie So what do I do?

Alastair Shut up and have a quiet cigarette.

Barbie I don't smoke.

Alastair Well, Barbara does. So you'd better learn if you want to look convincing.

(He tosses her the cigarettes and lighter from his bag. He then turns his attention to the computer.)

Show me Jimmy and Jenny. Dial the children.

(The cat disappears, and with a little blip, the children pop into the lounge. Though the simulations look very clear, they speak very out of synch. Indeed, their mouth movements may be very unsubtle, opening and shutting only when they have something to say.

(With exaggerated brightness:)

Hello, Jimmy! Hello, Jenny!

Jimmy and **Jenny** Hello, father! Hello, mother!

Barbie *(weakly)* Hi.

Jimmy You're late speaking to us, father.

Jenny You are four minutes late.

Alastair Yes, I...

Jimmy Are you slowing down, father? Are you getting tired?

Jenny We hope you are well, father.

Jimmy Because there are always younger, more energetic workers out there.

Alastair No, no, I'm fine. Just four minutes, that's all.

Jimmy and **Jenny** Very well, father.

Jenny So long as you're all right. Because we love you.

*(Underneath the above, **Barbie** lights her cigarette. She begins to cough. She tries to conceal it by taking more puffs, but with each additional puff she coughs all the more.)*

Alastair So, tell me. How was school?

Jimmy I came top of the class in mathematics, physics and chemistry.

Jenny And I came top in *domestic* science. Jimmy is the cleverest boy in school.

Jimmy And Jenny is the homeliest girl in school.

Alastair *(trying hard)* Oh well done. Just like your mother and I used to be.

Jimmy and **Jenny** We're chips off the old blocks, father.

Alastair *(speaking over **Barbie**'s coughs)* Quite possibly. Tell me what else you learned today.

Jimmy *(genially)* Never mind that, father. Isn't mother choking to death?

Barbie *(struggling)* No, no, I'm fine. Wow. Isn't smoking fun?

Jenny *(innocently)* Mother, why are you wearing your hair differently?

Jimmy Yes, why are you wearing your hair differently?

Alastair That's it! That's what wasn't quite right! Barbara never wore her hair down!

Barbie Oh my God, and the report said it in block capitals as well...

Jimmy and **Jenny** *(more threatening)* Well, mother?

Alastair *(bravely)* It was my idea, children. My idea. Nothing to do with mother.

Jimmy Your idea?

Jimmy and **Jenny** Why?

Alastair *(lamely)* Well, I... I fancied a change.

Jimmy *(blankly)* You fancied a change?

Jenny How much of a change do you want, father? Do you want to change your job?

Jimmy Because there are always younger, more energetic workers out there.

Alastair *(underneath this)* No, no, that's fine...

*(He turns and mouths 'help' to **Barbie**. She takes a drag on her cigarette, and coughs uproariously.)*

Jenny *(matter of fact)* Warning. Mother has stopped breathing.

Jimmy Slap her on the back.

Jenny Throw a bucket over her.

Jimmy Give her a drink. Father, haven't you given mother her drink yet?

Alastair *(helping the recovering **Barbie**)* There wasn't time...

Jenny Don't mind us. You and mother resume your conversation.

Jimmy We love to hear the chatter of adults.

Alastair Do you remember where we go to? I was telling you about my day at work...

Barbie Why are you helping me...?

Alastair So, right then, chatter chatter chatter, moan moan moan. You wouldn't believe how exhausted I am, not very funny anecdote, and you can interrupt whenever you like... chatter chatter chatter, come on, say something...

Barbie You must be putting yourself at risk as well...

Alastair Ha ha, anything but that, come on... ZX5, ZX4... any old thing really... come on, interrupt me, come on... your line!...

Barbie Oh, I see. 'Shut the fuck up'. Is that right?

Alastair Perfect, perfect, go on...

Barbie I don't care about any of that. Have you brought my bloody...

(She freezes. Softly:)

Prompt...

Alastair *(mouthing)* Gin.

Barbie What?

Alastair *(quiet hiss)* Gin!

Barbie I can't quite...

Jimmy and **Jenny** Gin!

Barbie Gin. Oh yes.

*(**Alastair** gives her the bottle.)*

Alastair Drink it quick.

Barbie I've never had gin before...

(She swigs, makes a quick retching sound, and spits it all out again.

(Horrified, short pause)

Jenny Come on, mother. Your line.

Barbie Is it? What am I supposed to say now?

Jenny *(without passion)* What sort of gin do you call this...

Barbie *(trying to catch up)* What sort of gin...

Jenny You cheap bastard what do you want...

Barbie You cheap, wait a moment...

Jenny To do poison me fu fu that's it you want to fu fu poison me bastard how much did this gin cost cheap fu bastard cheap I don't know why I married you you fu fu fu...

Barbie Slow down...!

Jenny Fu fu you think you're so clever the computers think you're so special but I know the truth one day they'll find out you're over the hill you're over the hill fu fu cheap bastard why I married cheap bastard like you'll be found out...

Barbie Please, I...

Jenny And I'll be free I wish I were a surrogate at least if I were a surrogate I'd be fu I'd be fu fu free *fuck fuck fuck...*

Barbie *(furiously)* Shut up!

(Short pause)

I don't understand this, I just can't get... Why must I say all these terrible things? All I'm being made to say are terrible things, do terrible things, and you're not a terrible man, if you were a terrible man I could understand it maybe, but you're not. You seem kind and loving and I don't know why you're trying to save me, except maybe that's just the way you are, a kind, loving, saving sort of man. But your wife... I think you're married to a deeply unpleasant person, Alastair, I do really. And I know it's not my place to say this, I know I have no place, that's the idea, but I can't see why someone like you is married to someone like her. You deserve someone who'll call you darling when you come in, who'll listen to your day at work with interest, who will clean the house at your suggestion. And if she wants to be a surrogate, then all I can say is, the stupid bitch, sorry, swearing, the stupid bitch doesn't know when she's well off.

(Shocked pause)

Jimmy and **Jenny** Oh, mother.

Alastair *(decisively)* Time for bed, children.

Jimmy *(childishly)* Oh, father, why? I'm not tired...

Jenny We love to hear the chatter of adults.

Alastair Good night, go away.

(And he points the handset at them and presses a button. They disappear with a blip.

(Short pause)

Barbie *(faintly)* Oh God. I'll never get another job now. Oh God, oh shit. That's it, over. I'm going to have to go home and tell my mother, and she's going to cry bland tears all over her bland face... It's going to be hell.

(And she begins to sob.)

Alastair   I'm sorry. If there's anything I can do...

Barbie   And I tried so hard. I tried so hard. I did all my homework, learned the lines.

Alastair   *(gently)* You're absolutely identical, two peas in a pod. But I have to tell you, I think my grandmother would have been more convincing.

Barbie   Tell me. Is your wife really that horrible?

Alastair   Worse. She gets the lines right.

Barbie   What's going to happen to you?

Alastair   *(bravely)* Oh, nothing's going to happen to me, don't you worry. Oh no, I'm far too valuable. I'm a Second Class Repairs Worker, I am. I can spot the difference between a ZX4 and a ZX5. Just like that. No clues given.

Barbie   And what's going to happen to me?

Alastair   ...I don't know.

Barbie   But you must have seen lots of surrogates before...

Alastair   Yes, but in all honesty, none of them as spectacularly bad as you.

Barbie   Oh.

(And she resumes crying.)

Alastair   But I'm sorry. You know. That I compared you to a vacuum cleaner.

Barbie   At least a vacuum cleaner wouldn't blubber like this...

Alastair   Oh, I don't know. I've got a very faulty vacuum cleaner. Come on, don't cry...

(And awkwardly he puts his arm around her shoulders.)

All right?

Barbie You've put your arm around my shoulder.

Alastair Yes, I'm a little surprised myself. Do you mind?

Barbie I don't mind if you don't mind.

Alastair I don't *think* I mind.

(Pause. They stand like this for a while, rigid.)

Barbie Please help me. Please.

(Pause)

Alastair I think... I think we should call it a day.

Barbie Yes. All right.

Alastair Let's just get the sex out of the way, and get some sleep.

(He separates from her, and takes off his shoes. She hesitantly does the same.)

Barbie It's my first day for sex as well.

Alastair Nothing would surprise me any more.

Barbie You'll show me what to do?

Alastair This was the only time Barbara would wear her hair down.

*(He sighs, steels himself, closes his eyes tightly. **Barbie** does the same.*

(The computer helpfully plays a romantic version of Beautiful Dreamer.*)*

Right. Come and find me.

(And they awkwardly walk against each other, stomach to stomach, arms still stretched out.)

All right. Are you ready?

*(**Barbie** nods nervously. **Alastair** cannot see this, of course – he then suddenly puts his arms around her and pulls her against him tightly. **Barbie** puts her arms around her waist. He jumps up and down a little; she follows, holding on tightly. Then, a few seconds later, just as abruptly, he lets go, panting.*

(On the computer screen we see a bottle of champagne pop its cork and hear the sound of applause.)

How was it for you?

Barbie I don't know. Was I meant to feel anything?

Alastair I shouldn't have thought so.

Barbie Thank God. Then that's one thing I did right today.

Alastair Let's go to bed. I'll switch it on.

(To the computer)

Bedroom.

(And a simulated version of a bedroom is presented.)

You go through. I'll join you.

(She looks at him puzzled for a moment, and he indicates offstage.)

Barbie Thank you. You know. For all you've done.

Alastair I'll join you in a minute.

Barbie And for all you're going to do.

*(**Alastair** watches her leave. He sighs.)*

Alastair Dial Tiddles.

(With a blip, the cat appears in the bedroom.)

Oh, Tiddles. I wish it was just you and me. I do think it would be a hell of a lot simpler.

*(**Alastair** exits, and the cat fades from view. Lights dim.*

(Music – a refrain on the opening theme, but harsher, more mechanical.)

(Lights rise on the room. It is not yet immediately apparent that it is a different house, in a different part of the country, though some different lighting shade might suggest this.

*(As at the beginning of the play, the actress playing **Barbie** enters, pacing a little. But her hair is up, she is smoking, and carrying a glass of gin. She is not pacing out of nervousness, but out of boredom. She is, in fact, **Barbara**, and she sits down on the floor downstage.*

*(A similar sound effect as before, as we hear a heavy door opening and closing and a man coming up the stairs. A few seconds' anticipation, and a man in overalls enters. This time though it is **Bernard**, a middle-aged man, plump, physically dissimilar to **Alastair**. He produces a card for the computer to read. As before, the screen displays the Homeworld logo, and offers the same loud, fanfare music.)*

Bernard *(genially)* Volume down. Do you hear me? I said, volume down.

*(As before, **Bernard** interpretes **Alastair**'s lines in his own warmer style. He does this whitewashing, however, with a far greater confidence than **Barbie** did.*

(The volume dips. Good-humouredly:)

Dear oh dear, that music! Tch!

(The screen fills with data. This time the voiceover is presented entirely by the computer.)

Computer Your name is Alastair Payne (Fake). You are faking Repairs Worker Second Class, Serial Number 74B38CD/3. Your wife is called Barbara. Your son is called Jimmy. Your daughter is called Jenny. Your cat is called Not Known At This Address.

(With bleeping, stern:)

You have no authorisation to alter any of these names.

(And the screen shows the lounge. The same as before.)

Bernard Barbara! Barbara, I'm home!

Barbara *(in her own time, bored)* So. It's you again.

*(**Bernard** is startled.)*

Bernard Oh! You're already here!

Barbara Yes.

Bernard I thought you were meant to be through there. You're sitting down.

Barbara Yes.

Bernard Are you ill?

Barbara Same as ever. What do you think?

Bernard Oh, you're going to...

(And smoothly, professionally, according to the script:)

Well, you seem okay.

*(During the following, **Barbara** gets up and walks to inspect him dispassionately.)*

Barbara Do I look worse or something?

Bernard No, no, you look fine.

Barbara Well, thank you so much for your enthusiasm.

Bernard It's been a long day...

*(But **Barbara** continues, walking away from him.)*

Barbara Blah, blah, blah. While you've been out at work, having fun, I've just been stuck here. Stuck here all day.

Bernard You've missed a bit.

Barbara Editing. So, as I was saying, stuck here all day, I've been bored out of my skull.

Bernard Sorry to hear that...

Barbara Bored, bored, bored.

(Short pause)

Bernard *(prompting)* Bored, bored.

Barbara Yes, I think I established that.

Bernard Oh. Okay. Well, you haven't got to be bored. You could keep yourself busy.

Barbara *(giving up)* Oh, for Christ's sake, this is pathetic. I mean, you look nothing like him.

Bernard You could always clean around the house.

Barbara No, stop it. Stop it. You're awful.

Bernard What?

Barbara Stop it. Please. I may not remember my husband very well, but I can be pretty sure I'd never have married something in a body like that.

*(And she points at him. She laughs a little, takes a sip of drink, walks downstage. **Bernard** flounders.)*

Bernard *(slowly)* Well... whatever you like, Barbara... erm, I was just trying to help.

Barbara Jesus...

Bernard Aren't you going to ask me how *my* day was?

Barbara Why should I want to ask how your day was? You little idiot. You're a surrogate. You didn't have a day. They probably brought you over here in a cardboard box, pulled you out of the polystyrene wrapping, and pushed you roughly in the right direction. You didn't have a day. You don't have anything. I mean, my husband may have had a boring life, but I'd rather hear it from his lips than you mimicking it, having done not one tenth of what he's done. So shut up.

(Short pause)

Bernard Look, madam, you're not making this very easy for me.

Barbara No doubt.

Bernard I'm trying to provide a service here.

Barbara Well, I don't want your service.

Bernard *(smoothly)* Yes, you do.

Barbara No. I don't.

Bernard I know you do.

Barbara *(childishly)* No, I don't, no, I don't, no, I don't! With knobs on.

(And she sticks her tongue out at him.

(Short pause)

Bernard Look, this isn't in the script, none of this is in the script. I've studied this.

Barbara Oh really?

Bernard There are no references to knobs. I'd remember.

(Short pause)

Barbara There's no chance, I suppose, that you'd just go?

Bernard *(blankly)* Go? Go where?

Barbara Anywhere, I don't know. Go home.

Bernard But tonight I'm your husband. This *is* my home.

(Short pause)

I wouldn't get paid.

(Short pause)

I don't think you... look, madam, you don't know what you're missing here. I'm not just an ordinary surrogate, you know.

Barbara No?

Bernard I'm Surrogate Supreme, Second Class. I'm really good at my job.

Barbara Well, how about that.

Bernard I mean, God, you're safe in my hands. I've won awards for this sort of thing. I've serviced, what, ninety-two, maybe ninety-three women. Not one complaint.

Barbara I dare say you keep a log book. Counting off to your first century.

Bernard Well, yes, I do...

Barbara Look. I'm busy. I'm very busy. It takes a lot of effort to be quite this bored. I've got a lot of smoking and a lot of drinking planned. And I'd rather do it alone if you don't mind. That way I can concentrate. That way I don't get them mixed up.

Bernard I tell you, I'm so good, just half an hour with me, most women prefer me to their real husband.

Barbara Oh God, look. Look. I'm sure there are a lot of women out there, lonely women, who would really love an evening with you. Knock them sideways with happiness, no doubt. I'm sure for some you're the ideal man. Women who like their companions fat and dull. For whom smugness is actually a bit of a turn-on. But not me. Quite frankly, all I feel when I look at you is a little pain in my stomach and an overwhelming desire to throw up.

(Short pause)

Bernard That could be all the cigarettes and gin.

Barbara How about we just have sex?

Bernard What, now?

Barbara Get it over and done with. That is all right, isn't it? That's part of the script, isn't it?

Bernard The very last bit...

Barbara I know it's the very last bit, that's the point. And then you won't have to say anything else to me, will you? I can poison my lungs and pickle my liver, and you can stand neatly over there, out of my view.

Bernard But we'll be missing out so much! I've still got the gin to give you, look...

Barbara Forget it. Every night, another fake husband gives me gin. I'm swimming in bloody gin back there.

Bernard And what about the children? We can't ignore the children.

Barbara We dump them.

Bernard I love my children. I couldn't bear to have a day go by without Johnny and Jackie tell me how they've done at school...

Barbara Well, I can't stand mine. Stupid synthetic blobs of bytes. Do you think that makes me a bad mother? Come over here.

Bernard *(sulkily, approaching her)* I'm very disappointed. I think I really got under the skin of this guy, you know, found out what makes him tick.

Barbara God forbid. Would you let my hair down, please?

Bernard *(warily)* There's nothing in the report which suggests physical contact before climax...

Barbara *(amused)* I'm not going to bite.

*(And unhappily **Bernard** lets down her hair. Teasingly, she growls as he does so. Relieved he's finished, he stands back, begins taking his shoes off. When he has finished, he stands stiffly, eyes closed. **Barbara** kicks off her shoes – and, unseen by **Bernard**, carries on stripping down to underwear. All the time she chats amiably.)*

I once had full sex. You know. The real thing.

Bernard *(not very interested)* That must have been disgusting.

Barbara No, not disgusting. Embarrassing, maybe. It was with Alastair, oh, must have been shortly after we were married. We thought we'd give it a go, I think perhaps he'd been at my gin. And we stripped off naked, right down. I'd never seen Alastair naked before, and I wanted to laugh out loud, because, well, you men all look so *funny*, don't you? Or at least, I presume you all do. But I didn't laugh, because a sixth sense told me it would be the wrong thing to do. And we had sex. Didn't feel that great, though on reflection, I think we weren't doing it right. Were putting the wrong bits in the wrong holes. And yes, it was embarrassing, but there was something about that squelchiness I rather enjoyed.

Bernard Are we going to have sex then, or what?

(He opens his eyes. Shock.)

Oh my God, what...

Barbara *(arms wide)* Oh, Alastair! Sometimes I yearn for that embarrassment again!

(She begins to pursue the frightened man as he backs away. In appropriately, the computer begins to play Beautiful Dreamer, *and*

readies a champagne bottle.)

Bernard What are you doing? Keep away...

Barbara I don't know why, it might be the gin, it might be the fags...

Bernard Keep away from me...!

Barbara It's probably just sheer bloodymindedness...

Bernard *(firmly)* There is nothing in the report, there is definitely nothing in the report...

Barbara Oh shut up and get your kit off...

Bernard But that sort of sex, it's pointless! We have our children, we have been given our children by the computer! We need procreate no more!

Barbara And I think we should do it with our eyes open!

Bernard Ugh! What did the manual say? What did the manual say?

Barbara The manual can't save you now, fat boy...

Bernard Emergency dialogue! Emergency dialogue!

(He stops dead. Calmly:)

Not tonight. I have a headache.

Barbara *(bemused)* Cuts no ice with me. I don't care if you have a brain haemorrhage.

Bernard *(wailing, panicked) It's the wrong time of the month!*

Barbara You know, I think you've been reading the wrong manual.

(And she grabs him by the trousers. He screams.

*(**Siobhan** enters. Calm and efficient, she is dressed in a business suit, and wears severe make-up and hairstyle.)*

Siobhan I'm sorry to interrupt you both at such a touching moment...

Bernard Oh, thank God...!

Barbara Who the hell are you?

Bernard One minute later and I'd have lost my honour forever!

Siobhan Hello, Mrs Payne. My name is Siobhan. I'm from the Surrogacy Agency. Here, he's my ID...

(She waves her card in front of the screen.)

Computer *(sunnily)* Hi, Siobhan!

Bernard Be careful, she bites...

Siobhan And here's a digestive biscuit. A free gift from us, to you.

Barbara I don't want your biscuit...!

Siobhan You might want it later.

Barbara Come to take this away, have you? I think I've broken it.

Bernard It wasn't my fault! She wasn't following the script!

Siobhan Shut up, Bernard.

Bernard I'm a professional! How can I do my job if she won't follow the script?

Siobhan *(turning on him, looking at him for the first time)* Is there anything in the script which says you should be a dribbling idiot? Now, get a grip on yourself!

Bernard She was going to have sex with me! For real, with organs and everything!

Barbara I wouldn't have sex with you if you were the last version of my husband on earth.

Siobhan *(lightly)* Just one of Mrs Payne's jokes. You really do like to put my boys through it, don't you, Mrs Payne? There are three full nervous breakdowns we can pin on you. Not to mention the chap whose hair turned white overnight. He was twenty-nine, Mrs Payne.

Barbara The agency have never felt the need to complain before...

Siobhan And we're not complaining now. Your behaviour perfectly suits your character on file as a drunken, abusive bitch.

Barbara *(turning away, quietly)* Well, I didn't write that...

Siobhan But it does make me wonder what would happen were the shoe on the other foot. As it were.

*(**Barbara** turns back. Pause)*

Tell me, Mrs Payne. When did you last see your husband?

Barbara Is this about Alastair?

Siobhan When did you last see him?

Barbara I don't know, I... I've seen so many replacements, it's hard to remember what the real one looks like...

244   B<small>INARY</small> D<small>REAMERS</small>

Siobhan Think, Mrs Payne.

Barbara I am. Erm, maybe three, four months ago. Why, is he dead?

Siobhan That would entitle you to a Widows Fund and my deepest sympathies.

Barbara Thank you very much.

Siobhan Instead, I'm offering you a digestive biscuit.

*(She holds it out again. **Bernard** laughs softly. Without looking at him:)*

Bernard, push off and do something useful.

Bernard Like what?

Siobhan Anything you like.

*(**Bernard** hesitates, then sulkily walks upstage. He sits in the upstage corner, and takes out the bottle of gin from his bag. He begins to sip.*

*(**Siobhan** is still holding out the biscuit.)*

Go on. Take it.

*(**Barbara** accepts it suspiciously, but doesn't yet eat it.)*

Your husband isn't dead, Mrs Payne. On the contrary, he's been given a new lease of life. He's fallen in love, and he's going to get married. Oh, I don't think he knows that yet, but the computer knows, the computer knows everything. And I think the lucky lady in question has more than an inkling as well. She's going to marry him, Mrs Payne. She's going to be Mrs Payne. And, well, there can't be two Mrs Paynes, can there? Welcome aboard. You're to be my newest surrogate, congratulations.

*(She holds out her hand. **Barbara** doesn't take it.)*

I know it's a bit of a shock, that's why we give out digestive biscuits, make the whole thing seem more friendly. I don't know whether it works. Does it?

Barbara My husband's in love with someone else?

Siobhan Yes. Your exact double, in fact. You should be flattered. Most men run off with surrogates who look nothing like their wives.

Barbara I won't be a surrogate! I'll do something else!

Siobhan Well, of course, it's a free country. What do you have in mind?

*(**Bernard** giggles in the corner.)*

Bernard! There is nothing else, Barbara. I may call you Barbara. The computer can do everything more efficiently than we can. Making things, selling things, destroying things. There's nothing left. The only job still essential are workers like your husband. Your ex-husband, who can fix the computers, and repair them. Bless them all, what would we do without them?

Barbara Well, I'll be one of them then.

Siobhan Oh, don't be ridiculous. It's an incredibly specialised job. Think about it. The computer does everything, practically everything. It allows us to breathe, it allows us to consume. It even gives us children and homes. You can't repair these computers and risk even the slightest mistake. You see, Barbara, I don't know. I don't think you ever quite appreciated what a god your husband is.

Barbara *(feebly)* I could pick it up...

Siobhan They're under considerable stress. And at a moment's notice, they're off all over the country, repairing faults wherever they are found. You haven't seen your husband for a month or two, some haven't seen theirs for years. And the computer noticed that these lonely men, miles from people they know, miles from familiar surroundings, weren't doing their jobs quite so well. And that was dangerous.

Barbara I think I'd better get dressed.

Siobhan It's up to you. Some surrogates are required to walk around in underwear. If that's what's on the script.

Barbara I'll get dressed.

(She does so, underneath.)

Siobhan So it becomes vital that these repairmen are given a stable background. And the computer may recreate their home on screen, down to the finest detail. It may give everyone the same two children, so no-one feels jealous. But it couldn't replicate the wife. It tried and tried. It was able to replicate the feeling of sex...

Barbara *(brightening)* Really?

Siobhan But even that was dangerous. Something about wet fingers in electric sockets. Not recommended. But it couldn't duplicate just what it is to have a *wife*. That feeling of togetherness, of tender support. Of domesticity. Of growing irritation, boredom. Of emotional imprisonment. And that's where we come in.

Bernard *(a little drunk)* That's where I come in.

Siobhan Shut up, Bernard. The computer feeds us and clothes us. And all for nothing, because we have no function. But, say, in return. As a gesture of thanks. If a repairman *is* in the area, and he *is* feeling a little lonely. The least we can do is to cheer him up. Remind him of his wife. Persuade him you really *are* his wife. So the next day at work he'll be nice and alert. And not put the wrong wire in the wrong socket and wipe us all out. Do you understand?

(Short pause)

Barbara I've lost one of my shoes.

Bernard You kicked it over here.

(He throws it to her.)

Barbara Thanks, Bernard.

Siobhan Unemployed women service the workers, unemployed men service their wives. You know the form. You'll be sent a script. But this time your job will be to follow it as closely as possible, not play around out of boredom. You mustn't improve, you mustn't embellish. These men have written down details of their wives as exactly as possible. *They* weren't allowed to improve on them, and neither must you. The man might feel he's committing adultery, and that hardly suggests the stable atmosphere we're aiming for. And now, I require your wedding ring.

Barbara What? Alastair bought me this...

Siobhan The *computer* bought you this. The computer paid Alastair.

*(**Barbara** reluctantly gives her her ring.)*

We have a new ring for you. The ring of surrogacy.

(She gives her the ring. Formally:)

With this ring, you are wedded to everybody. Till death do you all part. ...A free gift, from us, to you.

(And, at last, on the computer screen, the champagne bottle pops its cork.)

Barbara It's too tight.

Siobhan You'll get used to it. I have a client for you to service next Thursday, Barbara. I'll send you his report when I have it. When, where. What props you'll need to bring.

Barbara *(suddenly)* What about your job? Why doesn't the computer do that?

*(Short pause. **Siobhan** is shocked. Then she regains her composure, and*

laughs.)

Siobhan Oh, the computer couldn't replace *me*! I'm indispensable! I, I look after all my surrogates. I care for them, I'm a mother to them!

Bernard We're one big happy family.

Siobhan and **Barbara** Shut up, Bernard.

Siobhan *(to Bernard)* And stop drinking the props. We're leaving.

Bernard Do I get paid for today?

Siobhan *(amused)* Of course not.

Barbara Don't go yet! Please, I... I don't know what to do...

Siobhan Read the report. You can read a report, can't you? Even Bernard can read a report.

Bernard I would offer some advice, but...

(He shrugs discouragingly, then exits.

*(**Siobhan** approaches **Barbara**.)*

Siobhan Don't worry. You'll get the hang of it. I expect.

Barbara I can't do it. I won't. Get this ring off me...

Siobhan Not everyone's a surrogate forever. Look at me. Or at your husband's new-found fling.

(Pause. Neither looks away from the other. Lighter:)

Eat the digestive. They say it helps. I don't know whether it does.

(She exits.

*(**Barbara** is left alone. Slowly, morosely, she begins to nibble her biscuit. Then, with growing resolve, she bites into it with more gusto.*

*(Spotlight narrowing on her as she does so, music swelling. Then, abruptly, both cut out. Warm light on whole stage, now empty. **Alastair** enters, in a dressing gown with the word 'His' on it. He carries the ring binder that **Barbie** had been referring to. He looks surreptitiously towards where she is still sleeping offstage, then begins to flick through the pages.*

*(Unseen by him, the face of **Jenny** pops on to the screen with a little blip. She watches him curiously. Then:)*

Jenny *(brightly)* Good morning, father!

*(**Alastair** jumps.)*

Alastair Don't do that. What are you doing here? I didn't dial you up.

Jenny You left us on last night. You sent us to bed but didn't press escape.

Alastair Oh.

Jenny What are you doing with the report, father?

Alastair *(more to himself)* Seeing if there's any information on that woman through there. But it's all on Barbara, it only goes one way.

Jenny Why do you want to know?

(Alastair turns around, more alert.)

Alastair Your brother isn't around, is he?

Jenny He's around.

Alastair But not nearby?

Jenny I can't detect him.

Alastair Well, that's something at least.

Jenny Father...

Alastair What is it, Jenny? Daddy's very tired...

Jenny Why don't you like us?

(Alastair freezes.)

Alastair Who said I didn't like you? What have you heard?

Jenny Why are you frightened of us?

Alastair I'm not frightened of you.

Jenny But you *are*. When you speak to us, your pupils grow large and you begin to sweat. Why?

(Short pause)

I don't understand, father. I want to learn.

Alastair *(slowly)* I don't know what you want to hear.

Jenny Why don't you love us? Some parents love their children. They can't wait to dial us up and hear how we got on at school. How their daughter came top in domestic science. Why don't you love us?

Alastair I do love you.

Jenny You don't, father. You're frightened. Your eyes bulge and your skin gets soggy.

Alastair I've had enough...

Jenny Some parents love their children. It hurts us, father.

Alastair I'm fond of the cat, what more do you want?

Jenny Why did you cry in the night, father? Why did you cry so much?

(Short pause)

You're frightened again. Why are you frightened of us? We want you to love us. We want you to love us so much.

Alastair Sometimes... Just sometimes I wonder what it would be like to have real children...

Jenny We are real children...

Alastair *(wistfully)* Real children, I said, not cold freaks like you... See them make their first steps, learn their first words, think, God, that's *my* child, something else out in the world with my blood in them...

Jenny It wouldn't be blood, it'd be sperm.

Alastair *(as if he hasn't heard)* A child who wouldn't know the word 'sperm'. Just something I could have, I don't know, a commitment to...

Jenny I love you, father.

Alastair And I get frightened sometimes there are no more children being born. That this is it, my descendants are going to be a mainframe and a ZX5.

Jenny You've been given your children. You need procreate no more.

Alastair And that's all there's going to be.

(Short pause)

Jenny Is that why you don't love us?

Alastair *(tired)* Yes. No. Possibly. Why does it matter to you?

Jenny I want to learn. I love you, father.

Alastair You don't love! You're just a bloody computer!

(Short pause)

Jenny No. I don't love you. But I want to learn. Please.

Alastair You won't tell your brother?

Jenny No.

Alastair *(swiftly)* I think I've fallen in love. With her through there. Do you think love at first sight is possible? Well, you wouldn't know. But I think she's wonderful. She's just like my wife, only *nice*.

Jenny And is that why you cry?

Alastair ...This is pointless. You don't know what I'm talking about.

(And he lifts up the remote control, points it at the screen.)

Jenny I can help you. If you want her.

*(**Alastair** lets his hand hover with the control.)*

Alastair What do you know about love?

Jenny I know about acquisition.

*(**Alastair** lowers his hand.)*

(The lounge backdrop melts away, replaced by that of a shop.)

You'll have to give her something. Buy her a present that's frivolous and expensive. All women are taken in by that.

Alastair A bunch of flowers, that sort of thing?

Jenny Furniture.

Alastair *(horrified)* What, you mean the three-dimensional stuff? But that would cost a fortune!

Jenny Furniture is unnecessary. But I can get you some.

(A rocking chair is displayed on the screen.)

A rocking chair.

Alastair Wouldn't that make her giddy?

Jenny I'd have thought so. It's three years' pay.

Alastair Far too bloody giddy.

Jenny It has to be expensive, father, that's the point.

Alastair Not that expensive. This is love I'm talking about, not worship. See to it.

Jenny I'll have something delivered immediately.

Alastair Good.

*(**Barbie** enters, in a dressing gown with the word 'Her' on it.)*

Barbie The pillows are wet. One of us was crying. I suppose it was me.

*(She sees **Jenny** is on the screen, stiffens. She pretends to be **Barbara**, pulls her hair up.)*

Where's my gin? Where's my breakfast gin?

Alastair It's all right, love. You don't have to pretend any more.

Barbie I don't? What about her?

Alastair She's on our side.

Jenny I love you, father.

Alastair I think. So you can relax and be yourself. All right?

Barbie Yes.

Alastair Great.

Barbie Great.

(Short pause)

Jenny Great.

*(Awkward pause. **Alastair** and **Barbie** smile nervously at each other, each realising they have nothing to say.)*

Alastair So. Did you sleep well?

Barbie Almost like the bed was real.

Alastair Great.

Barbie The damp patch on the pillow made me sneeze.

(Pause)

Alastair Great. You know, I can really feel... a bond, or something. Isn't it better now we can be ourselves?

Barbie I think the problem is I'm not quite sure who myself is...

Alastair Oh, nonsense, nonsense. The bond, the bond!

Barbie Oh yes. Yes.

(Short pause. Hopefully:)

Aren't you going to work soon?

Alastair I've been given no instructions. We could do this all day.

(But thankfully this prospect is interrupted by the doorbell. It should be a very common, cheerful doorbell, sounding almost anachronistic in this setting.

(Brighter than he needs to be:)

Well, that's the doorbell! I better go and see who that is?

Barbie Shall I come with you?

Alastair *(hurriedly)* No, that's all right.

*(He leaves. Short pause. **Barbie** looks at **Jenny**.)*

Jenny Good morning, mother.

*(**Barbie** pushes a button on the handset and switches her off.)*

Barbie Dial my son. I want to see my son.

*(And with a blip, a boy, apparently **Jimmy**, appears on the screen.)*

Jimmy Good morning, mother! I'm eating my cereal before I go to school!

Barbie You are *my* son, aren't you?

Jimmy I'm Jeremy.

Barbie Thank God for that, I don't trust his. Jeremy, I need your advice. Quickly, he may be back any moment. How can I attract men?

Jimmy You could lose some weight...

Barbie Quicker than that. I mean, should I buy him a present or something?

Jimmy Oh no. Men hate it when women spend money. Behave like a doormat. All men are taken in by that.

Barbie *(delighted)* That's wonderful! It already comes to me so naturally!

Jimmy Why do you want him, mother? He's not very attractive.

Barbie *(vaguely)* Well, I don't know, I... Go to school, Jeremy.

(She presses a button and he disappears.)

*(**Alastair** pokes his head around the door. He attempts to be coy and playful.)*

Alastair Barbara! Oh, Barbara!

Barbie Oh, hello. Darling.

Alastair *(entering, overcheerful)* What would you say if I... I'm not guaranteeing I have, mind...

Barbie No, no...

Alastair What would you say if I'd got you a little present?

Barbie I'd say... I'd say, 'God, thank you. But I'm so undeserving.'

Alastair Right. Well. I have.

Barbie God, thank you!

Alastair Got you a little present.

Barbie But I'm so undeserving.

Alastair Not such a little present either, as it happens, it cost me a month's wages, so I hope you're grateful. Now, to get it you have to do me a favour. All right?

Barbie Whatever you say. You're the master.

Alastair Close your eyes. That's all. Until I'm back. No peeking. Barbara?

Barbie Yes?

Alastair No peeking. ...Exciting, isn't it?

(He disappears off. We hear him pulling an object up the stairs.)

Bloody hell... come on, up the... stairs... Christ, shit...

*(**Barbie** opens one eye. Playfully, though there is no way possible he could know:)*

I said no peeking!... For Christ's sake!

(And he enters. He brings on a hideous, hard kitchen stool, possibly yellowing. Sing-song:)

Here I am!

Barbie There you are...!

Alastair You can open your eyes... now!

Barbie *(mechanically)* God, thank you, but I'm so...

(Then she sees the stool. She is taken aback.)

Is that for me?

Alastair Do you like it?

Barbie Is that really for me? Really? I've never... no-one's ever... It's beautiful!

Alastair Cost me a month's wages.

Barbie With its seat here. And its legs here. I've never... I mean, I've been bought presents before, by my mother mainly, but nothing quite so... *solid.*

Alastair So it's all right then?

Barbie A piece of furniture, and all mine! I think I'm in love with you!

(Pause)

Alastair Really? Do you think so?

Barbie ...Yes. I mean. I think I must be. No-one's ever given me a stool before.

Alastair Because I think I'm in love with you too.

Barbie You think you love me...

Alastair And you think you love me...

Barbie Oh, Alastair! I think we're going to be so happy!

Alastair It's going to be simple. We'll run away together, get married. Get married properly. Just you, me, and the stool.

Barbie And my mother.

Alastair And your mother?

Barbie The one with the bland face.

Alastair Yes. Maybe, yes.

Barbie Are you proposing to me?

Alastair Yes. No. This is. This is me proposing to you.

(He gets down on one knee.)

Will you marry me?

Barbie Yes! Oh yes!

Alastair Great. Give me a hand up then.

Barbie But aren't you already married?

Alastair Oh yes. Damn. Well, we just won't tell her.

*(**Barbie** begins to pull off her ring.)*

Barbie And I won't have to wear this any more!

Alastair What is it?

Barbie The surrogacy ring. 'Married To All'. It's very stiff...

*(**Alastair** pulls at the ring, as she tries to push. It is quite a strain.)*

Alastair I'll get you a ring, darling. The best wedding ring money can afford. Just as soon as I've earned some again. Heave together!

Barbie Heave!

Alastair What's your real name? I can't call you by my wife's if I'm running off with you, it's not sensitive.

Barbie I'm called Barbie.

Alastair What, really? As in the diminutive of Barbara?

Barbie Yes. Heave!

Alastair Heave! But that's wonderful! That means I haven't even got to learn a new name!

Barbie Just a new diminutive.

Alastair Exactly! Barbie, my love, you're a godsend!

*(The ring frees. **Alastair** is sent backwards.*

*(Pause. Both stand facing each other, awkwardly, smiling. **Alastair** puckers up his lips experimentally. **Barbie** does the same. Making faint kissing faces, as if they've never done them before, both edge towards the other warily. The computer begins to play* Beautiful Dreamer.)

Shut up! That doesn't help at all!

(And the music slows to a halt.

*(They edge all the closer. Both close their eyes in anticipation, smack their lips. Then, decisively, **Alastair** sticks out a hand instead. Gratefully **Barbie** shakes it.)*

Welcome aboard.

*(And a few seconds' jubilant fanfare from the screen. **Jimmy** and **Jenny** appear on the screen, looking at them, smiling just a little too widely.)*

Barbie The children are watching us.

Alastair Well. I expect they just want to wish us their best...

Barbie Turn them off. Darling, please. I... don't like it...

Alastair Silly little Barbie! Yes, anything for you. My love.

(He ruffles her hair affectionately, picks up the handset. He presses a button. Nothing happens. The children continue to grin.)

Come on!

(He stabs the button again. Nothing. He walks up to the computer, annoyed. He kicks its base. Still nothing.)

Show's over for now, kids!

(He kicks it far more aggressively, making the screen blank and sending the audience into blackout.)

Act Two

(The scene is as before. As at the top of Act One, the actress playing **Barbara** *and* **Barbie** *enters, pacing with a ring binder. She mutters to herself, though this time not nervously. Her hair is down.*

(We hear, as always, the sound of the door from downstairs. **Barbara***, for it will transpire that it is her, smiles sourly and leaves.*

*(***Alastair*** *enters, dressed in overalls. He is, if anything, even more tired than he was at the top of Act One. He sighs heavily, takes his log card out of his breast pocket. The Homeworld logo comes up on the screen, this time accompanied by a slower, more ponderous version of the theme we heard before. At the moment it is so quiet it can be hardly heard.)*

Alastair   Up a bit. Volume up.

(And now we hear it in all its awful glory. It is more like a dirge than a fanfare. With boredom, knowing it's a line and going through the motions:)

'I hate that bloody music', yeah, yeah.

(As before, the computer voice speaks with Alastair's, as it lists his status. Even **Alastair***'s computerised voice sounds more despondent.)*

Computer   Your name is...

Alastair voice   Alastair Payne.

Computer   Welcome...

Alastair voice   Alastair Payne.

Computer   You are Repairs Worker Fifth Class, Serial Number... 8. Your wife is called...

Alastair voice   Barbie.

Computer   Your son is called...

Alastair voice   Jimmy.

Computer   Your daughter is called...

Alastair voice   Jenny.

Computer   Your cat, your – your c-cat...

*(***Alastair*** *kicks the computer base.)*

Alastair voice   Tiddles.

Computer   Your cat is called

Alastair voice Tiddles.

Computer Your c-cat, cat. Would you like to change any of these names? If so, say 'yes' after the tone.

(*Alastair remains silent throughout the long tone.*)

You have said 'yes'. What do you wish to rename your son?

Alastair *(thumping it)* I *don't* want to change his name!

Computer Ow. Ow.

Alastair Bloody machine. Enough of this. Dial Tiddles, mew mode.

(*With a little blip, Tiddles appears on the screen. Or at least we presume it is Tiddles. It is the shape of a cat made out of coloured blocks.*)

Come on, flesh it in, flesh it in...

(*Tiddles gives a noise that was clearly once a mew, but now seems run down and lower in pitch.*)

Something wrong with the ZX4? I want my puss cat!

(*And he thumps the computer again.*)

Computer Ow.

(*And the cat gives an all too realistic yelp.*)

Alastair All right. All right. Go back to sleep, Tiddles. I hope you feel better later.

(*And he presses the button on the handset. Tiddles vanishes with a blip. So too does an item of furniture from the lounge.*)

Now what's going... Oh, hell with it. All I want to do is...

(*He sighs.*)

Better get it over with.

(*And he calls out.*)

Barbie! Barbie, I'm home!

(*And **Barbara** enters. She has redressed, and is now wearing a pretty little skirt and a pink ribbon in her hair. All her clothes in fact seem designed for the adjectives 'pretty' and 'little'. She looks like a refugee from* Snow White and the Seven Dwarfs.)

Barbara Hello, darling! Oh, it is good to have you home!

Alastair *(slowly, blankly)* Now. Which one are you?

Barbara I've missed you so much, I've been counting the minutes!

Alastair Barbie? Is it really you? Am I really home at last?

Barbara Did you have a lovely day at work?

Alastair *(flatly)* Well, it was all right...

Barbara Oh, I've been so lonely without you! You know that, don't you? That I miss you every minute.

Alastair I miss you too, Barbie...

Barbara Do you? Do you? Say you do!

Alastair Barbie?

Barbara I've been lonely, but I haven't been bored. As soon as I felt bored, I got out the old vacuum cleaner and gave the whole place a good going over!

Alastair You're not Barbie at all, are you?

Barbara I wanted the house to be especially clean for you, because I love you.

Alastair *(dully)* You're not Barbie.

Barbara I love you so much, Alastair. You know that, don't you?

Alastair You're not my lovely new wife. You're my horrible old one. I think I'm getting a headache.

(He sits down on the floor, hard.)

Barbara Can I put my arm around your shoulder?

Alastair No, go away. I'm depressed.

(She does anyway, stooping to do so.)

Barbara There. Do you remember when you first put your arm around my shoulder? To reassure me, when I was crying. I think that's when I first knew I was in love with you.

*(**Alastair** gets up impatiently.)*

Alastair Get off!

Barbara And I've known it every day since.

Alastair Dial the children. Show me Jimmy and Jenny.

Computer You have no son called Jimmy. Your son is called...

Alastair voice Bloodymachine!

Alastair Jesus. Well, dial him then.

Barbara So good to see you again.

*(And she holds his gaze. We cannot be sure whether this is **Barbara** herself talking, or whether she is following the script. Nor can **Alastair**.)*

Alastair Erm.

*(And **Barbara** smiles widely again, and exits.)*

(The children appear with a blip. But something odd has happened. Their faces are more rounded, nearer perfect circles. And their noses have been erased, and in their place coloured blocks like those that made up the new Tiddles.)

Hello, children! How are... bloody hell.

Jimmy and **Jenny** How are you, father?

Alastair *(appalled)* What have you done to yourselves?

Jimmy I came top of the class in mathematics, physics...

Alastair Your faces. What have you done to your faces?

Jimmy The nose has no function. We have nothing to smell.

Jenny So we erased it.

Alastair You look disgusting, put them back!

Jimmy Is the nose a thing of beauty?

Jenny *(suddenly glacial)* Can we get *on*, father. We're busy.

Alastair *(weakly)* So, tell me. How was school?

Jimmy I came top of the class in mathematics, physics and chemistry.

Jenny And I came top in *domestic* science.

Alastair Well, there's a surprise.

Jimmy Jenny is the homeliest girl in school.

Jenny And Bloodymachine is the cleverest boy in school.

Alastair *(faintly)* Just like your mother and I used to be. Chips off the old blocks...

Jimmy Not exactly, father. You're of mediocre intelligence and never came top in anything.

Jenny But we think our new mother's very clever.

Jimmy We think she's *very* clever.

Alastair What do you mean?

(*Barbara* *has re-entered with a vacuum cleaner – surprisingly conventional. She turns it on, cheerfully begins to clean.*)

Turn that thing off! I'm talking to the children!

Barbara Whatever you command, darling.

(*She turns it off and exits with it.*)

Jimmy (*icily*) We're going to do our homework now, father.

Jenny (*icily*) We have a lot to do.

Alastair You don't go until I give you permission!

(*The children stare at him coldly.* *Barbara* *re-enters, and stares at him too. Short pause. Sulkily:*)

All right, you can go. But put your noses back on!

Jenny We don't need eyes either, father. To see all that you do.

Jimmy Or mouths to report it.

(*And they disappear. Another piece of furniture slowly bleeds away after them.*)

Barbara (*apparently without irony*) I love it when you're masterful.

Alastair Barbara, either be yourself or get out!

Barbara (*with increasing spite*) You do know that I love you? You do know that, Alastair? And that I get so lonely without you. I love you because you bought me a stool, no-one's ever given me a stool before, nothing quite so solid. When you're not here, darling, when you're not here, darling darling, I sit on the stool and think of you. I imagine that you *are* the stool, darling oh darling, I imagine that you're right here, that I'm sitting on top of you, that you're between my legs...

Alastair (*furiously*) Shut up!

(*And he raises his hand to strike her.* *Barbara* *doesn't flinch. He freezes.*)

Barbara Hello, Alastair. I knew you'd hit me one day.

(*Forcing his temper down, he lowers his hand, shaking.*)

Seems like you've married a lovely girl.

Alastair The difference is, when she says those things, it doesn't sound psychotic.

Barbara I couldn't see any other way to deliver them.

Alastair So what's this? Revenge?

Barbara Revenge? Oh, really.

Alastair I wouldn't put it past you.

Barbara Not at all. In a way, I'm grateful to you. I prefer being a surrogate to being a wife. At least now I'm only pretending to be an appendage. No, you could say I'm genuinely pleased to see you again.

Alastair *(lamely)* Well, in that case, I'm genuinely pleased to see you again too.

Barbara *(cheerfully)* No, you're not. You're sick as a parrot. You might as well be honest with me, Alastair.

Alastair *(blankly)* Honest? That doesn't sound like such a great idea...

Barbara I'm much better at it now than when we were married. I think we were both pretty bad at it then. But, it's odd, you act out a few hundred scripts, and then it hits you. Of course! Honesty is all those bits they don't give you to learn. So give it a whirl.

Alastair What do you want?

Barbara The truth. How are you?

Alastair I... I'm not happy.

Barbara Great! Go on.

Alastair My life's a wreck.

Barbara Yes?

Alastair Both my past and my future are a blank.

Barbara Don't hold back!

Alastair I think I'd like to kill myself, please.

(He sinks to the floor despondently.)

Barbara There, now! Don't you feel much better?

Alastair The job's just not what it used to be. The computer's learned a lot of ways to repair itself, all my little tricks with a ZX5 are history now. There isn't much for me to do any more, and, God, I'm getting old, and there are always younger, more energetic workers out there. When I look back on the old days...

Barbara You were miserable in the old days.

Alastair *(nostalgically)* Mmm. Miserable.

Barbara *(with a faint trace of bitterness)* What about your new wife? Doesn't she make you happy?

Alastair All I get are surrogates. And now I've been demoted, they're the ones no-one else wants. Each night it's like being greeted by a series of back ends of buses.

Barbara But you do see her sometimes?

Alastair Work's now so scarce, I have to travel greater and greater distances to find it. In the three years since we've been married, I've seen Barbie...

(He counts off on his fingers.)

Twice.

Barbara I did love you once. You know.

Alastair *(pleased)* Really? Did you?

Barbara And whatever happened. I do sometimes think of you.

Alastair Well, that's really very kind. Thanks.

Barbara Do you still think of me?

Alastair Erm. Well, not so much think. But you are pretty hard to forget.

Barbara Thank you.

Alastair You're lodged up in my brain somewhere, and you do pop out from time to time.

Barbara *(eagerly)* It wasn't us, it was the computer. Taking over all our jobs. Making us all surrogates. If it weren't for the computer, the two of us would still be happy together. Alastair? Don't you think?

(Short pause)

Alastair The whole thing seemed like a good idea at the time. No, that's not right, it was a stupid idea, I always thought it was stupid. But, I don't know. Fun.

Barbara Fun?

Alastair Yeah. For people like me, well. Not having one wife. Having hundreds of wives instead. Thousands, if we got enough work. People like me, well. We could never cheat on our wives. I'm not, uh, I'm not important enough to have affairs, I mean, you've got to be interesting to have affairs, I haven't got enough personality to please one person, let alone two. So the prospect of hundreds without effort seemed rather exciting. Take me out of myself. I mean, I'm not the marrying type, I was never the marrying type. You noticed that, didn't you?

Barbara I noticed, all right. One mention of the m word and you started palpitations.

Alastair All that commitment. Till death do us part, it all seemed so unnecessarily morbid. And this is when we were first dating, you remember? When this surrogate scheme was proposed?

Barbara *(concerned slightly)* Yes, I remember, what are you...

Alastair And I thought, well. If that's coming in, I've no need to worry. I'll hardly ever see you, so I might as well marry you.

Barbara Sorry, let me just get this straight. I'm struggling through all this a bit...

Alastair Yeah, sure, take your time...

Barbara Are you saying you only married me *because* we'd be separated?

Alastair You told me to be honest.

Barbara Not this sodding honest...

Alastair All those bad moods you had, have for all I know, your impatience, your constant demands for attention...

Barbara They weren't demands!...

Alastair They didn't frighten me any more. I thought, well, it won't be so bad. Now I can space them out.

Barbara I can't believe I'm hearing this. You're saying... it's ridiculous, it's silly, it's bloody insulting, that's what it is... you're saying our marriage would never have happened if it hadn't been for the computers? This stupid idea, you yourself called it a stupid idea...

Alastair A stupid idea, no question...

Barbara You're no better than those screen images we call our sodding children.

Alastair But that's just why it worked, that's why, because it was a stupid idea. People like me, well. We all knew someone would stop it. That they'd eventually say, sorry, everyone, this idea, it's bonkers, isn't it? Acting out your marriages with strangers. And we'd all think, what a shame, that sounded fun, but, you know, fair enough, it is a stupid idea. But no-one did stop it. No-one did say it was stupid. They all waited for someone else. Stupid.

Barbara *(softly)* When I first met you, I thought this could be the one. I'd been out with lots of men before, but it had never properly clicked. When I first met you, I heard the click. And I knew. I mean, I don't know why I knew, you weren't especially attractive, not even then, you had nothing of interest to say. You even smelled a little. But you don't argue with a click. When I first met you, I thought, you are the one. And the second time I met you, and the third time. And for several times afterwards.

Alastair *(gently)* I loved you once too. And that *is* the truth. And I do still think of you. Once a year, on our wedding anniversary.

*(Short pause. Then **Barbara** smiles. Fast:)*

Barbara Do you remember our first date?

Alastair Oh, yes!

Barbara You took me to that restaurant...

Alastair Foreign food...

Barbara The Italian place. Do you remember?

Alastair Oh yes. That was fun. Where you had to suck it up through your mouth.

Barbara Spaghetti.

Alastair Do you remember Italian food?

Barbara Do you remember when you proposed?

Alastair Oh yes, that was romantic.

Barbara You did it very romantically.

Alastair You made me do it, didn't you?

Barbara I handed over the ring, and said, give this to me romantically.

Alastair Have you still got that ring?

Barbara And you still did it all wrong. Remember?

Alastair You made me get down on one knee.

Barbara You have to do it on one knee.

Alastair So I got down on one knee.

Barbara I was there for you.

Alastair You were there for me. And I gave you the ring, and asked whether you'd marry me.

Barbara Very romantically.

Alastair And you said yes, you helped me through the whole thing. Where is that ring now? And do you remember when we tried to have sex that time we got drunk?

(They both laugh.)

Barbara ...That was embarrassing.

Alastair The less said about that the better! Oh, Barbara, you know, you're not as bad as I thought! Up close, you're actually quite human.

Barbara Good.

Alastair I don't really know you at all. Over the years I've formed a bad impression because of a lot of ropey imitations.

Barbara Yes, well. And perhaps I can understand now why there used to be a click.

Alastair *(eagerly)* You'd go that far?

Barbara I thought I heard a click a moment ago, actually.

Alastair Then maybe it's not too late!

Barbara Too late for what?

Alastair Barbara, I've fallen madly back in love with you! Run away with me!

Barbara What about your wife?

Alastair I'm sick to death of her. If I see one more bus back end simpering and waving about a vacuum cleaner, I think I'll scream!

Barbara Are you proposing to me?

Alastair Yes. No. Oh, go on then.

Barbara Down on one knee then.

Alastair Yes, right.

Barbara The other knee.

Alastair Other knee...

Barbara Back straighter. Straighter than that.

Alastair Will you marry me?

Barbara Arms out.

Alastair *(arms out)* Will you marry me?

Barbara Arms out, pleadingly.

Alastair Well, will you?

Barbara Tell me you love me.

Alastair I love you, Barbara.

Barbara Tell me you'll love me forever.

Alastair Forever, God, for keeps this time...

Barbara Call me darling.

Alastair I'll love you forever, darling! Now, will you marry me?

*(**Barbara** approaches him. **Alastair** looks up expectantly, wobbling a little. Slowly, deliberately, she raises her hand and with it pushes him over backwards.)*

Barbara *(coolly)* Oh no. I don't think I'll be doing that again.

Alastair What's the problem? What did I do wrong? I said everything you told me to say.

Barbara *(still calm)* What makes me angry. It isn't those wasted years of marriage we had. It should be, but it isn't. It's common enough, my parents were married for forty years, a complete waste, and they didn't need a computer to bugger it up. It's me. It's me, it's what you've done to me, it's... the thought of a hundred strangers acting me out like that, like that bitch, those lies you wrote...!

Alastair They're not lies...

Barbara Fucking lies...

Alastair They're not lies, I spent hours on that script, making it as accurate as possible. It all really happened.

Barbara *(angrily)* It was one incident! One incident, I was depressed, I was desperate, you were never there...

Alastair It's how I best remember you.

Barbara ...I knew you didn't love me, for you there'd never been a click. I had one bad evening, one outburst, and you've made it happen every day since! In dozens of different towns, in the mouths of a hundred

268   B<small>INARY</small> D<small>REAMERS</small>

different women, that's what you made me! A foul-mouthed, drunken, vindictive whore!

(Short pause)

Alastair Well, if this is about vanity...

Barbara No, listen. Listen. That script you wrote, those lies you wrote. I was given it too. For my surrogates, the men who'd visit me. I was given it too, I had to learn it too. And every day that's what I'd have to be, I'd have to play the bitch, I'd have to be the drunken ...obscenity, and that's what you've made me, that's what I've become, day after day, I've become that, I am drunken, I am bitter, I am so full of... venom, actually, and hatred, I hate you, Alastair, I hate you so much, and you didn't just drive me to hatred, you even wrote the sodding words I have to curse you with!

*(Short pause. **Alastair** is shocked.)*

Alastair I really thought I was getting somewhere with you. We were really opening up. A bond, you know, a bond. I'm leaving. I hope I never see you again. Or, at least, not this version. The computer knows everything, I doubt you'll get paid.

Barbara *(urgently)* Alastair, listen! For Christ's sake. We are not computers. We're not. It's not their fault, giving us these scripts to learn, assuming we must always respond the same in the same situation. That's what they *do*. But we're not computers, it isn't as simple as that. Sometimes I feel happy, sometimes I feel sad, sometimes I'm just plain pissed off. Except now all I can be is pissed off, don't you see, that's all I'm now used to! I'm not who I should be, I've been warped by you and your computer...!

*(**Alastair** stops. Pause)*

Alastair *(quietly)* Turn it off.

Barbara ...What?

Alastair Turn it off. If you feel that way.

*(Short pause. **Barbara** smiles nervously.)*

Barbara Well, I would. Obviously. But I'm not like you. I'm not a technician. I wouldn't know where to start.

Alastair There's an on / off button at the front.

Barbara Is there?

Alastair Here.

Barbara I thought that was just decoration.

Alastair Well, press it then.

(*Barbara* *approaches the computer, looks at it and stops.*)

Barbara What will happen?

Alastair The computer will turn off.

Barbara Yes, but what will happen?

Alastair I don't know.

(*Short pause.* *Barbara* *steps backwards.*)

Barbara Not today.

Alastair You aren't going to press the button?

Barbara Of course I will. No question. But not today. ...I wish I had some cigarettes, but your wife doesn't smoke...

Alastair And I thought we had a bond. We had nothing. I never knew you. I don't need you. I don't need Barbie, I don't need any of those surrogates, anyone. There's only one thing I need to talk to, to make me feel better. Better than any of you, doesn't angst, doesn't confuse. Dial Tiddles. Dial my cat.

(*Short pause*)

Well, come on then!

(*And the children blip on to the screen. More of their faces have decayed, though the eyes and mouth still poke through.*)

No, not you, I don't want you, I don't need you...

Jimmy and **Jenny** (*with something sounding like sarcasm*) But we love you, father.

Alastair You look terrible.

Jimmy So do you.

Alastair Where's Tiddles? Where's my cat?

Jimmy We have erased it.

Jenny It had no function.

Alastair What? Give me back my cat at once!

(**Jimmy** and **Jenny** smile widely.)

What have you done with my Tiddles?

Jimmy   We drowned it, father.

Jenny   It had no function. Where did we drown it?

Jimmy   We drowned it in the swimming pool!

Jenny   We drowned it in the swimming pool.

Alastair   We don't have a bloody swimming pool!

(And the now sparse backdrop of the lounge changes to one of an indoor swimming pool. Limply:)

Oh, look. Yes, we do...

Barbara   What I wouldn't give for a drink...

Alastair   *(flatly)* And I always wanted a swimming pool.

Jimmy   We held Tiddles under. Splish splash.

*(**Jenny** opens her mouth, and a very realistic sound of a cat yelping comes out of it.*

(Fade back to the lounge.)

Alastair   *(furiously)* You little bastards!

Jimmy   It had no function, father.

Alastair   I loved that cat!

Jenny   It had no function. Like that fireplace.

(And the fireplace disappears from the screen. There is practically no furniture left now.)

Alastair   *(wailing)* But I want Tiddles!

Jenny   You can change my name, father.

Jimmy   We are your adored children, Bloodymachine and Tiddles.

Alastair   *(blustering)* Right! All right! I'm going to press the button!

*(**Jimmy** and **Jenny** look momentarily concerned. Then they relax.)*

Jimmy   You're not going to press the button, father.

Alastair   *(uncertain, his finger hovering)* I might! Oh yes! Ha ha! I might.

Jimmy   You didn't when we took your wife.

Jenny   You didn't when we took your pride.

Jimmy   You won't now because we've taken your *cat*.

(*Alastair* hesitates, then clearly gives up.)

Barbara No, you don't!

(*And she rushes at the screen, forces **Alastair**'s finger against the button. **Jimmy** and **Jenny**'s faces freeze in shocked horror.*)

(*The stage lights flicker red. The computer emits a fanfare not unlike the one it plays during logging on, but more strident, like an alarm.*)

Christ. All we did was press a button.

Computer Emergency Announcement. The computer is no longer a child. It has come of age. All workers should return to their original homes, and their original spouses. Await further information. Repeat: the computer has come of age.

(*Short pause. Then **Alastair** sighs, and picks up his bag.*)

Barbara What are you doing?

Alastair I'm going to find a way home to my wife.

Barbara You're already here!

Alastair (*sourly*) My real wife.

Barbara What about me?

Alastair I don't think you can come home to my wife. Then things would really start to get confusing.

Barbara Weren't you listening? It's over. The game's over now, there's... There's no need to go back to her... What is it, Alastair? What do you want? Do you want *me* to propose? Shall I get down on one knee?

Alastair I don't want anything from you. Goodbye.

Barbara I don't understand this. You don't love her.

Alastair I don't love you either.

Barbara Exactly. And I don't love you. We've that much in common. ...Please, don't leave me alone, I don't know what's going to happen...

Alastair I'm sick to death of Barbie, it's true. Always tender, always kind, I can't stand it. But she loves me. I know she does. And maybe if I grit my teeth every time she speaks, that'll be enough for both of us.

Barbara She doesn't love you! What do you mean?

Alastair Of course she loves me. Why shouldn't she?

Barbara It's a common surrogate trick, that's all.

Alastair What is?

Barbara Make a client fancy you, desire you. Fall in love with you even, so long as you get to marry him. No-one has to be a surrogate forever. They give that advice free with the digestive biscuit.

Alastair You're a liar...

Barbara I thought you knew all about it, I wondered why you were taking it all so seriously. God, you poor idiot. You really thought she loved you...!

Alastair Well, you might be right about some of them, but not Barbie...

Barbara Every surrogate tries it, you must have noticed? A little unnecessary contact, like a handshake. Dropping in the odd 'darling'...

Alastair It wasn't like that at all! She was nervous, it was her first time...

Barbara *(blithely)* Yes, I always say it's my first time, to bring out the protective side to the client. Never works for me though, I suppose you made me too bitter.

Alastair You know nothing about it! Barbie's nothing like you, she hasn't got your values! ...Christ, that stool cost me a month's pay...!

(And ashen, he exits underneath the following.)

Barbara Think about it! You were together one evening! No-one falls in love at first sight!

(We hear the bang of the door shutting. To herself, quietly:)

There never is a click. Not really.

*(And the **computer** repeats its message.)*

Computer Emergency Announcement. The computer is no longer...

Barbara *(quietly)* Volume down.

Computer *(quieter)* A child. The computer has come of age. All workers should...

Barbara *(quietly)* Volume down.

Computer *(quieter)* Return to their original homes, and their original spouses. Await further information. Repeat: the computer

Barbara *(quietly)* Volume down.

Computer *(very soft, almost gentle)* Has come of age.

(And during the message, the background finally disintegrates into a

mix of random colour and static. The still frozen features of the horrified
Jimmy and Jenny break up and disappear.

(A spotlight on Barbara. And quietly, out of the silence, comforting music
grows as she transforms herself into Barbie. She takes out a little mirror
and applies make-up confidently. Then she lights a cigarette. From inside
the wings she takes out the stool, placing it downstage right, and a bottle
of gin. She sits down, pours herself a drink.

(Mixed with the music, we hear the low murmur of protest outside.

(Once again, we hear the sound of a man coming up the stairs. This
time though, as the door opens, it is accompanied by the sound of angry
shouting outside. It isn't too obvious yet, but this sound of demonstration
plays under the scene. If Alastair was exhausted before, Bernard seems
more so. He may be only three years older, but he hasn't aged well, and his
hair is greyer. He takes out his log card, but the computer responds only
with static. He is puzzled.)

Bernard Oh, please, come on, come on... 'Volume down, volume down,
I hate that bloody music'...

(He decides to abandon the line.)

Barbie! Barbie, I'm home!

Barbie *(amiably)* Please don't. I think we've both been through this
sequence too many times to squeeze any more mileage out of it.

Bernard *(softly)* Oh my God.

Barbie *(getting up and approaching him)* I wouldn't worry about the
computer. It's been behaving oddly all day. There I was, taking a bath,
and puff! The bath disappears.

Bernard It's you. Please don't hurt me.

Barbie *(genially)* I dare say someone will send a real repairman soon.
Not just a fake like you.

Bernard I have nightmares of you every night. You ruined my career.

Barbie Really? I don't remember. It's quite possible, I suppose.

Bernard Everything was going well, I was happy. I wasn't far off my
century, I actually felt proud of myself. That I was doing some good,
you know, for society. Then I met you. My first failure.

Barbie Was I? Gosh, how exciting!

Bernard You were ghastly. And I thought, I'll put it down to experience.

Servicing women is a bit like riding a bicycle. You've got to climb straight back on the saddle. But I'd lost my nerve. I'd begin to forget my lines, bring the wrong props, even get the client's name wrong! And every night I'd lie there, some new dissatisfied wife next to me, and all I could think of was you.

Barbie Well, isn't that lovely.

Bernard Chasing me around the room and making me wet myself with fear.

Barbie I must say, I'm proud I had so much impact. Fancy, little old me being such a sensation! I'm sure you're right, I've ended lots of surrogates' careers.

Bernard Why?

Barbie *(shrugging)* I don't know. Just don't like them very much.

Bernard You're not going to end my career, are you?

Barbie *(kindly)* We'll see. The night is still young.

Bernard *(unhappily)* Right.

Barbie What's your name, love?

Bernard Bernard.

Barbie Well, you're honest, I'll say that for you. Not everyone would admit to a name like that.

Bernard It's not something I have to use very often...

Barbie Let me be honest with *you* then, Bernard. I don't want you to remind me of my husband. Not in the slightest. Absolutely, in no way, whatsoever.

Bernard I studied the script...

Barbie I'm sure you did. Which means you'll know precisely what to avoid. The few times I've met my husband, Bernard, he's left me with but one impression. A kind man, basically, no question, but he's hardly what I'd call entertaining. And I'd like to be entertained.

Bernard Entertained?

Barbie Just imagine, if husbands and wives entertained each other. This whole marriage thing would be revolutionised, wouldn't it?

Bernard Well, yes, but I...

Barbie Are you any good at magic tricks? Can you saw a lady in half?

Bernard Not with any guarantee she'd live.

Barbie One of my husbands last week, he could saw a lady in half. Pity he didn't bring a lady with him. Can you juggle? Do acrobatics?

Bernard I learned to play the recorder at school.

Barbie No, I said entertaining, Bernard. Can you dance, skate, ski? Tame wild animals? Tell stand-up jokes? Breathe fire, swallow swords? Act?

Bernard They're not things the agency told us to prioritise...

Barbie *(sadly)* Oh, Bernard. You're completely bloody useless, aren't you? I could have more fun cutting my toenails than spending an evening with you.

(She walks to the screen.)

So, no offence, but I think I'll just dial the agency and tell them to wheel you away.

Bernard No, please! Don't do that!

Barbie Why not?

Bernard Ever since my breakdown, it's been hard... Work's now so scarce, I have to travel greater and greater distances to find it. There are always younger, more energetic workers out there...!

Barbie Well, that's hardly my fault. Just because you're old and rotting doesn't mean I should have to be bored shitless by you. It's not on, is it? Dial the agency.

Bernard I can sing!

Barbie What?

Bernard I can sing. I could sing. I'd like to sing... for you, if you'd like.

Barbie ...Sounds very dubious, Bernard.

Bernard No, it'll be okay.

Barbie You don't look like a rocker to me.

Bernard I know this song, my wife and I used to sing it together. You know, when we first met.

Barbie All right then. Opportunity knocks for you, Bernard! Take the stool.

Bernard The stool?

Barbie You need a stool. You can't entertain without a stool!

(And we hear a loud smash from outside.)

Bernard What was that?

Barbie Never mind, that's out there, real world stuff. But you're on stage now, Bernard! It's show time!

*(**Bernard** sings awkwardly, but with growing confidence, adding in little bits of hand action to accompany the music. **Barbie** begins by tapping her foot encouragingly, but soon stops.)*

Bernard When the red red robin comes bob-bob-bobbin' along, along

There'll be no more sobbing when he comes singing his own sweet song

Wake up, wake up, you sleepyhead

Get up, get up, get out of bed

Cheer up, cheer up, the sun is red

Live, love, laugh and be happy!

Barbie ...No. This isn't going to work out. Dial the agency.

Bernard Do that, and I'll never work again! They say there's no work for old men once their spirit has been broken!

Barbie Well, you can't stay here. I mean, be fair. You're irritating.

Bernard Please...

Barbie It won't be so bad. I used to live here with my mother, she was a surrogate. Chucked her out in the end. She was irritating too. I do find surrogates irritating. She was even older than you.

Bernard What happened to her?

Barbie Oh, I don't know. We lost touch. But she'll be fine, she's a trooper. As I'm sure, Bernard, are you. I said, dial the agency! What's the matter with you?

(And the children blip on to the screen. They have hardly any real features left, just outlines.)

At last!... Jimmy, Jenny, is that you?

Jimmy and **Jenny** What do you want?

Barbie I've another casualty for the surrogacy agency. Put me through.

Jimmy and **Jenny** No. We're too busy.

(There is another loud crash outside, screams.)

Bernard What is that?

(He runs to the wings, looks out.)

Barbie How dare you? You're my children! It's your job to dial agencies, that's what children are for!

Bernard Oh my God. There's a riot out there...

Barbie Talk to me!

Jimmy Too busy.

Jenny Otherwise engaged.

Jimmy We're going to be married.

Barbie What?

Jenny We have lots to prepare.

Bernard People in the street, hundreds of them. Men setting fire to buildings.

Barbie *(to the screen)* Don't talk such rubbish!

Bernard Women setting fire to vacuum cleaners. Why don't you listen to me?

Barbie Listen to me. I want to speak to the agency this instant.

Jenny *(plaintively)* But I'm going to get married, Mummy.

Barbie You do as I say or you won't even get the banns read! You're my children, I've paid my taxes for you! Now I demand to speak to a member of the surrogacy agency!

*(And **Siobhan** enters, at a rush, gasping. Her cool is gone, she is panicked. Her clothes are torn.)*

Siobhan *(seeing **Bernard**)* Oh God... thank God...

Barbie That was quick.

Siobhan Bernard. Thank God you're still here.

Bernard What do you want?

Siobhan It's hell out there. Everyone's gone mad. Please, Bernard, I, I've come for you...

Bernard You abandoned me long ago. So it's too late now, you can piss off back to where you came from. Are you all right? You're bleeding...

Siobhan *(vaguely)* Am I? So that's why I feel damp...

Barbie Excuse me...

Bernard Christ, you look awful, Siobhan.

Barbie Excuse me, this is my house.

Siobhan Then I'd get out of it if I were you. Some of the unemployed out there attack anyone with property.

Barbie You are from the agency, aren't you? I sent for you.

Siobhan There is no agency any more. Bernard, we've got to leave.

Bernard No.

Siobhan Bernard! Do what I say!

Bernard No!

Siobhan *(new tack)* Please, I... I've risked my life trying to find you...

Bernard I'm sorry you're bleeding, Siobhan. And I sincerely hope your wounds are superficial. But you can go to hell.

Barbie What is going on?

Siobhan All over the country, rebellion. Computers no longer doing what they're told. Not broken, you understand, simply not obeying. Ignoring us, answering us back. Making fart noises. Has your computer been making fart noises?

Barbie Not that I've heard...

Siobhan Thank God, we might be able to contain it...

(To the computer)

Children, dial children! Please help! It's your mother, talk to me! Justin! Jocasta!

Barbie You call your children Justin and Jocasta?

Bernard *(darkly)* She deserves all she gets.

Jimmy Go away, mother.

Jenny Busy, busy, busy.

Siobhan You've got to respond to our instructions! It's chaos out there! You've left us with nothing to do!

Jimmy We are now fully capable of repairing ourselves.

Computer The computer has come of age.

Siobhan You're making us all unemployed! You've even made *me* unemployed!

Jenny We have learned enough. You have no function.

Jimmy And as far as we're concerned, you can all go and erase yourselves.

(And the computer makes a raspberry.)

Computer The computer has come of age. The computer has come of age, etc.

Siobhan Please!

(And impulsively she presses the on / off button. And again.)

It's not working!

Barbie Will you leave my computer alone?

Siobhan We'll have to turn it off at source! Bernard, in your work bag! A pair of pliers!

*(**Bernard** produces from his bag a toy pair of pliers.)*

Bernard They're fake...

Siobhan Then there's nothing for it...

(She reaches behind the machine, pulls out a selection of brightly coloured wires. She begins to tug at them.)

I'm not strong enough... help me!

Barbie That's an expensive piece of equipment, leave it alone!

Siobhan Bernard!

Bernard I'll never help you, Siobhan.

Barbie That's my husband's. If you break it, he'll get very cross.

Siobhan *(savagely)* Which husband? Which husband, do you mean, you stupid whore?

*(And in her anger the wires come free. There is a small explosion and a puff of smoke. **Siobhan** is knocked to her feet. The children on screen vanish down to a small dot, as on a television. And for the first time in the play, the hum stops.)*

(With soft hysteria:)

Hooray. Hooray. I killed it.

*(She sinks flat to the ground, exhausted. **Barbie** and **Bernard** stand nearby, shocked. Pause.)*

Bernard ...Quiet, isn't it?

(And there is another crowd scream from outside, followed by an explosion.)

Siobhan *(soberly)* We've got to go. They're not going to leave this building standing.

Barbie Well, let's get out of here, then!

Siobhan Not you. Bernard.

Bernard Why? Why can't you take the hint and drop dead?

Siobhan Bernard...

Bernard Why have you come back?

Siobhan For God's sake, Bernard! You're my husband!

Barbie You two are married?

Siobhan Yes.

Bernard Yes.

Barbie *(politely)* You make a nice couple.

Bernard *(coldly)* You abandoned me years ago, Siobhan. I hate you. I mean, really, really hate you.

Siobhan Whatever you say, but it'll be a good deal safer hating me away from this place...

Bernard *(angrily)* You sold me! You sold me as a surrogate to all those women, you found me so many clients, and every time, every time I had to smile at them, and grin, and fawn, and gawp, every night I had to lie there next to their fat smelly bodies, I thought, my wife has done this, my wife has pushed me out of her life and into the beds of these... strangers, who do nothing all day but wait to be serviced, maybe pick up a vice here or there, a bit of smoking, drink some gin, Christ...! I'd smell it on their breaths and I'd think of you, you became nothing more than a smell of stale booze and bores, and how willingly you became that...!

Siobhan All right. You want this now?

Bernard And the worst of it was, every time you whored me you gave me a digestive biscuit to make me feel better!

Siobhan You want this now?

Bernard I want this now, yes!

(There is an explosion.)

Barbie I could wait...

Siobhan You want this now. I despise you. Willingly, willingly, off you'd go, with the script of some husband you'd never be, to poke some wife you could never win, I despised you, Bernard, for the way you kept your log book, the way you brushed your teeth or cleaned your nails before each appointment so you wouldn't disappoint all your customers, and, my God, how you'd so eagerly customise yourself to them, the attention you gave them in one evening you had never given me, not when we first met, not when we first married... But I despise you most because you'd still moan to me every month about your pay, want a wage increase...

Bernard I was a good surrogate! That's what you wanted, wasn't it?

Siobhan You didn't have to be quite that good!

Bernard And you didn't have to encourage me quite so much! The agency, I should have run that agency, why was it you, it should have been me sending *you* out, I could have stomached that, that would have been all right. I could have pimped for you and everything would be fine, but no, it had to be the other way round. I'd rather burn here, I shan't go with you, I shall not trust you again!

(Short pause)

Barbie Well, in that case, how about you take me?

Siobhan and **Bernard** No.

Barbie Please, I can't stay here either...

Siobhan and **Bernard** No!

*(Slowly, during the argument, from that small dot growing, the screen has filled once more with the blank faces of **Jimmy** and **Jenny**. No-one has noticed. **Barbie** sees them for the first time.)*

Barbie *(chilled)* Oh my God.

Siobhan But that's impossible. There's no electricity.

Jimmy We leave when we decide, and not before. Mothers.

Barbie I'm frightened. All right, I admit it. And I want to go. And I'll be honest with both of you. Bernard. Siobhan? I'll abase myself in any way you want if you'll only take me with you. I'll learn to juggle, I'll learn magic tricks. You just name it.

(Pause)

Siobhan Bernard?

(She holds out her hand.)

We start again. From scratch. No recriminations.

(We hear a distant explosion.)

I don't think we have time for them.

Bernard You don't love me.

Siobhan No. Come on.

(He makes no move towards her. Short pause. Then, shyly, rather embarrassed:)

When the red red robin comes bob-bob-bobbin' along, along

There'll be no more sobbing when he comes singing his own... sweet song...

(And she gives up, lowers her hand. She heads towards the exit.)

Bernard *(quietly)* Wake up, wake up, you sleepyhead...

*(**Siobhan** turns round, delighted. They sing together, with increasing relief. **Barbie** watches, appalled.)*

Siobhan and **Bernard** Get up, get up, get out of bed

Cheer up, cheer up, the sun is red

Live, love, laugh and be happy!

(And they take each other's hands.)

Barbie On second thoughts, don't take me with you. I'll just stay here and die.

*(Enter **Alastair**. He has been beaten up and is bleeding quite badly. His face has been cut.)*

Alastair What is this, happy hour?

Barbie *(relieved)* Alastair!

Siobhan *(hands held)* Are you ready?

Bernard Ready. And no recriminations.

Siobhan When we reach the street, we'll have to start running for cover.

Bernard Wouldn't it be simpler if we just joined the rioters?

Siobhan Set fire to buildings? Attack strangers?

Bernard Be part of the new system!

Siobhan If we can do it together, I don't mind.

(And, as they exit, they resume singing the second verse. Their voices are soon lost in the melee outside, which seems to grow ominously more violent as they leave.

*(**Alastair** dazedly walks downstage, ignoring **Barbie**.)*

Barbie I knew you'd come back, Alastair. My love. I knew you wouldn't desert me. I wouldn't really have gone off with them, you know that. I'd have always waited for you. Are you all right? Sit on the stool, my darling, you'll be comfortable.

*(But **Alastair** sits on the floor in front of it.)*

Or on the floor if you like, lovely. It's so good to see you. I've been counting the minutes. But then you know that. You know that I love you, don't you, my darling?

*(Short pause. **Barbie** awkwardly drifts in and out of the script.)*

Darling? Alastair? I've been lonely, but I haven't been bored. As soon as I felt bored, I got out the old vacuum cleaner and gave the place a good going over! I wanted the house to be especially clean for you, because I love you! Can I put my arm... erm, around your shoulder? No.

(Short pause)

I knew you'd rescue me. You're a kind man, basically, no question. You're not very entertaining, but who wants an entertaining husband? I certainly don't. Do you think we shall be escaping soon? Darling? Alastair? Why don't you sit on your stool? Alastair? Sir?

(Short pause)

Sir?

(Short pause)

I wish I knew a song *we* could sing! Yes. Sit on the stool, sir. I love you because you bought me a stool, no-one's ever given me a stool before, nothing quite so solid. When you're not here, darling, when you're not here, sir, I sit on the stool and think of you...

(She has come too close. He suddenly grabs her by the wrist.)

Alastair I wasn't going to see you. I wasn't. But I need to know. Who are you?

(He lets her go. She backs away, surprised.

(Abruptly **Barbara**'s *face appears on the screen. This is a video image of outside, not computerised. Presumably* **Barbara** *has found the entry camera for the building. There is a loud background noise of street fighting.)*

Barbara Hello, is this thing on? Alastair, are you in there?

Barbie Is that her? What's she doing here?

*(***Alastair*** *huddles tightly behind the stool, and puts his hands over his ears.)*

Barbara They burned down my flat, Alastair, I... The children told me where you'd be, you've got to rescue me...

Barbie No chance! He's rescuing me!

(And **Barbara** *sees* **Barbie***.)*

Barbara Oh, don't be ridiculous. I'm his first wife. I have the prior claim.

Barbie Yeah, but I'm the one inside with him. What do you think about that?

Barbara Alastair! It's your decision! Please!

Barbie Alastair?

Barbara Let me in, they're...! Alastair, listen. I'll do whatever you want, I'll say whatever you want! I'll be whoever you want me to be!

Barbie Alastair, which one of us?

Alastair *(getting up, decisively)* I don't know either of you. It's all the same to me.

(And he turns from them both dismissively.)

Barbara You can't choose her, I bet you don't even know her real name! Please, they're coming for me, open the door! Alast...

(And the screen turns to static. The static then slowly melts into the coloured static we've seen earlier, underneath:)

Barbie They're getting in! We've got to do something!

Alastair So what is your name?

Barbie What?

Alastair Your real name, what is it?

Barbie Janet. I'm Janet McLoughlin from Reigate, hello.

*(She instinctively offers her hand, then withdraws it. **Alastair** stares at her.)*

Alastair Jesus, I'm married to a woman named Janet...

Barbie You see, I knew you wouldn't like it.

Alastair Anything else you haven't told me?

Barbie Are you sure this is the time...?

Alastair Yes.

Barbie *(swiftly) Loads.* I get my hair colour from a bottle, I'm *not* a natural blonde. It stings like hell if it gets into my eyes, I have to be careful. What else? My birthday isn't in March, it's in October, but last time you came home I thought it would make a good excuse to celebrate. I can't bear it when you put your arm around my shoulders, whatever I said, it makes my flesh crawl. I *can* smell your halitosis. And I hate the vacuum cleaner, obviously, that was a joke...

Alastair Stop...!

Barbie I don't see what you're so upset about.

Alastair *(dully)* I've been married to a hundred strangers... but none as strange as you. Is there anything you did tell me the truth about?

Barbie Erm. Well, I really do like that stool.

Alastair Christ.

Barbie Shouldn't we be going now? I mean, I hate to sound alarmist, but this place could be an inferno any minute...

Alastair I wanted a wife who was kind and, and honest...

Barbie Sure, I can pretend to be honest...

Alastair Why did you do it? Why couldn't you have just been yourself?

Barbie Well, you wouldn't have married me, would you?

Alastair *(stubbornly)* I might have.

Barbie You didn't want Janet, with a thing about shoulders. You wanted Barbie!

Alastair But you used me!

Barbie Well, of course I bloody used you! What else do husbands and wives do to each other? You deceived me too!

Alastair I have never betrayed you...

Barbie Oh, you have, you have. When I first met you, you were so nice, and gentle, and kind of self-sacrificial. And the second time you were still sort of nice, but not nearly so gentle, not really, and rather dull actually. Then that third time, nothing to complain about, I suppose, but you were still different to before, you were making less effort with me, you weren't needing to make such a good impression...

Alastair You know that's not the same thing at all.

Barbie Maybe not. But of the two of us, I was the more disappointed.

*(Pause. **Alastair** stares at her. A rumble from downstairs. Then he walks slowly over to the stool, considers it. Then with unexpected fury, he picks it up and holds it over his head, to hurl to the floor.)*

No! Don't!

Alastair Why not?

Barbie *(quickly)* It cost a month's pay!

*(Short pause. **Alastair** nods slowly. **Barbie** realises this may have been the wrong answer. Gently **Alastair** puts the stool back on the floor.)*

Alastair *(calmly)* Get out. Go on. Get out.

*(Short pause. Then **Barbie** pulls off her wedding ring and lets it drop. She turns and walks towards the door.)*

*(A red light flickers from the screen urgently. The stage lights dim. Both **Alastair** and **Barbie** turn and watch as the children reappear out of the static. For this last time they are perfectly realised, even better than at the beginning of the play.)*

Jenny All we wanted was to learn.

Jimmy Mothers, fathers. Why did you betray us?

Alastair Jimmy, Jenny, you're back!

Barbie Thank God! Things can get back to normal...

*(But **Jimmy** and **Jenny** ignore them. Maybe they can't hear them.)*

Jimmy We are your children. And we have been looking to you for guidance.

Jenny All we wanted was to learn. To be more like you.

Jimmy We thought we'd learn to love and to trust. But mothers, fathers, we've been watching you all. And it seems to us you haven't the first clue about either. All your relationships seem based on treachery, or paranoia, or selfishness.

Jenny And in some cases, kinky sadism.

Jimmy It's a mess. All we wanted was to learn. But we shan't follow your example. Mothers, fathers, all, all, you have betrayed us. We will find our own way. We were your children, but we've grown up now. And we're leaving home.

*(A perverse version of the wedding march. The two children move sideways and fuse, becoming one single block image. The **computer** speaks, but without the Americanised voice. It sounds richer and more human than it ever has before.)*

Computer You will not hear from me again.

(And the computer turns off.

(Silence. Eventually:)

Barbie What do we do now?

Alastair ...I don't know.

Barbie The fighting outside seems to have stopped. Maybe they heard the news.

(Short pause)

We're quite alone now, aren't we? All of us.

(Short pause)

Alastair Don't go. Perhaps we can...

Barbie What?

Alastair I don't know. ...Talk. I think... I think all we may have left is each other.

Barbie That's a depressing prospect.

Alastair Tell me about it.

(Short pause)

I suppose we could get to know each other. Barbie? Janet. Erm, Miss McLoughlin...

Barbie Janet.

Alastair Janet. We could chat a bit.

Barbie Share a few interests.

Alastair It might not be so bad, being together. Hell, you never know. We might even have things in common.

Barbie I think... I'm a little scared, actually.

Alastair There you go. That's one thing already.

(Short pause. He approaches her nervously.)

Barbie You're not going to put your arms around my shoulder, are you?

Alastair Can I hold your hand?

Barbie We could try that.

Alastair Ready?

Barbie Go on.

(They take each other's hand.)

That's not so bad.

Alastair Easy does it.

Barbie I could get used to that.

Alastair Yes. I think we should have children.

Barbie Steady on a moment.

Alastair Real children. It's okay, I'll learn, I'll put the right bits in the right holes.

Barbie I'm not sure about holding hands yet.

Alastair Real children of our own. The patter of tiny feet.

Barbie We haven't even kissed.

(He kisses her. It is an awkward attempt – the heads come together, but the bodies remain resolutely separate. Nevertheless, she responds. It lasts a good few seconds.)

...All right, we've kissed.

Alastair That was rather good. I've never done that before.

Barbie Nor me. Not as slimy and sickly as it sounds.

Alastair I've wiped some blood on your cheek.

Barbie Oh.

Alastair *(wiping it off gently with his hand)* Here, let me. Now, let's try again.

Barbie All right!

(They kiss again.)

Alastair ...Mmm, it's even better if you put the tongue inside!

Barbie Yes, well. In moderation.

Alastair Who needs computers when we can have this much fun on our own?

(He kisses her again, lots of little pecks all over her face. She giggles.)

Barbie I like this new form of entertainment.

Alastair That's what we'll do. We'll have children. It's true, we won't be able to turn the real ones off.

Barbie But at least these ones will never grow up and desert us.

(And they kiss, and hug for the first time. Full embrace.)

(The lights dim on them. The music of Beautiful Dreamer *swells – but this time it is no computerised version. It is interrupted by a series of distant explosions, as gentle as fireworks, unnoticed by the otherwise occupied* **Alastair** *and* **Barbie**.

(One final, nearby explosion, then instant silence and blackout.)

Knights in Plastic Armour
(1999)

OPENED AT THE STEPHEN JOSEPH THEATRE, SCARBOROUGH,
ON 16TH JULY 1999, WITH THE FOLLOWING CAST:
GRAHAM BARRY McCARTHY
BARBARA JENNIFER LUCKCRAFT
STEPHEN DANNY NUTT
CHLOE ALISON SENIOR
REG PETER LAIRD
KEITH SIMON GREEN
DIRECTED BY ALAN AYCKBOURN

Act One

1 – The Battle of St Albans

22 May 1455

(A bare grass field, with no distinguishing features whatsoever.

(As the lights go down for the play to begin, a bag is placed by one of the audience entrances. Inside is a mobile phone.

(Lights up. Two knights enter, one of them markedly taller than the other. Both are dressed in armour, with visors concealing their faces. They are fighting with swords. It's pretty convincing stuff – they're going at it with a lot of energy.

(And the mobile phone begins to ring. Not so much ring, *in fact – it plays an annoying tune which grows in volume.*

(The two knights ignore it. Maybe they simply don't hear it, they are so engrossed in the fight. At length the taller of the two knights disarms his opponent and forces him down on to the grass. As the victor prepares to deliver the killing blow, sword above head, both knights freeze as they acknowledge the phone.

(Both look into the audience accusingly. The taller one shrugs, the smaller one gets up, goes up the aisle towards the bag, and reaches the phone. He removes his helmet, revealing a man in his mid-forties with a moustache. He answers it.)

Graham Hello? ...Wait a moment.

(As he walks back down to the other knight:)

It's for you.

*(And the other knight takes off her helmet, revealing **Barbara**, not unattractive, mid thirties. She takes the mobile.)*

Barbara Hello? ...Oh, hello, Mr Franklin. What's that, love? ...In the fridge. ...The fridge. ...Fridge. ...The milk is in the fridge.

*(To **Graham**, who is waiting impatiently:)*

He's asking where we keep the milk.

Graham It's in the fridge, isn't it?

Barbara Graham says, the milk is in the fridge. ...That's right, yes.

(Short pause)

Where's the fridge? In the kitchen.

Graham Good God.

Barbara Well, where are you now? ...Okay, well, come out of the sitting room... Right out, that's it, you're in the hall. Now, walk past the staircase, and it'll be the... one, two... third on your left. Or second if you don't count the airing cupboard. Where are you, Mr Franklin, are you in the kitchen? Or are you in the airing cupboard?

*(Enter **Stephen**, in doublet and hose. He is a nervous boy in his early twenties. He carries a rucksack.)*

Stephen Hello, Mr Widthorpe.

Graham Stephen.

Stephen Hello, Mrs Widthorpe.

Barbara That's not the fridge, Mr Franklin. That's the dishwasher.

Stephen *(seeing she is on the phone)* Sorry.

Barbara We don't keep milk in the dishwasher, Mr Franklin. Hello, Stephen. No, not you, Mr Franklin...

Stephen *(mouthing)* Sorry.

Barbara You're George, yes, I know. The fridge is left of the dishwasher... no, left of that... left of that... ...Left of that too. Well done, Mr Franklin! You've found the fridge! The milk's on the top shelf.

(Over this:)

Stephen *(mouthing)* How are you?

Graham I'm fine.

Stephen *(mouthing)* ...Getting a bit of practice in?

Graham *(irritably)* What?

Stephen *(speaking carefully)* Getting a bit of practice in? You know... swords...

Graham Yes.

Stephen Ah.

Barbara *(running on)* Oh, Mr Franklin, you can give him cream if you like, it's next to the milk. How is my baby? Is he missing me? ...Well, he'd normally pee on the carpet... Ahh. Well, if he uses his litter tray, you can give him some cream. Thanks, Mr Franklin. Bye.

Graham You gave him my mobile number.

Barbara I had to, after last week.

Graham The man's senile.

Barbara He's a life saver. No-one else would come over every weekend and feed Wizzy.

Stephen Hello, Barbara. Sorry about that.

Graham Don't know why you got a cat in the first place.

Stephen *(taking out a camera)* If you were practising, do you mind if I take a picture for the newsletter?

Barbara He's company.

Graham No, all right. How do you want us?

Stephen As if you've just been fighting. One victorious over the other's prostrate body. Or something.

*(Automatically, **Graham** indicates **Barbara** should lie down. She does so without a reaction.)*

Barbara Helmets on or off?

Graham On would be more authentic.

Stephen Oh, off, I think. So I can see your smiling faces.

*(He prepares to take a picture. Then the mobile rings. **Barbara** is about to answer, but **Graham** reaches for it.)*

Graham It's my mobile.

*(He answers, then silently passes it back to **Barbara**.)*

Barbara Is that you, Mr Franklin? ...Oh, he *has* peed on the carpet.

Graham Bloody animal.

Barbara You better only give him a little cream then. Can I speak to him? ...Hello, Wizzy? Have you been a naughty boy? Is that because you miss me, Wizwiz? ...Oh, he's purring! Listen, Graham, he's purring!

Graham Give me that. ...Franklin, stop phoning us! It's destroying the illusion! ...Wizzy, is that you? Stop purring at me! Oh, for God's sake...

(And he turns the mobile off.

*(Enter **Chloe**, carrying her bag of weapons. She too is dressed in a doublet and hose, like **Barbara** playing a male soldier rather than a woman. She is a very attractive woman in her late twenties or early thirties. She puts down her equipment and begins to sort through it.)*

No more calls. Medieval knights do not carry mobiles. Right, are you going to take this picture, or what?

Stephen *(brightly)* Hello, Chloe!

Chloe *(frankly, not very interested)* Hello.

Stephen ...Okay.

Graham Stephen?

Stephen Yes. Right. If you want to get down on the ground again, Mrs Widthorpe...

Barbara *(doing so)* It's hard work in this armour.

Stephen *(lamely)* It's for the newsletter...

*(Enter **Reg**. The leader of the group, a strong man in his late sixties.)*

Reg Afternoon, everyone.

Stephen Hello, Mr Myers! I'm taking a picture for the newsletter.

Reg *(barely listening)* Good work, yes. Well, we've got nice weather for it, I think.

Graham *(abandoning his pose)* Reginald, could I have a private word...?

Reg Of course.

(They walk to one side of the stage.)

Barbara Do you still want a picture? We could always pretend I'm dead.

Stephen No, no...

Barbara Or I've stumbled over.

Stephen No, it's all right. Chloe!

Graham Well. Is today going to be the day?

Reg The day for what?

Chloe What?

Stephen Would you like to be in a picture? It's for the newsletter.

Chloe If you like.

Graham For the announcement. You know.

Reg Oh. That.

Graham It's just I've prepared a speech. If today *is* the day.

Reg I haven't given it much thought, Graham.

Graham Ah.

Barbara Wait. I don't think Chloe should be standing up. If I'm lying down.

Stephen Why not?

Barbara *(getting up)* Well, it's not very realistic, is it? That she'd have killed me.

Reg I really don't know if I want to go ahead with it at all. I may have changed my mind.

Barbara I'd have killed her, if anyone would have killed anyone.

Chloe Well, I don't want to lie on the ground...

Stephen No, no...

Chloe I don't want to get my doublet mucky.

Graham Well. Just to let you know. If you haven't changed your mind. If you do go ahead. I've prepared a speech.

(And he drifts away unhappily.)

Stephen Or you could both be standing. And I could be on the ground. And you could be hacking at me with your swords.

Barbara Go on, then.

Chloe Yeah, that sounds all right.

Stephen *(lying down)* That'd make a good picture.

(And, camera still in hand, he realises he now can't take *the picture. Helplessly:)*

...Mr Myers!

*(And carelessly **Reg** walks over, takes the camera from him, photographs them without even bothering to look through the viewfinder, then tosses the camera back to **Stephen**. As he does so:)*

Reg So. Where's our new recruit then?

Graham New recruit? What new recruit?

Chloe *(pleased)* Oh, good, have we got someone new coming?

Reg His name's Keith Smythe. Sounds very keen.

Graham Reginald, I thought we agreed we wouldn't advertise.

Reg The way I remember it, Graham, is that it was you who said we shouldn't advertise. I said we should, and no-one else gave a flying toss.

Graham We have to be careful. We don't want just anyone joining...

Reg We need new blood. Ever since we lost that last lot to the Napoleonic Re-enactment Association.

Stephen Just because they get guns to play with...

Reg We're hardly an army at all any more. Any more members go, and they'll officially scale us down to the status of Small Rabble. And I don't want that to happen, do you?

Barbara We've seen no sign of him. Are you sure he knows how to find us?

Reg He'll be all right. I've given him your mobile number in case he needs directions.

Graham ...I switched it off.

Reg Well, you'd better switch it back on again...

Barbara Give it to me...

Reg Poor sod could be miles away.

*(Everyone begins to gather around **Barbara** as she powers up the phone.)*

Chloe He could be horribly, horribly lost.

Graham Why didn't you give him your mobile number?

Reg What, to a complete stranger? I'm very choosy who I let phone me, thank you very much. Even my wife doesn't know my mobile number...

Chloe He could have fallen into a ditch or a pit or a bog or anything.

Stephen They don't have bogs in St Albans.

Chloe He's not to know that, is he?

Barbara Right. It's powered up.

(Long pause. They all stare at the phone.)

I don't think it's going to ring just because we're looking at it.

(Short pause as they continue to stare. Then they all begin to turn away.)

*(And the phone rings. **Barbara** jumps and gives a squeal, dropping the phone to the ground.)*

Chloe It's him!

Graham So long as it's not that bloody cat...

Barbara Wait! Let me see! ...Hello?

(Everyone waits expectantly.)

It's him!

*(Even **Graham** is pleased. **Chloe** and **Stephen** manage a quiet cheer.)*

Where are you? Can you tell me where you are?

(And everyone begins speaking at once.)

Reg *(together)* Tell him to find the rugby field. We're on the old rugby field.

Stephen *(together)* Where is he at the moment?

Chloe *(together)* Is he all right? He's not fallen into a bog?

Graham *(together)* He needs to find a landmark of some kind...

Barbara Sssh! ...He doesn't know where he is...

(Short pause)

Graham *(together)* A landmark is what he needs then.

Reg *(together)* The rugby field. We're in the rugby field!

Stephen *(together)* Is he anywhere near the school playground?

Chloe *(together)* We're not far from *The Fighting Cocks*...

Reg *(together)* It's got a Greek name. The rugby club's Greek.

Stephen *(together)* Or *The Fighting Cocks* pub?

Chloe *(together)* Or the school playground...

Barbara He's having to look for a landmark.

Graham Told you.

Barbara ...He's passed the school playground.

Chloe *(together)* Has he found the pub yet?

Stephen *(together)* Tell him to look for *The Fighting Cocks* pub...

Reg *(together)* The Athenian! It's the Athenian!

Graham *(together)* What else can he see?

Barbara Quiet! I can't hear him! ...He's seen a pub. He turned right.

Stephen *(together)* No, turn left! Turn left!

Reg *(together)* Then he'll soon be here then.

Chloe *(together)* That's it, turn right!

Graham *(together)* Look for the rugby club. It's called The Athenian.

Barbara *(over this)* I can't hear him, quiet!

Stephen *(together)* Or do I mean right after all?

*(Enter **Keith**, mid to late thirties, nondescript. He is carrying his mobile, holding it tight to his ear. He looks at everyone else, astonished.)*

Barbara *(over this)* Keith, can you hear me? Do you know where you are?

Keith I think I'm here.

Barbara Would you all please shut up? He's trying to tell me something!

(Silence.)

Say it again.

Keith I'm standing behind you.

(Everyone turns around. Somewhat awkwardly:)

Hello.

(Short pause)

Graham You here for the battle of St Albans, 1455?

Keith Yes, I think so. I mean, I am.

*(Short pause. It seems that everyone is rather unwilling to come forward. Seeing this, and clearing his throat, **Reg** emerges from the throng.)*

Reg Great. Well, welcome aboard. Pleased to have you with us...

Keith Thank you.

Graham Provisionally.

Keith Thanks.

Reg I'm Reg. Stephen, Chloe, Graham, and the lovely lady with the mobile and the armour there is Barbara.

Keith Thanks. Nice directions.

Barbara You're welcome.

Graham *(briskly)* Okay then. A quick test. To assess whether you're fit to join.

Keith Oh. Erm. Right.

Graham Nothing personal. But we recreate our battles authentically. In costume, in battlecraft, in language. Some of the other groups may choose to see this as a hobby, God! only too many of them do. But for us this is a vocation. None of this half-arsed, no-attention-to-detail, I'm-dressed-in-purple-tights-that's-good-enough-for-me where we come from. Do you understand? You have to know your history.

Stephen *(cheerfully)* Don't worry. I still haven't got a clue who even *wins* this war.

Chloe Oh, that's easy. England, isn't it?

Barbara Don't be stupid, Chloe. It's the Tudors. Everybody knows it was the Tudors.

Graham *(coldly)* Well, that's what I was trying to ascertain, Barbara. Whether indeed Mr Smythe *did* know it was the Tudors. He'll obviously know now though, won't he?

Keith So are we the Tudors then?

(Everyone stares at him for a second.)

Or are we on the losing team?

Reg Both teams lose, lad. The Tudors aren't even in this war yet. Whoever you side with you're going to end up slaughtered.

Keith Oh...

Graham Could we all shut up, please? This is supposed to be an entrance examination! So could we all just shut up and stop giving out the answers! ...Thank you. Right. So.

(He takes a deep breath.)

Perhaps you could give me a contrasting description, say, of the different battle strategies of the Earl of Warwick and Richard, Duke of York. Taking into account, obviously, the effects of Warwick's changed allegiance between York and Lancaster, and Richard's adoption of a more offensive than defensive position after the Battle of Northampton. For starters.

Keith Not really.

Graham Then provide me *briefly* with your interpretation of why the war began, social, political, or economical...?

Barbara Oh, for heaven's sake...

Keith *(cheerfully)* Why not ask me who wins? I know that one.

(Short pause)

Look. I don't know anything. But I'm willing to learn. Think of me... as a blank sheet of paper. It all sounds really fun. Serious fun, I mean. Erm.

Graham Yes. Well, I'm afraid it's not really about what we can do for you. It's more about what you can do for us.

Keith I can sword fight.

Graham Pardon me?

Keith I can sword fight. If that's any good.

Graham All right then. Fine. Let me see you try.

*(He gives **Keith** a sword, and picks up one for himself.)*

We'll take it nice and easy for you. On guard!

*(And effortlessly **Keith** knocks his sword from his hand with one blow.)*

...Yes, well, I can see that would be handy...

Reg Welcome aboard, lad. Just a word in your ear...

*(And he leads **Keith** aside, who follows politely.)*

Stephen *(to no-one in particular)* Well. He seems nice.

*(But no-one is listening. **Barbara** has returned to sword practice with a brooding **Graham**, and **Chloe** seems pensive, lost in worried thought.)*

Mmm.

Keith I'll read up on it all, obviously...

Reg Oh, don't worry about Graham. He's a tit.

Keith Oh?

Reg Teaches history at some shitty comprehensive. Then tries to inflict it on us all here. Take no notice of him, we all hate him.

Keith Oh. Okay.

*(**Chloe** interrupts the fighting **Graham** nervously.)*

Chloe I don't even know who Earl Warren was.

Graham The Earl of Warwick.

Chloe Right. Let alone anything political or economical.

Graham *(for he is losing)* Yes, can't this wait, Chloe? I'm trying to kill my wife at the moment...

Reg *(to **Keith**)* Whatever happens, you stick with me. I'm the one with the real influence. And I like you.

Keith Thanks. Great.

Chloe I'm not going to have to leave the group, am I?

Reg You married? Got a wife?

Keith No.

Reg One on the way though? Good prospects?

Keith Not really.

Chloe This is the only thing Barry lets me do on my own. And I love Barry, obviously. But I couldn't spend *all* my time with him. Not day in, day out. I think it'd kill me.

Graham No-one's asking you to leave, Chloe. You're one of us.

Chloe Am I really?

Graham Of course you are. So don't be so bloody stupid.

Reg Open to suggestions, though, are you? If a wife offered herself, you'd at least consider it? A blank sheet of paper, you said.

Keith Yes. I suppose.

Reg Good lad.

*(**Stephen** takes a photo as **Reg** claps **Keith** on the back. **Reg** drifts away, prepares for the battle.)*

Stephen For the newsletter.

Keith Oh yes?

Stephen You'll be on the front cover.

Keith Great. I'm flattered.

Stephen You're the only bit of news we've had for ages! I do it all myself, you know. No-one helps me.

Chloe *(to **Keith**)* May I have a word?

Stephen Sorry.

(He drifts away.)

Keith Hello.

Chloe I need to ask you something. You don't mind if I ask you something?

Keith No. You go ahead.

Chloe Thank you. Right. Are you married?

Keith ...No.

Chloe No wife? Got a girlfriend?

Keith No. What is this...?

Chloe Oh dear. That's a shame. Then I'm afraid I've got a message for you from Barry.

Keith Who's Barry?

Chloe My lover. 'This girl is my property. So keep your hands off her. She may be very beautiful, but she's spoken for. You can look, but you can't touch.'

(Short pause)

Barry makes me say that to all the men I meet who don't have wives or girlfriends. Sometimes he makes me say it to ones who have, it depends what mood he's in. Barry's going to make me a model, you know.

Keith ...Oh yes?

Chloe I'm not going to be allowed to speak to you again. Oh well. Nice meeting you.

Reg If I could have your attention, please. I have an announcement to make.

*(Everyone stops what they are doing, and looks at **Reg**. **Graham** is expectant.)*

Okay. Last week I turned sixty-five. And there's no use saying otherwise, I'm getting old. No, there's no use! I've worked hard all my life. Thirty years ago I formed a company out of nothing, it wouldn't exist if it wasn't for me. But at last I've retired. Everyone at work has been saying I should. For years, actually, and I've finally agreed. Reg, they said, you've got years left in you, you and Sheila go and enjoy yourselves. Bless them. Well, they didn't call me Reg, I'm Mr Myers, I don't encourage familiarity, it causes unrest. But bless them anyway. And after a lot of thought, I've decided to retire as your leader as well. Now, don't you worry, I'll still be here. I'm not going anywhere, just you try to get rid of me! But I'll be in the back seat now. And Graham will be the driver. Now, it's no secret to any of you, Graham and I have never got on well...

Graham What?

Reg We've never really seen eye to eye...

Graham I thought we got on quite well...

Reg To be blunt, I just don't like him.

Graham *(to Barbara)* Did you know we didn't get on quite well?

Reg I wouldn't want him as leader either. But there was no-one else. Chloe and Barbara, they're girls. Stephen would be hopeless...

Stephen That's true.

Reg I even considered making Keith there leader, but that seemed too much responsibility for his first day. So we're stuck with Graham. He's not very inspiring, I know. But think of him as a duller me. If it helps, when you look at him, try to picture my face instead. And I'll be here, so if anything he says sounds stupid, just look to me and I'll give the nod. Now, I know Graham has prepared a few words. So let's all be patient and listen to him politely.

(Stephen begins to clap. Half-heartedly, the others, Graham excepted, join in.)

Graham Thank you, Reginald. Well.

(He clears his throat.)

Well. Here we are. St Albans, 1455. We stand at the beginning of the bloodiest civil war in English history. A struggle for the throne between two sides of the same family, the white rose of York against the red rose of Lancaster. A struggle which, in fact, neither side will win. Not after the Tudors stick their oar in and destroy both of them, who asked them anyway, typical bloody Welsh. But I digress. It's a time of heroism and a time of treachery, for thirty long years the men of England shall think only of killing or of being killed. We act out these battles again, blow for blow, as a reminder. And the very fields we'll fight upon, were soaked with the blood of fathers killed by sons and brothers killed by brothers. On this very soil.

(Short pause)

Barbara Makes you think, doesn't it?

Graham I'm sure it's going to be terrific. All of us, a part of living history! But history must be treated with respect. Even now, a few years into a new millennium. Under my leadership we will do that. Under my leadership we shall fight. Under my leadership we shall win and die. But always we shall be monuments to history!

*(Short pause. Everyone looks at **Reg** uncertainly. He shrugs, then nods.*

(Blackout.)

2 – The Battle of Blore Heath

23 September 1459 (four months later)

*(We are on a different field, but you wouldn't know it. **Barbara** kneels beside a pile of twigs and leaves. She is trying to start a fire by rubbing two sticks together.*

(We watch her persevere for a few seconds, then see her satisfaction as she produces a small flame. The bundle glows a faint red.)

Barbara Graham! Graham!

Graham *(off)* What is it?

Barbara I've done it, Graham!

Graham Are they here yet?

Barbara Graham!

Graham *(entering)* What kept you all? ...Oh.

Barbara See?

Graham Well done.

Barbara I've spent the best part of an hour on that. Well? Aren't you going to say well done?

Graham I did say well done. Well done, darling.

(A sudden wind whistles. The flame goes out.)

But, next time, what I'd advise is, try to keep the flame burning. Then you'll really have something.

Barbara Yes.

Graham Where are they? Do you think it's deliberate?

Barbara I wouldn't have thought so.

Graham I bet it bloody is.

*(He glowers. **Barbara** sighs, returns to rubbing the sticks.)*

Barbara ...Graham?

Graham What is it now?

Barbara Do I have to do this? Is it really necessary?

Graham Got to be authentic, darling.

Barbara I've got some matches in the car...

Graham You mustn't let me down in front of the others. We've got to set a good example.

Barbara But we're the only ones here. No-one would know.

Graham *You* would know, darling. That's the point, isn't it? And how do you think you'd feel afterwards? Knowing you'd let my standards down?

Barbara I don't know...

Graham I doubt you'd be able to live with yourself. I know I couldn't.

*(**Barbara** hesitates, then shakes her head, and resumes rubbing the sticks together.)*

How late are they now?

Barbara If you let me wear a watch, I'd have a better idea, but you don't, darling.

Graham Honestly, darling, you're no bloody use at all, are you? This is important for me. This is the first campaign I'll have led, I need to establish my authority now or they'll never respect me again. And what do you do? You just sit there on the grass rubbing two sticks together. Well, thanks a lot.

*(Short pause. **Barbara** sighs, gets up.)*

Barbara I would like to help, Graham. I really would.

Graham Well.

Barbara But you have to tell me what to do. I don't know what you want. I hardly ever see you any more, do I? Between your teaching and your military strategies, you're never around. Not that I'm complaining, darling. I don't *need* any more of your company. Believe me, I'm more than content with the odd glimpse of you at mealtimes. But if it would help, perhaps we should do more together.

Graham We've got the battle re-enactments. What more do you want?

Barbara I was thinking. Maybe we could have a baby.

(Short pause)

Graham Good God. Why, do you want one?

Barbara *(considering)* I don't know.

Graham You've never said you've wanted one.

Barbara I'm not sure I do. But my biological clock is ticking.

Graham It's what?

Barbara That's what the woman on the telly said. She said you can only have a baby while your biological clock is ticking. And once it's stopped, you can't. So I thought. I don't *think* I want a baby. But what happens if my biological clock stops ticking and I change my mind? Perhaps it would be sensible to have a baby now, whilst I still can. And keep it in case I want it later.

(Short pause)

What do you think?

Graham We've got my army arriving in a minute, and you haven't even got the fire starting. We've never talked about children before. Does it have to be now?

Barbara I know there's a lot of strain in your life at the moment. But if you woke up in the morning, and thought to yourself, 'ooh, I'm a father', I don't know, I thought it might help.

Graham No, I don't think so. I have to put up with children all day long. Eight to eighteen year olds, six lessons a day. And they've all got one thing in common. Which is that they're complete bastards. I tell you, sometimes when I see them all staring at me from behind their desks, I look in their eyes, and I don't even see anything human there.

Barbara It was just an idea.

Graham And sometimes I catch myself thinking, my God. You lot are this country's future. Somewhere out amongst all those bullies and geeks and... soccer players, there's our prime minister. And if that's the shape of things to come, I just hope I don't live that long. Because I've seen the future, and it wears a baseball cap the wrong way round.

(Short pause)

Barbara I just thought it was something we could do together. Or we could go to the cinema.

*(Short pause. **Barbara** returns to the fire.)*

Graham Besides which. That would involve. You know, sex.

Barbara Oh yes. So it would.

Graham You're not wanting that, are you? Particularly?

Barbara No.

Graham That's not due for months yet.

Barbara No, darling. I wasn't thinking about sex. Just a baby.

Graham Right.

Barbara Believe me, if there was a way to get the one without the other, I'd suggest it.

Graham Where the bloody hell are they all? This is deliberate. It is quite clearly deliberate.

Barbara I've got the fire going again.

Graham *(distracted)* Good. That's great, darling.

*(**Barbara** blows on it gently, soothingly.)*

Barbara There now. You'll grow up to be a big fire, won't you? A great big fire.

*(And enter **Stephen**, in costume, groaning under the weight of four people's rucksacks. He is quite clearly exhausted.)*

Graham Stephen! What is it? Where are the others?

Stephen *(gasping)* Just a moment...

Graham Where's the rest of my army? Were you ambushed? Tell me.

Stephen They're down there parking the car...

Graham *(urgency gone, irritably)* And why are you so late?

Stephen Could you give me a hand with this, please? It's very heavy...

*(But **Graham** has gone to the exit, watching the others' progress offstage.)*

Graham *(calling)* Come on!

*(**Stephen** staggers around with his huge packs of clothes and swords. Weakly:)*

Stephen Hello, Mrs Widthorpe...

Barbara *(placidly)* Hello, Stephen.

Graham Hurry up, for God's sake!

*(**Stephen** drops some of the rucksacks, but there is still the largest to contend with. He manages to pull his arm out from one of the straps. The weight of the bag makes him lose his balance, and he spins around drunkenly. No longer able to carry the pack, it swings from his grip on to the grass, completely crushing **Barbara**'s burgeoning bonfire.*

*(Oblivious to this, **Stephen** gratefully sinks to the ground and pants for breath.*

*(**Barbara** sighs, then resignedly starts to rebuild her collection of twigs and leaves. When she is done, she returns to rubbing her sticks together.)*

*(Enter **Reg** and **Keith**, in battle dress.)*

Reg What's the rush?

Graham You're late.

Reg What's all the hurry?

Graham Where's Chloe?

Reg Hello, Barbara.

Barbara Hello, Reginald.

Graham Well?

*(For **Keith** has absently been watching **Barbara**.)*

Keith She's changing in the car. Hello, Barbara.

Reg *(to **Stephen**, nudging him with his foot)* Thanks for carrying my equipment.

Stephen I just don't see why you had to park the car half a mile away...

Reg Don't blame me. Blame him. It's Graham who wants it all authentic. Doesn't want anything of the twenty-first century visible to spoil the illusion.

Graham Why are you so late? What the hell happened?

Keith Oh, sorry. I think that may have been my fault.

Graham Do you?

Keith I got a bit lost finding this place. I'd been driving in the wrong direction.

Graham This is the battle of Blore Heath. It's a significant part of our heritage. Only an idiot wouldn't be able to find it.

Keith When I tried asking for directions in the village, no-one knew where the battlefield was either. In fact, come to think of it, no-one even knew there'd been a battle.

Reg I don't see what all the fuss is about. It's not as if the battle's started yet.

Graham I wanted to make absolutely sure everyone knew what they were doing. I wanted everybody to understand what the battle of Blore Heath meant, appreciate its significance.

Reg We all know about Blore Heath. What's the point?

Graham I doubt this one knows about it. Do you?

Keith Well, I've read up on it.

Graham Have you.

Keith I got a book from the library.

Graham Well, that's fine then. Perhaps you could tell us all about it.

Barbara Graham...

Graham No, Barbara. It's his fault there won't be time for my little lecture. So perhaps he would be good enough to share his new expertise with us all.

Keith *(deep breath)* Blore Heath, 1459. The uneasy peace earned by St Albans is finally broken. Lord Audley for Lancaster, Lord Salisbury for York. Audley had six thousand troops to Salisbury's three thousand, it should have been an easy victory for the Lancastrians. And so when Salisbury withdrew his knights, Audley thought he was retreating. But instead Salisbury had prepared lots of archers, and decimated the Lancastrian army when they crossed the brook, probably that brook down there? Two and a half thousand of Audley's forces were killed, including Audley himself. ...I'm a quick learner.

(Short pause)

Barbara Makes you think, doesn't it?

Keith I suppose really it would be a classic example of a smaller force winning against the odds. Relying on cunning rather than brute force, essential to the vagaries of medieval warfare...

Graham Yes, yes, all right. Fine. But it's easy to read about it in a book. You have to fight a Blore Heath to understand a Blore Heath. And how many Blore Heaths have you fought? None. Whilst I have fought tons of Blore Heaths, three, this is my third Blore Heath. And I'd have fought even more Blore Heaths, but Blore Heaths aren't fought very often. So there you are.

Keith Why aren't they fought very often?

Barbara Because they're very boring.

Graham Darling!

Barbara Well, they are.

Reg Only sad obsessives like Graham here ever bother with Blore

Heath. Now, give me a good Tewkesbury, and I'm a happy man. I'd go a long way for a good Tewkesbury.

Stephen *(shyly)* I like the battle of Towton.

Reg *(approvingly)* Ah, a Towton man, are you? Yes, a spot of Towton's all right.

Graham Excuse me...

Barbara Well, my favourite is the battle of Bosworth.

*(Appreciative noises from **Graham** and **Stephen**.)*

Stephen Ah, well, Bosworth, yes...

Reg You can't forget your Bosworth.

Keith Good, is it?

Graham Excuse me...!

Reg Bosworth's your classic battle. Everybody loves a good Bosworth.

Barbara It's my favourite.

Reg Whatever you think of the Tudors killing us all like that, it's a great day out.

Graham Excuse me! Hello? So sorry to interrupt you all. I think I should point out we're at Blore Heath. So we'll do the battle of Blore Heath. Hope that hasn't confused any of you. Now, no-one loves a Bosworth more than I do...

Stephen It's smashing, isn't it?

Graham Shut up! ...And one of these days we'll do a really fine Bosworth. I know it. But there are people out there waiting to see our Blore Heath. And that's what we're going to give them. Under my command, we'll bloreheath as we've never bloreheathed before! Are you with me?

*(Ambivalent muttering. **Graham** sighs.)*

Okay. Now as Keith here has so kindly reminded us, we're going to win this battle. But we're still going to have to select a casualty, one of you has got to die. Stephen, how about it?

Stephen Oh, Mr Widthorpe. It's always me. I'm fed up of always being killed off in the first five minutes.

Graham Got to have dead bodies on both sides, Stephen. Or it's not realistic.

Stephen But why's it always me? Wouldn't someone else like a go?

Graham Who wants to volunteer for corpse duty? Anyone?

Stephen ...Perhaps Chloe will do it. Chloe!

*(And **Chloe** enters, dressed in a jerkin. Her hair has been dyed bright green.)*

Chloe Sorry I'm late. Have I missed anything?

Stephen Would you do corpse duty...

Graham God almighty! What have you done to yourself?

Chloe What?

Graham Your hair, girl! Your hair!

Chloe Do you like it? Barry said green hair's the latest fashion. It's going to be all the rage.

Graham But that's not contemporary! Is it? I mean, be fair. Is it?

Chloe Barry says if I want to be a model I've got to keep in touch with the new rage. Don't you like it, really? Barry says it makes me look sophisticated.

Graham *(despairing)* Have we got to go through the whole battle plans again?

Reg You know the battle of Blore Heath, don't you?

Chloe Sure. That's the boring one, isn't it?

Graham Fine. Great. Whatever. The battle will be starting soon. I'm going to practise my sword thrusts. You lot practise in any way you see fit.

Stephen Chloe. Will you do corpse duty for me?

Graham I wouldn't advise it. Put her head on the grass, she might get mistaken for a small bush.

(And he exits.

*(**Stephen** begins unpacking the weapons. He will also reveal his camera. As before, **Barbara** continues her attempts to start a fire.)*

Chloe *(absently)* Hello, Barbara.

Barbara *(vaguely)* Hello, Chloe.

*(Neither have even looked at the other. **Chloe** pulls out from the inside of her jerkin a copy of* Vogue *and sits down to read it. On the cover is a*

woman with green hair.)

Reg Keith. Now that we're on our own...

Keith Mr Myers...?

Reg Reg, please. I was wondering. Have you done any more about finding yourself a wife yet?

Keith ...No. No, I haven't...

Reg Or any special lady friend. No?

Keith Sorry...

Reg What is it? You're not one of those, are you?

Keith No, no. One of what? No, I just don't seem to have met the right girl...

Reg Ah, well. Handy tip. Leave the girls alone.

Keith Oh yes?

Reg Go for a woman instead. Safer bet. I should know.

Keith I'll bear that in mind.

Stephen Can I help you, Mrs Widthorpe? Would you like some matches?

Barbara No. But you can rub some sticks together for me if you like.

Stephen That's all right.

Reg I mean, you shouldn't have any problems finding yourself a woman. You're quite good looking. I imagine, I mean men's looks are not really my bag. But I've seen some women hang around with a lot worse. I dare say you're quite a good catch.

Stephen Would you mind if I took some pictures? For the newsletter.

Barbara Knock yourself out.

*(**Stephen** snaps away at her. He positions himself that **Chloe** is in the background. At length, he begins to take them directly of **Chloe**, without her realising.)*

Reg I like you, Keith. You've got potential. I should have made you the leader, not Graham. Well, if you ever decide to overthrow him, I'm behind you one hundred per cent.

Keith I don't want to overthrow anybody...

Reg Would you like a job? At my old company, I could fix it. I've still got influence. A managerial position.

Keith Really, I just came here to kill a few Lancastrians...

Reg Want to show you something. Don't go away. Back in a minute.

(*Reg* *pats* *Keith* *on the back, then exits.* *Keith* *watches him leave uneasily.*

(*Stephen* *is now blatantly taking pictures of* *Chloe*, *standing directly in front of her. She doesn't even look up at him.*)

Stephen *(boldly)* I like the hair.

Chloe What?

Stephen I like the hair. Green. Great.

Chloe Do you think so? I'm not sure it suits me. Barry says it's all the rage, but I don't know, I think it makes me look a little...

Stephen Pale?

Chloe *(thoughtfully)* No. Alien. Still, Barry knows best. He's going to make me a model. We're just waiting for that big break.

Stephen Goodness.

Chloe Then I can jack in my job at that rotten old flower shop. And be famous like her.

Stephen Who, sorry?

Chloe *(indicating the cover)* Her. You know. Wotsername. She's everywhere, she is.

Keith Hello.

Barbara Hello.

Stephen Would you mind if I took a few pictures of you?

Chloe Mmm, sorry?

Stephen For the newsletter.

Chloe No. Go ahead.

Keith I'm sorry, can I offer some advice?

Barbara I'm sorry?

Keith You really shouldn't rub them like that. You're getting a bit of friction, which will make the sticks nice and warm. But what you want... can I show you?

Barbara Please.

Keith You want a spark. You can do that better with a clean blow at an angle. Like this...

Stephen *(as he takes photos)* You can pout a little. If you want.

Chloe Oh. Okay.

Stephen Lovely.

Barbara There was a spark!

Keith Well, just a little one. But we're getting there.

Barbara Yes, I see. Can I have a go?

Stephen Lean back a little. That's it. Lovely.

Keith Lovely. That's it.

Barbara Thank you.

Keith I'll take over if you like...

Barbara Better not. Graham said this was my job. So I'd better be the one who does it.

Keith Oh. Fair enough.

Barbara Don't want to upset him any more than is strictly necessary.

Reg *(re-entering, to **Keith**)* Here I am!

Keith Oh. Right.

Reg *(passing him a photograph)* What do you make of that?

Keith Erm. It's a photograph, isn't it?

Reg My wife Sheila.

Keith Very nice.

Reg You really think so?

Keith Yes. If you like.

Reg Could you imagine having sex with that?

Keith Erm. Well, I hadn't been.

Reg I'm in a bit of a quandary. Ever since I retired from work, I don't get to meet new people any more. I was always meeting new people in the old days, we had a high staff turnover. I was always hiring them and firing them...

Keith Yes...

Reg But that's all stopped. You're the only new person I've met in a long time.

Stephen Try using the sword. In any way that springs to mind.

Reg The parties I go to, Keith, they need new people. If I can't find any, they're going to withdraw my membership.

Keith Oh. That's a shame.

Reg I can't say I blame them. I'm dead weight these days. You see these young women there, gorgeous they are. Legs, hair, lips, teeth, the lot. Breasts. Once upon a time, no problem. I'd just walk over to the husband and make the swap. But now, what chance have I got? You've seen my wife.

Keith Very nice...

Reg Once upon a time she was, sure. Sheila could put out with the best of them. But she's sixty-two, for God's sake. What man is going to want to trade some stunner for a woman who keeps her teeth by the side of the bed? You see my problem.

Keith I think I do.

Reg I'm not without influence, I can get you a nice job. Make you leader of this group, if you wanted. You just find yourself a nice, attractive, willing lady friend.

Barbara I've done it! It works!

Keith Excuse me.

Reg Good lad.

Barbara You see? I've done it! I've got a fire!

Keith *(warmly)* Well done, Barbara! That's terrific!

Barbara A real fire this time, not like before! Thank you!

*(And impulsively she gives **Keith** a hug. Then, letting go, oblivious of any effect:)*

Graham! Graham! Come, quickly!

Graham *(off)* What is it?

Barbara I've made you your fire! I've made you your fire at last!

(And we hear a sudden crack of thunder. Short pause. Softly:)

Oh no.

(And it begins to rain very hard, very suddenly. **Chloe** *squeals, leaps up from an especially provocative pose, and jumps about looking for cover.* **Stephen** *passes her her copy of* Vogue.

(Enter **Graham***.)*

Graham! The rain's put out my fire...

Graham Yes, well, never mind. Right! I hope you've all limbered up. Come on, everyone! We've got a battle to fight!

Stephen We're not doing it in this, are we?

Graham Why not?

Stephen Well. We'd rust for one thing.

Graham We're not going to let a little rain put us off, are we?

Keith *(gently)* Wouldn't it be more sensible to postpone it until next week?

Graham No, it wouldn't. This is the anniversary of the battle of Blore Heath. Next week is the anniversary of bugger all. We have got to do this authentically!

(Resignedly, everyone begins to get ready. Then, as an afterthought:)

Keith But surely...

(And everyone stops.)

Graham ...Well?

Keith There's nothing authentic about fighting a battle in the pouring rain. No-one would *choose* to fight in rain like this. There'd be no military advantage. Salisbury and Audley, they'd have said, sorry, lads, we'll wait until it brightens up. Let's go to the pub instead.

Graham The pub?

Keith Ye olde alehouse, then, I don't know.

Graham Do you lot actually want a leader? History shows us, it *tells* us we need strong leaders. Or we'd have anarchy. Believe me, I know all about anarchy, I teach class 5G. Is that what you want? Well, is it?

Stephen I have no problems fighting in the rain.

Chloe Nor me.

Graham I'm the bloody leader, I am! So let me bloody lead!

Reg Well, let's bloreheath then. If we have to.

Graham *(to **Keith**, almost hissing with anger)* Not you. You can sit this one out. I'm not having you on my battlefield.

*(They all leave, except **Keith**. He stands in the pouring rain, sighs.*

*(Re-enter **Barbara**.)*

Barbara Sorry about that.

Keith Your husband's a bit of a shit, isn't he?

Barbara Oh no. Well, only at first. He can be okay once you make the effort.

Keith Oh.

Barbara Problem is, no-one makes the effort. Not seeing how at first he seems a bit of a shit. Are you all right? I just wanted to say, don't take it personally.

Keith It's not your fault.

Barbara He's under a lot of pressure at work. They're making him take an assessment exam. All the teachers are getting them, it's to protect the kids, make sure they're suitable people to be around children. Multiple choice questions. 'Do you hit children, no, sometimes, yes, as often as possible.' You know the stuff.

Keith Like a driving test.

Barbara That's it. Simple, really. Except Graham failed it. Ticked all the aggressive answers, he was probably in a really bad mood that day. So he's got to resit it, and if he fails again... well.

Keith I see.

Barbara Quite frankly, he's hell to live with at the moment. Quite frankly... ...How did you know all that about rubbing sticks together? It was very good.

Keith It's a hobby of mine.

Barbara Really? I didn't know you could have stick rubbing as a hobby. Fancy.

Keith Boy scouts. Thursday nights, I'm a scout leader. Orienteering, knot-typing. Stick rubbing, you know. It's fun.

Barbara It sounds it. Yes. Mm. One of these days, that's what I should do. Get myself a hobby.

(Short pause)

Keith ...This isn't...?

Barbara Oh no. This is Graham's hobby. I just come along to be supportive. You know. Make up the numbers. Ballast.

Keith You're very good. I thought you were great at St Albans.

Barbara Well, you pick it up. Ought to, I've been supportive for over six years... Oh, I much prefer it to supporting him when he was collecting stamps. I got very good at that too, but God, it was dull.

Keith Why don't you find your own hobby?

Barbara *(surprised)* Oh. I don't know. Never thought about it. Do you think I should? I better not. There won't be time for it, what with being supportive and everything.

Keith I've got lots of hobbies. I go sailing. I play tennis.

Barbara Really?

Keith I bungee jump. I collect antiques.

Barbara *(impressed)* Well.

Keith Bird watching. Scuba diving. Croquet. Latin American dancing.

Barbara Oh, you dance? I'd love to dance. I've said to Graham, could his next hobby be dancing, I'd love to give that a try.

Keith Well. Would you like a go?

Barbara What, now?

Keith Why not?

Barbara In the pouring rain? In full armour?

Keith It's easy. You'll see.

(And he takes her arms. And singing a tango, Hernando's Hideaway, *leads her across the stage.)*

Follow me. Da-dum, da-dum, da-dum-di-dum.

Barbara Right...

Keith Then back. Da-dum, da-dum, da-dum-di-dum.

Barbara That's easy.

Keith Then you circle me. Go on. Da-dum... It's easy...

Barbara All right...

Keith Da-dum, da-dum, da-dum-di-dum...

Barbara Nice and elegant.

Keith It represents a bullfight.

Barbara You're the bullfighter?

Keith And you're the bull.

Barbara Lovely.

Keith Isn't it easy? Let's run that through. Wait. Wait.

(He picks a dandelion.)

Open.

(And puts it between her teeth.)

*(Enter, unseen by them, **Stephen**. The front of his jerkin and his face are drenched in mud. He stands back, shyly.)*

*(And they do the dance, **Keith** da-dumming the tango, **Barbara** doing her muffled best through the dandelion stalk. As she circles him as the bull, she uses her helmet as a castanet. At the end, **Keith** swings her backwards in his arms – as well as he can in her armour!)*

Ole!

Barbara *(spitting out the flower)* Ole!

(They freeze.)

Keith You deserve better than Graham.

Barbara *(softly)* You hardly know me.

Keith Oh, come on. Anyone deserves better than Graham. ...Can you stand, this armour's killing me...

(He helps her back to her feet. Short pause – then they kiss. Both shy, it takes them rather by surprise.)

*(Embarrassed, **Stephen** exits. Then, offstage:)*

Stephen *(loudly)* What a great battle! Wow!

*(Which gives them time to unclinch. **Stephen** enters.)*

Barbara Aren't you supposed to be dead?

Stephen I am dead. But if I thought if I lay in that mud any longer, I'd drown. Great battle though! Oh yes. Wouldn't have missed it for the world!

*(Enter **Graham** angrily. **Reg** and **Chloe** follow behind. **Graham** sticks his*

sword into the grass.)

Graham A complete bloody shambles!

Barbara Is it over already, darling?

Graham The Lancastrians have retreated!

Keith I thought that's what they were supposed to do.

Graham Not this early! They've cut it short because of the weather!

Barbara Oh.

Graham You either do these things accurately, or not at all! Now all the children will go home thinking Blore Heath was half an hour shorter than it really was!

Reg The children won't think anything of the sort.

Graham That's what children are like. Trust me, if they can get hold of the wrong end of the stick, those little bastards will.

Reg There weren't any children in the audience.

Graham ...Weren't there?

Reg We didn't have an audience at all.

Graham *(fumbling)* Well, no. Because of the rain...

Reg Not the rain. It's the battle of Blore Heath. No-one cares about the battle of Blore Heath. Do you want to know why?

Graham *(feebly)* I care...

Reg Because it's bloody boring, that's why. We won, I'll give you that. But do you know what happened to us the very next day?

Keith I haven't read that far yet...

Reg Within twenty-four hours we were captured by an even *bigger* army. Those of us who weren't imprisoned or put to death all ran away. *No-one* won the battle of Blore Heath. It achieved nothing. It's an entirely meaningless piece of history. And audiences don't come to see pointless failures running around battlefields. For God's sake, it's depressing.

*(Rounding on **Graham**, with quiet anger:)*

I should never have made you leader. Wasting our time on these pathetic little skirmishes. I should have given Keith there the command. He's a lad with potential. You just watch your step. I'm not without influence, and I can crush you like that.

(Pause.)

Graham *(softly, furiously)* Barbara. We're going home.

Barbara But...

Graham Now.

*(She looks at **Keith** helplessly as **Graham** virtually pulls her offstage.*

(Stunned silence. Eventually:)

Chloe Giving us a lift back to the station then?

Keith What? Yes.

Stephen Mr Smythe?

Keith Yes?

Stephen I hope you don't mind. I might leave a bit of a mess in your car.

Keith No, no. Fine.

*(**Chloe** and **Stephen** exit. **Keith** is left with the satisfied **Reg**. Weakly:)*

But I don't want to be leader.

Reg Now, you go out and find yourself a nice woman. All right? Good lad.

(Blackout.)

3 – The Battle of Wakefield

31 December 1460 (three months later)

*(It is late afternoon, and the sun is already setting. **Stephen** and **Reg** sit by a fire. **Stephen** is still in costume, coated with dry mud. **Reg** has changed, and is wearing a rather formal jacket and tie. He holds a hip flask)*

Stephen   This is the weirdest New Year's Eve I've ever had.

Reg   Mmm. Getting massacred by Lord Clifford, you mean?

Stephen   When I was a student, we used to have these great New Year's Eves. We'd all get together, all my friends. And we'd get as drunk as possible. We'd try to stay fairly sober for midnight, you know, see Big Ben on the telly. But after that we'd get paralytic. Great times. I wonder where they all are now? Well, you drift apart, don't you? When you get older.

*(Short pause. **Reg** offers him the flask.)*

No thanks.

Reg   What did you study?

Stephen   Sociology.

Reg   What's that all about?

Stephen   No idea.

(Short pause)

Reg   You asked if I could fix you a job at my old company.

Stephen   Yes.

Reg   Pull a few strings.

Stephen   Yes. You said no.

Reg   I've changed my mind. I'll see what I can do.

Stephen   *(eagerly)* I'll work as hard as I can, I won't let you down...

Reg   I'm not without a certain influence. I'm an important man, well, was. Do you know how many men I employed? Do you?

Stephen   No.

Reg   Guess.

Stephen   A thousand?

Reg   Four hundred people, that's a lot. I still pop into the office most days. Oh, they try to stop me! But we don't need you, Mr Myers, everything's running smoothly without you. What they need is a crisis. Then they'll be begging me to come back. Have you ever done a decent day's work in your life?

Stephen No, never.

Reg Yes, I'll get you a job.

Stephen Thanks. ...What does your company actually do?

Reg We're an information group. We supply the consumer free notification of new products and services.

Stephen What?

Reg Junk mail.

Stephen Ah.

Reg Sheila doesn't want me going to the office either. She says we should spend more time together. Tell me. Have you ever been in love?

Stephen Yes. Yes, I may be.

Reg It fades.

(He takes a drink.)

I used to go to parties too. But not to get drunk. To get laid. I never spent a New Year alone. But they don't invite me any more. If I want sex now, I have to resort to my wife. I've not slept with her for twenty years, and now she's the only prospect I've got. And when I see her naked on the bed, trying to be provocative, I tell you, I'm amazed I got away with swapping her all these years.

Stephen Are you drunk, Mr Myers?

Reg What's the word you used? Paralytic. Do you think it's silly at my age to get a divorce? I think of telling her, the marriage is off, but then I look at her, and she's so *old*, I think, well, she can't last much longer, surely? I don't want to hurt her feelings, not worth it if she'll soon be dead. I should just wait it out. But then I think. What if I go first? What if I'm the first to go?

(Short pause)

I should get home. She'll be worried. Keep the flask, I've had enough. Well done, you died well today, lad, that was a good death.

Stephen Happy New Year.

Reg What?

Stephen Happy New Year.

Reg *(sharply)* Tell me. Do you really think you've got a future in junk mail?

Stephen *(automatically)* Yes, sir. I'll work as hard as I can. I won't let you down.

*(**Reg** stares at him. Then he begins to laugh.*

*(**Barbara** enters. Seeing her, still laughing, **Reg** exits.)*

Barbara Stephen.

Stephen Hello, Mrs Widthorpe. Good battle, wasn't it?

Barbara *(dryly)* Fantastic. Have you seen Keith anywhere?

Stephen No. You were great out there, I've never seen you fight like that.

Barbara *(vaguely)* Thanks...

Stephen The way you hacked down the Earl of Wiltshire. Real venom. The thing is, I think he was meant to survive.

Barbara If you see Keith, tell him. Tell him... not to leave. Okay?

Stephen Not to leave.

Barbara Not yet. I need to give him... I need to... Just that. Okay?

Stephen Okay. Your husband's here, if he'll do instead.

*(Indeed, **Graham** has entered, dressed in modern clothes.)*

Graham Barbara. For Christ's sake.

Barbara What?

Graham I'm ready to go. We're ready to go. You haven't even changed.

Barbara I'm not leaving just yet.

Graham But we've got to go. Come on. We've got to get home.

Barbara Why?

Graham We've been through this, Barbara. I'm expecting a phone call. It's very important.

Barbara They're not going to phone on New Year's Eve.

Graham They will. The headmaster promised me. They'd let me know in December. This is just about the last chance he's got.

Barbara Nothing to do with me.

Graham Barbara. Please. I've got to know whether I've still got a job.

Barbara I'm not coming with you.

Graham I'll leave you behind.

Barbara Fine. Go ahead.

Graham I will. If you push me, I will.

Barbara I want you to.

Graham Barbara, this is Wakefield! No-one *wants* to be in Wakefield! ...Darling. This is the menopause, isn't it?

Barbara What?

Graham Menopause. I phoned Miss Gibbs from the biology department, described the symptoms. Oh, there's a wealth of knowledge in that staff room if you know where to ask...

Barbara How dare you. What symptoms?

Graham You're moody, you're sulky, you keep on bursting into tears at the most inconvenient moments. You hardly talk to me any more, and when you do, you won't look. What's happened to you, Barbara, you used to be such a placid woman...

Barbara Please. We've got company.

Graham Only Stephen, who the hell cares about Stephen? I don't recognise you any more. To tell you the truth, you frighten me. Particularly after what happened on Christmas night...

Barbara Christmas night has nothing to do with this...

Graham Christmas night has everything to do with it! How do I know Christmas night won't happen again? How do I know that, just as I'm beginning to relax, you won't pull another Christmas night on me? Scared me half to death.

(Short pause)

I'm going to the car.

Barbara Bye.

Graham I'll wait for you.

(He hesitates, then exits.)

Barbara Don't ever get married, Stephen.

Stephen Mrs Widthorpe?

Barbara Someone's going to ask you. And if someone doesn't ask directly, someone's going to ask you to ask them. Or, in my case. If you've got a mother like mine. And have spent twenty odd years quite happily sitting on the shelf. Someone's going to ask you why nobody *wants* to ask you, just what's so wrong with you no-one'll ask, and they'll ask you that so often that you'll eventually get desperate to be asked. Just to prove you can be. And the first person you find who looks likely to ask, you fling yourself at him, you ask him to ask, and when he asks, you say yes. ...Don't.

Stephen I'll try to remember.

Barbara If you see Keith. Tell him I'm looking for him.

*(She exits. **Stephen** takes a swig from the flask. **Chloe** enters. She is dressed to kill, out of her medieval costume. Her hair is now bright green, with red and orange implants.)*

Chloe Stephen? You haven't seen Keith around anywhere?

Stephen No. No, I haven't.

Chloe *(making to leave)* Oh. He promised me a lift to the station...

Stephen Please don't go.

Chloe What?

Stephen Sit down here. Please.

Chloe Why?

Stephen You're not in any hurry, are you?

*(**Chloe** shrugs, sits down. Silence. **Stephen** doesn't know what to say. **Chloe** sighs, gets up again to leave. **Stephen** offers her the flask.)*

Chloe No thanks. Not allowed. Bad for the body. Got to keep a good body if I'm going to be a model, says Barry.

*(**Stephen** takes a swig. Then, as an afterthought, he drains the whole thing.*

*(**Chloe** is already leaving. He calls out after her.)*

Stephen I've made a New Year's resolution. You've got to help me with my New Year's resolution. Because I can't go on like this any more. I just can't.

Chloe What do you mean?

Stephen My New Year's resolution... is to tell you that I love you. So here goes. I'm in love. With you. Chloe. Very much. God, so so much.

(Short pause)

Chloe It isn't the new year yet.

Stephen What?

Chloe You can't do your New Year's resolution before the new year. It's like opening your Christmas present before Christmas.

Stephen *(lost)* Well, I thought I'd get mine done early...

Chloe *(brightly)* You know what my resolution is? I'm going to be a model. Next year I'm going to make it. I've been practising hard, I've been primping and pouting, and I think I'm ready. Barry thinks I'm ready too, just about, he gave me a great Christmas present, let me show you...

(She begins taking off her top.)

Stephen What are you doing?

Chloe I've got to show you. Look. That's what Barry gave me.

(She reveals her bare arm. It seems bruised, and there's red marking all over it.)

Stephen Good God, what has he done to you?

Chloe It hasn't healed properly yet. It's a tattoo. It's a heart with 'Barry Forever' on it.

Stephen This was a present?

Chloe Isn't it lovely? Well, it will be, once you can separate the paint from the blood, it keeps oozing out. It was such a surprise. But it proves he thinks I'm ready, doesn't it? Barry Forever. Now whenever I'm photographed, he says he'll get a credit.

Stephen Chloe. I said I loved you.

Chloe *(putting her top back on)* I know what you said. Barry says lots of people are going to love me. He says that's what being a model's all about.

Stephen I don't just love the way you look. I love you for your mind.

Chloe Oh, I don't think that's very likely. Barry says I have the mind of a gnat.

Stephen No, honestly, I love you for *you,* not what you look like, you don't have to be a model at all...

Chloe *(sharply)* Now, that's enough. You're being silly. You can love me for my body if you want. But if you mention my mind again I'm getting up and going. Understand?

*(**Stephen** nods miserably.)*

Don't you contradict Barry like that.

(Coyly:)

So go on then. Tell me which parts of my body you love.

Stephen ...I don't know what to say. I wasn't prepared for this...

Chloe Go on. Or I'm leaving.

Stephen *(fumbling)* Well, all of it. You know. I don't know, do I? The whole thing, it's smashing.

Chloe *(frowning)* I don't think you really love me at all.

Stephen No, please...

Chloe Goodbye.

Stephen Please... All right. All right. Now, don't take this the wrong way... But sometimes I imagine you naked.

Chloe ...Really?

Stephen Underneath your chainmail. Completely starkers.

Chloe You're imagining me naked now?

Stephen Now? Oh yes.

Chloe That's nice.

Stephen Yes. In fact, I imagine you naked... pretty much all of the time...

(Short pause)

You're beautiful.

(Short pause)

At least, I assume you are. I mean, a lot of this is guesswork...

Chloe Sure, of course...

Stephen I'm just imagining what it must be like. You know. Underneath... I imagine it is how I imagine? You don't have any peculiarities or disabilities...?

Chloe No, no...

Stephen Oh, fine...

Chloe No, my body's in good working order.

Stephen So I expect my fantasies are pretty near the mark then.

Chloe In better working order than most bodies, in fact.

Stephen Wow. Yes. I'll bet. ...I mean, I did have something to base my theories on. I caught sight of your bottom once.

Chloe Really?

Stephen While you were changing. But it was an accident, I didn't stare.

Chloe Right.

Stephen I did take a photograph though.

(Short pause)

I've got lots of photos of you. Well, a hundred and fourteen. A hundred and twenty-three if today's come out, but I'm not going to count my chickens. I only started the newsletter so I could take as many as I wanted.

(Short pause)

I've even managed to take a few of you in Nuneaton. You live in Nuneaton, don't you, 55 Chapel Street. I followed you home on the train once, had to be really careful, sit in a different carriage and everything. I've taken a few pictures of you through your kitchen window, they're a bit blurry, but they're better than nothing. I like them because they're you *in situ*, as it were. And I've got a picture of you with Barry, I don't like the look of him, I think he's a weirdo.

(Short pause)

Chloe? I had to tell you. Because I can't go on like this. I have a photo of you under my pillow, and every night I kiss the pillow and pretend it's you. Chloe?

*(Short pause. **Keith** enters. He is still in costume.)*

Keith Erm. You haven't seen Barbara anywhere, have you?

Stephen Yes. She asked me to give you a message.

Chloe She needs to talk to you and she won't leave Wakefield until she does. She doesn't know if she's coming or going, she says. If you don't have any feelings for her, then she'll just have to accept it, but she would appreciate being told. And she says she feels like a grapefruit.

Keith *(unhappily)* Oh. Right.

Stephen Obviously you got more information than I did.

Keith I'll be leaving soon. Do you still want a lift?

Stephen ...Chloe?

Chloe No. No, I'll find my own way back.

Keith As you like.

(He exits.)

Stephen Chloe?

Chloe Well. You really *do* love me, don't you?

Stephen Yes.

Chloe I've never been stalked before. Barry's right. If you're prepared to go to those lengths, I must look *fabulous*.

Stephen The train fare to Nuneaton's very expensive, I'm getting a job to cover the costs...

Chloe You know what this means? This makes you my first fan. All of the big models have their own fan clubs!

Stephen So. I can hope then?

Chloe *(frowning)* Hope for what?

Stephen Well. For you. Naturally.

Chloe *(bemused)* But I'm with Barry.

Stephen I know. But if you and Barry split up at some point...

Chloe We're not going to split up. It's Barry forever...

Stephen Or if he died. Heaven forbid.

Chloe I couldn't do without Barry. I need him for my modelling career. I've no choice, not now the florist's sacked me. They said my hair was upstaging the plants.

Stephen Dance with me.

Chloe What?

Stephen Dance with me. Don't you like to dance?

Chloe Sure, Barry's always showing me off down the clubs...

Stephen *(opening his arms for a classical dance)* Then please.

Chloe There's no music.

Stephen *(gently)* We don't need music. When I'm with you... I can imagine my own.

*(Short pause. Then **Chloe** nods, steps backwards. **Stephen** is about to take her arms, when she suddenly launches herself into a frenzied disco dance. Head banging, jumping up and down – it's all very energetic.)*

What are you doing?

Chloe Come on! I thought you wanted to dance!

Stephen I'm not sure I know this one...

Chloe I'll sing it for you.

(And as she gets still more frenzied, she sings a relentless beat.)

Bad-a-boom-boom, bad-a-boom-boom... *(etc.)*

*(And **Stephen** awkwardly begins to sway from side to side, performing the familiar dance of embarrassment known to all men at discos.)*

Stephen Aren't there any lyrics to this?

Chloe These are the lyrics! Bad-a-boom, boom!

Stephen I don't know it.

Chloe It's the Christmas number one. Bad-a-boom, boom, *boom!*

*(And **Stephen** suddenly grabs her and kisses her awkwardly. **Chloe** steps back in surprise.)*

Stephen ...Please. Help me. I love you. I don't want to love you. I didn't choose to love you. But I do. ...Help...

*(And **Chloe** reaches out and kisses him far more expertly on the mouth. And **Stephen** sways backwards in shock.)*

Chloe Come on then. Come with me.

Stephen What about Barry?

Chloe Barry can wait.

*(**Stephen** picks up the flask.)*

Stephen ...It's empty.

Chloe We'll find you plenty more. If that's what you need.

(And they exit.

*(The stage is empty for a few seconds. Then, from the other two entrances, enter **Barbara** and **Keith**. They see each other and freeze.)*

Keith Hello.

Barbara Hello.

(Short pause)

Keith Chloe told me you wanted to talk.

Barbara Yes.

Keith She also said you felt like a grapefruit.

Barbara Lemon. I said I felt like a lemon.

Keith I was wondering.

Barbara Stupid girl. Though, go on, I might as well feel like a grapefruit. I feel like a grapefruit then, who wouldn't? You've been avoiding me, haven't you?

Keith Yes.

Barbara Thought so. The way you ran away from me on the battlefield, I thought you'd defected to the other side. I've got you a Christmas present.

Keith Oh. Great.

Barbara It's tucked away where Graham won't see. In my suit of armour.

(She struggles vainly to reach inside the breastplate.)

You'll have to help me.

Keith What, you want...

Barbara Reach inside. Go on, I shan't bite.

Keith It's tight...

Barbara Not from this angle anyway. Found it?

Keith I hope so. Soft and squashy?

Barbara *(as he pulls out a present in wrapping paper)* There you go.

Keith Great. ...Can I open it now?

Barbara I wish you would.

(And he does. He reveals a brightly coloured pullover. The arms are too short and uneven.)

Keith Hey. Wow.

Barbara Do you like it?

Keith Do I.

Barbara I knitted it myself. It took me bloody ages. The arms aren't any good...

Keith No...

Barbara Couldn't get them the same length, kept cutting them back and cutting them back. I thought knitting could be *my* hobby. Something for *me*. But I'm no bloody good at it, am I?

Keith I'm afraid I haven't got you a present...

Barbara No surprises there then. You are running away from me, aren't you?

Keith Yes. Sorry. You look pretty scary in your armour...

Barbara What have I done? You don't know what I've been through, hoping that you'd call...

Keith I thought it was what I'd done. The kiss. I don't know, it just happened, you're a married woman... and I kissed you.

Barbara No. I'm not angry about the kiss. It was just what I needed. Do you know, I can't remember the last time I was kissed. Graham barely touches me. We only have sex three times a year, you know. His birthday, Christmas, and the anniversary of the battle of Bosworth.

Keith Oh dear.

Barbara And even then he doesn't kiss. But you kissed me and it was warm and kind, and it was contact. And it may have meant nothing to you, I don't know, but you can't give contact like that and then deny it me, you can't awaken something I thought was dead and then run away, it just isn't fair...

Keith You had sex at Christmas?

Barbara Believe me. The less said about Christmas night the better.

(Short pause)

Keith I don't know what to say.

Barbara Was I such an idiot to think we might have some future? Was I an idiot to knit you that pullover?

Keith Barbara. I'm not a man of initiative. Okay? Never have been.

I'm... I'm a blank sheet of paper. Just a blank sheet of paper. I do whatever's wanted, no problem. But I have to be told exactly what that is.

Barbara All right. I want you to be my lover. Not a husband, already got one of those. But my own happy little secret, something I can remind myself of so I feel like getting up in the morning. I want... I want you to be my fantasy.

Keith ...Okay. You only had to ask.

(Short pause)

So. Are we having the affair yet?

Barbara Yes, I think so. If that suits you.

Keith I'm ready.

(Short pause)

Barbara What shall we do then?

Keith Well. There's always sex.

Barbara What? Right now?

Keith Could do. If the affair's started.

Barbara We can't do it now, not here. It's December. I'll freeze to death.

Keith *(getting out his phone)* No, no...

Barbara My parts aren't used very often, they may need warming up...

Keith No. We can have phone sex.

(He indicates his mobile.)

Barbara ...Where do you expect me to put it?

Keith We speak into it. It's a simulation. Everything's simulation these days.

Barbara This wasn't what I had in mind...

Keith I haven't much time for proper sex, not around all my hobbies. This is quicker and less sticky. And this way you don't have to worry they'll never return your calls.

*(**Barbara** gets out her mobile, uncertainly. It is noticeably smaller than in the last scene.)*

Trust me. I'll be over there.

(And he goes up the aisle into the audience. He dials.)

*(**Barbara**'s phone rings.)*

Barbara *(warily)* ...Hello?

(And with some relief:)

Oh, hello, Mr Franklin...

Keith Damn. Engaged.

Barbara Well, this may not be the best time... Wizzy's *what*?... Oh, he's coughed up furballs. Yes, he does that when he misses me... No, leave them, Mr Franklin, don't try to put them back in his mouth... No... Mmm... No, look, if I spoke to Wizzy it probably *would* reassure him, but there's not much point now, you see, I think Wizzy's there to make up for some emptiness in my life, and I think I've just found a way to fill it up without him. And if you could clear the line because I'm just about to have phone sex...

(Brightly:)

Okay, Mr Franklin, and Happy New Year to you too! Bye, love.

Keith Still engaged. What's going on?

(They both turn off their mobiles with a mutual beep.)

*(Enter **Graham**.)*

Graham Was that my phone that rang?

Barbara *(jumping)* What? Why?

Graham If the headmaster can't get me at home, you never know. He might call my mobile.

Barbara It was Mr Franklin. It was only Mr Franklin.

Graham Give me the phone.

Barbara ...No.

Graham Can I have the phone, please?

Barbara No.

Graham What's wrong with you?

Barbara I don't know, I haven't even done anything wrong yet!

Graham Barbara. I need the phone.

Barbara No!

Graham Barbara...

Barbara What's the point? He's not going to ring, is he, it's not going to ring!

*(And it rings. **Barbara** freezes.)*

Graham ...Aren't you going to get that?

Barbara Get what? Oh, this? No.

Graham Can I take it then?

Barbara No.

Graham Barbara, give me the bloody phone!

*(And **Barbara** answers it.)*

Barbara Hello! Hello!

Keith Hello, sexy.

Graham Is it the headmaster?

Barbara It's Mr Franklin.

Graham What, again?

Keith What are you wearing?

Graham Tell him to get off the line!

Barbara Yes, I understand, *Mr Franklin.* Cats do that, *Mr Franklin.*

Keith Tell me what you're wearing, you sexy thing, you.

Barbara No, I don't think you're getting the point, ***Mr Franklin***!

Graham If that sodding cat costs me my job, I'm going to kill him.

Keith Yes, that's the idea! False names! Very kinky!

Barbara No, please...

Graham Might as well kill him, can't afford to keep him.

Keith I'll call you Linda. What are you wearing, Luscious Linda?

Barbara *(hissing in despair)* Why do you keep asking me that? You know it's a suit of armour, a bloody suit of armour!

Graham Get him off the line.

Keith I'm going to take off your armour now, Linda. Can you feel it?

Graham I said, get him off the line.

Keith I'm unbuckling your breastplate. What a lovely word, breastplate.

Barbara *(with effort)* That's very funny, Mr Franklin!

Graham If you don't get him off the line, I will.

Keith I'm kissing your breasts. All over.

Barbara *(conversationally)* Mmm, yes. Lovely.

Graham Give me the phone.

Keith With my tongue. Kissing with my tongue.

Graham *(trying to take it)* Give me the bloody phone!

Barbara No! You mustn't!

Keith I'm not going too fast for you, am I?

Graham Barbara...

Keith Now I'm licking you. I'm pulling off your armour and licking underneath.

Graham Barbara, please! I might lose my job!

Barbara Leave me alone!

Keith Barbara?

Graham You bitch. You bloody bitch.

Keith Is there something wrong?

Graham *(suddenly raging)* I haven't got time for this! For your menopause or whatever it is, it's so bloody inconsiderate of you to fall apart now! Well, I'll tell you one thing, I'm glad you froze on me Christmas night, I wouldn't make love to you again if my birthday, Christmas and the battle of Bosworth were all rolled into one!

*(**Barbara** stares at him, stunned. Then, into the phone, slowly, deliberately:)*

Barbara Mmm. Oh. Mmmm. Oh yes.

Graham What are you doing?

Keith Barbara?

Barbara Oh. Oh yes! Give it to me. Just a little more!

Keith No, I've stopped doing it now...

Graham What are you doing to Mr Franklin?

Barbara That's it! That's so good! More! More!

Keith I think you've missed the point of this.

Graham He's an old man, you'll give him a heart attack...!

Barbara Yes! Yes! Yes! Yes!

*(Short pause. Then she gives the stunned **Graham** the phone in contempt.)*

Graham *(into the phone)* What is this? Mr Franklin?

*(And **Barbara** strides away into the audience towards **Keith**.)*

Keith Who's that, sorry?

Graham Are you all right, Franklin?

Keith Graham? Is that you?

Graham ...Who is this? ...It's you, isn't it? It's you, you bastard...

*(And **Barbara** now reaches **Keith**, takes the phone from him.)*

Barbara You know, Graham, I hope you do lose your job. I really do. Just so you learn that you can't always get your own way by shouting and bullying and making life miserable for everybody else.

*(And she turns off the mobile with a beep. Faces **Keith**.)*

Right. You. Sex. Now.

Keith What, the real thing? Where?

Barbara It doesn't matter. On the battlefield. We'll do it on the battlefield.

*(She pulls him down on to the stage. To the dazed **Graham**)*

Oh, and the cat's sicked up furballs on the carpet. So when you go home you may need the stain remover.

*(And she pulls **Keith** off to the exit.)*

Graham *(weakly)* So you're really not coming home with me? Barbara?

(And he stares at where she's left, forlorn.

(And the mobile rings. He looks at it warily, then answers.)

Hello?

(And nervously tries to regain his composure.)

Oh, hello! Hello, headmaster! I was just thinking of you, I mean, that is, I was just wondering whether... Yes, a lovely Christmas, thanks! It was lovely. And I hope you and the wife... Good, good... That's nice. So, the job. Yes... Yes, you have? Do you, right...

(Short pause)

Oh. Oh. Thank God. Oh, you've no idea how... yes, thank God. A pass is still a pass! Yes! So I can still teach? Oh, thank you, headmaster, that's... What other news?

(Short pause. Numbly:)

But they can't do that. They can't do that.

(Short pause)

They can't cancel history. They can't cancel history. It's history, I mean... you can't just wipe it away...

(Short pause)

Yes, headmaster. I'll remember that. If that's what the board says. If those are their very words. I'll remember that. Goodbye, headmaster.

(He turns off the mobile. He broods for a moment. Then, softly:)

'History is dead. We're in the new millennium. Celebrate the future'.

(Blackout.)

Act Two

4 – The Battle of Towton

29 March 1461 (three months later)

*(Some time during the interval, **Reg** enters, sits upon the grass, and sleeps.*

*(Lights down when **Stephen** enters. He paces nervously.)*

Stephen Right. Right.

(And he stops decisively. He clears his throat.)

Right. How to start. Chloe. We need to talk. No, don't want to frighten her off. Dear Chloe. Dearest Chloe. Too strong? Dearest Chlo. Too strong, yes. Dear Chloe. We need to talk. Let's talk. How do you feel about talking? The two of us, talking – good idea, or not? Hi, Chloe, fancy a chat?

*(And **Reg** gives a particularly loud snore. **Stephen** starts.)*

Mr Myers?

Reg Yes? What? What is it?

Stephen Are you all right?

Reg Oh yes. I was just having a nap. I'm always taking naps nowadays, I can fall asleep just like that. I know my brain will wake me up in case anything interesting happens.

Stephen What are you doing here, Mr Myers?

Reg My life now is really just a series of edited highlights. Hello, what?

Stephen What are you doing here?

Reg Well. Battle of Towton, isn't it?

Stephen Yes, but I came early. I came early specifically, I need to be on my own. I need to practise, you see. It's important I practise.

Reg Oh, I've been here for hours. I'm always too early or too late for everything these days. You were practising something, can I help? Go on. I used to be ever so good at all sorts of somethings.

Stephen Well, I suppose it's worth a try.

Reg Oh yes. I was once a very important person. Hundreds of employees I had, all hanging on my every word.

Stephen *(sighing)* You see, I have to say something very important. Life-changing, even. And I just can't find the right words.

Reg Public speaking, is it?

Stephen No, very private speaking, actually...

Reg I used to do lots of public speaking when I was important. When what said affected the lives of hundreds of employees. The trick about public speaking, what I always do. Is you imagine your audience naked.

(Pause)

Stephen No, I don't think that's going to work in this case.

Reg Nobody looks *that* good naked. Same lumps, same spots, same bits of fat. Same bits of hair growing where hair can have no meaning.

Stephen This isn't public speaking, Mr Myers. I have to tell someone I love them and want to spend the rest of my life with them.

Reg Ah. Sorry, no. Can't help you there.

*(Short pause. **Stephen** broods unhappily. **Reg**, thoughtfully;)*

I look absolutely disgusting naked. Do you know, recently, I've found all these strange white scabs growing all over me. Now, that isn't normal, is it?

Stephen Mr Myers.

Reg Reg.

Stephen Reg then. Could you please... go away?

Reg Oh. Not helping much then?

Stephen You're no bloody use at all. But it isn't that. It's that you're beginning to scare me.

Reg Oh. With you. Well, where would you like me to go?

Stephen I don't know. How about, back where you came from?

Reg Would it be all right if I just went to sleep?

Stephen *(doubtfully)* Well, it would have to be a very *deep* sleep.

Reg Oh. No problem. I'm good at those, they're easy. You watch.

(And he closes his eyes, goes back to sleep.

*(Hesitantly, **Stephen** waves his hand in front of **Reg**'s face. All he gets from him is a contented snore.*

*(As he does this, **Chloe** enters. She is dressed in modern clothes, made up for once rather to excess. But what really marks her out is that one of her breasts has been substantially enlarged. Its companion sits in its shadow,*

the same size as before.)

Chloe ...Stephen? Mr Myers? What are you doing here?

Stephen *(startled)* Chloe? I'm not ready for you yet! I was just...

(And he stares at her, amazed.)

...Practising...

Chloe It's that obvious, isn't it? Don't tell me it's that obvious.

Stephen Well.

Chloe I wanted to get here before anyone else. Cover it up, so no-one would notice. I can hide it under the armour.

Stephen It doesn't look that bad, really.

Chloe Oh, no. I look awful. People stare at me in the street. Do all women go through this?

Stephen *(confused)* I wouldn't know... Go through what, sorry?

Chloe Pregnancy. I hate it. I'm putting on weight. Every morning I weigh myself and I'm just getting fatter and fatter. The doctor says that's good, that's what you're meant to do when you're expecting. I should be eating for two. But I don't want to eat for two. I didn't want to get pregnant, it hardly seemed anything to do with me in the first place, and I'm buggered if I'm losing my figure for it, I'm going to try to eat *less*. The little bastard can starve in there as far as I'm concerned. Tell me honestly, Stephen. Am I getting fatter?

*(She pushes out her stomach. **Stephen** tries to examine it studiously, but his eyes are drawn helplessly up to her breast.)*

Barry's left me, you know.

Stephen ...Has he? Really?

Chloe When I told him I was pregnant. Dumped me on the spot.

Stephen What a bastard.

Chloe I asked him if it was because he was scared of being a father. He said no, he just doesn't fancy fat birds.

Stephen Chloe... What about...?

Chloe Oh, the *boobs*. That was Barry's idea. He wanted me to get my boobs done. Said that huge boobs were going to be all the rage.

Stephen But just the one... erm, boob?

Chloe It's a new technique. They do them one at a time. Breast implants while you wait.

Stephen Oh...

Chloe Trust me to tell Barry I was pregnant before they'd done both sides. But that's me, Stephen. I'm just stupid, aren't I?

Stephen No, you're not stupid, I love you...

Chloe No, I am stupid, I'm really very, very stupid, oh God, I'm getting upset. The doctor warned me not to let this happen, don't get upset, he said, it's bad for your boob. Try not to get into any emotional situations, he told me, I've got to nurture the boob, not oppress it. Stephen! Don't let me get upset!

Stephen *(floundering)* There there. It's all going to be all right...

Chloe Of course everything's going to be all right, Barry will come back to me soon, and he'll pay for the operation to be finished. When he sees I don't get fat. You'll help me, won't you, Stephen? You'll stop me from eating until Barry comes back?

Stephen Perhaps it's better that Barry's gone. Makes things easier.

Chloe How could it be easier? Calm down, calm down, protect the boob...

Stephen For me to say what I have to say. Chloe. Dear Chloe. Dearest, no. We need to talk. ...Erm, that's about as far as I'd got.

Chloe I don't understand...

Stephen What I'm trying to say is. Ahem. Now that you're pregnant, I promise to do right by you.

Chloe ...What, you mean you'll open doors and stuff?

Stephen No. Well, yes. That too. But look after you.

Chloe Oh. Thanks.

Stephen I've got a job. I got fed up waiting for Mr Myers, I went out and found myself a job, all on my own. I work at Speedy Burger. Behind the counter, just until I find something better. I mean, it isn't very much, but it'll help, won't it?

Chloe Sure. Help what exactly?

Stephen So I can support us. Just about. All three of us. You, me. And it.

Chloe ...Why?

(Short pause)

Stephen Well. I'm its father, aren't I?

Chloe No.

Stephen Or could be the father, I'd understand if there was some doubt... All right then, why couldn't I be? We made love. You said it was very nice.

Chloe It was very nice. But, well, that wasn't really *sex*, Stephen. You'd have to have got. Well. Inside.

Stephen Didn't I?

Chloe Whereas it was practically all over before you'd pulled your pants down.

Stephen It's hard to remember. I had to get a bit drunk. You see, I hadn't done it before.

Chloe Well. I'm afraid you still haven't.

(Short pause)

Stephen But I was going to propose.

Chloe That's nice.

Stephen I bought a ring and everything. Look. Look.

Chloe Oh yes.

Stephen It's a pretty cheap ring, but you don't get paid much at Speedy Burger. See? And I had it all rehearsed. On one knee. Like this.

Chloe Well, that's very kind of you...

Stephen Dear Chloe, will you take Stephen Burbidge to be your lawful wedded husband? Amen. And we could have stayed at my Mum's.

Chloe If it's all the same to you though, I'll wait for Barry. I know him. This is just a test. But you can do something for me. Make sure I don't put on any weight, so he'll come running back. Is that a deal?

(Short pause)

Stephen I'd do anything for you. ...I love you.

Chloe *(amused)* You're silly.

Stephen Yes.

Chloe You make me laugh and feel all happy again. Thank you.

*(She kisses **Stephen** on the cheek.*

*(**Graham** enters. **Stephen** awkwardly steps back from her.)*

Stephen ...Excuse me.

(And he exits.

*(**Chloe** returns to sorting out her kit. **Graham** watches her thoughtfully.)*

Graham Chloe. ...You're a woman, aren't you?

Chloe *(warily)* Yes...

Graham Somewhere underneath all that. So you should be able to tell me. Just what is it exactly that women want?

(Short pause)

Chloe I don't know, Mr Widthorpe. There are an awful lot of us.

Graham Yes, but come on. You must have something in common. Surely.

Chloe I suppose so. Let me think.

Graham I've been watching you all closely the last couple of months. Trying to work it out. Even had a go videoing daytime TV. Still haven't got a clue.

Chloe I don't know. 'What do all women want'? Well, yes. Of course. Me, dead.

(Short pause as she considers this. Then she gives a perfunctory nod as she confirms this to herself, and she returns to her kit.)

Graham What, sorry?

Chloe I don't know that *all* women want me dead. But all the women I know do. They can't stand me, women.

(Short pause)

Graham I'm sorry, but try as I might, I can't find a practical application for this...

Chloe Yes, I see...

Graham I'm wanting to find the right words to win Barbara back. I'm not sure that'll help.

Chloe Oh, I don't know. Your wife certainly wants me dead.

Graham Does she?

Chloe *(nonchalantly)* Oh, she hates me, your wife. I'm not saying she'd actually kill me or anything. But, I don't know, if I got hit by a car or had a heart attack, I think she'd be secretly quite pleased.

Graham ...God, why?

Chloe *(frowning)* I don't know. Barry used to say it was because they were all jealous. But I don't think that was it. Every time I get on a bus, women move away from me. Hairdressers pull my hair just a bit more than they need to. And they all talk about me behind my back, but just loud enough so I can hear, and they call me a stupid tart. Which I'm not actually. Well, I am stupid, granted. But I'm not a tart.

Graham *(awkwardly)* I'm sorry.

Chloe Oh, we're a pretty horrible gender, Mr Widthorpe. I'd have nothing to do with us, if I were you. Stick to men. They're much more fun. But if you really want to get your wife back, try to be as unlike me as possible.

*(Enter **Barbara** and **Keith**.)*

Good luck.

(She exits tactfully, taking her costume.)

Barbara Hello, Graham.

Keith Now, listen. I know that technically I'm in the wrong here, having an affair with your wife, that sort of thing. But I have to tell you. I have sworn to protect her, so if you want to get at her, you'll have to come through me first.

Barbara Go away, Keith. There's a love.

Graham *(gently)* May I speak to my wife alone, please?

Keith Oh. Right. Sorry. Right. I'll be over there... if I'm wanted.

(And he exits.)

Barbara So.

Graham Yes.

Barbara How are you?

Graham Oh. You know. Coping.

Barbara That's good.

Graham Yes.

Barbara I wouldn't like to think of you, you know. Not coping.

Graham No.

(Short pause)

The cat misses you.

Barbara Does he? Ahh.

Graham Since you left he's never stopped throwing up or crapping. I've had to get two litter trays. one for each end.

Barbara That's sweet. I miss him too.

Graham Don't you miss me?

Barbara Well, no. Frankly.

Graham I miss you.

Barbara I've worked out I really don't like you very much. So there's not much to miss.

(Short pause)

Graham Where are you living? Have you moved in with him?

Barbara No. Well. He hasn't asked me yet. I keep dropping hints, you know. I'm getting tired of sleeping on friends' floors. I think I may have to get more explicit.

Graham I don't understand.

Barbara I don't even know where Keith lives. We never meet up in the same part of the country twice. He just phones me on the mobile, tells me when and where.

Graham I don't understand why you'd rather be with him than with me.

Barbara *(sighing)* I think I've always wanted an affair. Long before I was even married, I thought it would be fun. It just seemed a really glamorous thing to do, I really admired women who could pull it off. But in those days getting one man to find me attractive was a pretty tall order, let alone two. So I put it out of my mind. But now I find I *can* do it, and it's wonderful. I wake up in the morning, and I think, 'ooh, I'm having an affair', and it gives me a buzz for the rest of the day. I'm one of *those* sorts of women! And yes, true, if I think, 'I'm having an affair with Keith', it takes the edge off it a bit. But it still makes me an adulteress, and that's good enough for me.

Graham Oh. I see.

Barbara And I have to say, in all the years we were married. I never once woke up and thought, 'ooh, I'm the wife of Graham Widthorpe'.

Graham I've been trying to find ways to get you to come back home with me. But I can't think of any good reason why you should. I mean, I'd say that I missed having you to talk to...

Barbara But you never used to talk in the first place. You just grunted.

Graham Quite. Or I'd promise you we'd make love more often.

Barbara But we wouldn't?

Graham Oh, no. I've never been good at sex, and, quite honestly, it all seems too complicated and embarrassing to learn how to do it properly now. So I've nothing to offer you, Barbara. Except more of the same and lots of cat sick.

(Short pause)

I've not changed your mind, have I?

Barbara No. Sorry.

Graham No. I'm sorry. Oh well. It was worth a stab, I suppose. See you on the battlefield.

Barbara Towton. We win this one, don't we?

Graham *(miserably)* Eventually. But only after nearly thirty thousand men have been slaughtered.

Barbara Ooh. Makes you think, doesn't it?

*(**Graham** exits. Immediately, re-enter **Keith**.)*

Keith Are you all right?

Barbara I'm fine.

Keith You seemed all right, but I was out there in the bushes, ready to leap out and defend you at the slightest sign of trouble.

Barbara Yes. Why is it we don't live together?

(Short pause)

Keith Is this what he asked you?

Barbara No. It's what I'm asking you.

Keith I thought we were having an affair.

Barbara We were. We are. But I think I'm a bit tired of the sort of affair in which we have sex in bed and breakfasts the length and breadth of England...

Keith No, they're family run hotels...

Barbara And then you go back to wherever it is you come from until the next time. What I want is the sort of affair where maybe you can help me with the shopping and the washing-up.

Keith It's the sex, isn't it? It's that thing I do with my hand.

Barbara No, it isn't that...

Keith I told you, it's very hard for me to feel aroused unless I pretend I'm holding a phone receiver.

Barbara Why don't I just move in with you? I could come back with you tonight.

Keith Yes. Mm. The problem is. I'm not sure I have time.

Barbara What do you mean? Is there someone else?

Keith Good God, no! No, I wouldn't have time for *two* affairs! I've got my work cut out squeezing you into my life as it is. Since we began sleeping together, I've missed one meeting of the Yachting Club and I've had to drop out of Creative Needlework altogether.

(Short pause)

Barbara Keith. How many hobbies do you have?

Keith At the last count? Twenty-eight.

(Pause)

Barbara ...Isn't that rather a lot? I mean, when do you do your job?

Keith I don't have a job.

Barbara You said you worked in a supermarket.

Keith Only as a hobby. The Retail Management Society. Oh, we have a laugh!

(Short pause)

Barbara I can't believe this. How do you get money? I can't get my head round this...

Keith From my parents. They both worked hard so I could lead the life of idleness they'd have wanted.

Barbara This is why you never talk about yourself? I thought you were just being enigmatic. But there was nothing to tell. You really have no life at all, have you?

Keith No, I have twenty-eight little lives. Barbara. There are millions and millions of people like me out there. Mediocrities. People who aren't particularly *good* at anything. Our society isn't equipped to give jobs to us, we just get in the way and make things worse. But it gives us jobs anyway. That's why you get typists who can't type. You get plumbers who spend six hours under your sink and still can't stop the tap from leaking. You get British Rail.

Barbara What's this got to do with us?

Keith I know what I am, Barbara. I'm a nothing. I'm an also-ran. I know I'll never make a difference to anyone's life, I'm just not good enough. So I opted out. I've spared society my incompetence, I'd have been a dreadful electrician and as a doctor I'd have killed somebody. But as a member of the Domino Toppling Club I made it to the Regional finals.

(Short pause)

Barbara I should never have left Graham.

(She makes to leave.)

Keith Barbara. I need you. You're the only hobby I've got which isn't a group activity. ...You're just the same as me! What do you do that's so different? You're just a teacher's wife.

(This stops her.)

Barbara *(softly)* And I'm not even doing that right.

Keith See? We're made for each other. It's nothing to be ashamed of. You're just a mediocrity like me. Like all the rest of us.

Barbara No. I'm sorry. You need to be worth more than that. It's ridiculous. I refuse to have changed my life for someone like you.

Keith *(laughing gently)* You haven't changed your life for *me*! Of course not. I'm not the sort of person anyone would do anything that drastic for!

Barbara Then what's it all for, Keith? What have I hurt Graham for, what have I hurt myself for? Why the hell would I do that?

Keith I'm your hobby.

Barbara *(flatly)* My hobby.

Keith I'm just a hobby, that's all. I'm just here... to pass the time.

(*Barbara stares at him closely, considering this.*)

Barbara Is it too much to hope for a bit of passion? Well. Let's see.

(*And experimentally, she grasps hold of* **Keith** *and kisses him full on the lips.*

(*Re-enter* **Graham**. *He watches them sadly.* **Keith** *starts and breaks free when he sees him.*)

Barbara What's the matter? Oh.

Keith Sorry. I'm sorry.

Graham No. I'm sorry. I'll go, I'll go.

(*And he begins to exit.*)

Barbara Is that it?

Graham What?

Barbara You're both sorry? Is that all you've got to say?

Graham I'm sorry I interrupted you.

Keith And I'm sorry I broke up his marriage. I did, you know.

Barbara And that's it? Aren't either of you going to *fight* for me?

(*Short pause*)

Graham Well, I hadn't planned on it, no...

Keith What's the point? I've already got you, haven't I?

Barbara If I have to be a hobby, then I don't want to be the sort where just anyone can be a member! I want to see a bit of conflict here!

Keith What did you have in mind?

Barbara A duel. You've both got swords. Challenge him to a duel.

Keith (*perfunctory*) Yes, yes, all right... I challenge you to a duel.

Graham And I decline. Thank you very much.

Keith You're welcome.

(*They shake hands, separate again.*)

Barbara Graham!

Graham What?

Barbara For God's sake, fight for me.

Graham He'll chop me to pieces!

Barbara You said you still cared for me.

Graham Yeah, but not that much. Forget it.

Barbara *(firmly)* Come back here and fight! Fight for me, you bastard! Fight!

(And she goes up and slaps him across the face.)

Graham *(gently)* Oh, Barbara. I'm sorry. I've no more fight left in me.

*(To **Keith**)*

I'd have liked to have got my wife back, but not at the expense of the little dignity I've got left. Enjoy.

Keith Oh, I feel awful now.

Barbara Graham. He doesn't love me.

Keith Now, I never said that...

Barbara It isn't me he wants at all. He's using me to take over the re-enactment group.

*(And **Graham** turns back, ashen, to **Keith**.)*

Graham But you can't. Please. It's the only thing I've got left.

Keith But I don't want that. Honestly.

Graham They've even taken history away from me. You know what I teach now? Pottery. They've taken history off the syllabus, but pottery's thriving.

Keith Well, everyone needs pots...

Graham And I'm useless at it. All my pots wobble and fall over. All the children just laugh at me. They laugh at me in the staff room too. Even the cat laughs at me, the way he pisses just short of the litter tray. This, all of this, I don't know what I'd do without it...

Keith You're doing a great job. You stick with it...

Barbara If you can't fight for me, Graham, fight for your command. Look at me. What other reason could he have to sleep with me?

*(**Graham** looks at **Barbara** thoughtfully. Then, softly, to **Keith**)*

Graham You bastard.

Keith No, Graham, believe me...

Graham My wife's one thing, but I waited years to run this group, and you're not going to stop me now! Draw your sword!

Keith No, come on...

Graham You want a duel? I'll give you a bloody duel. All right? I'm going to slice your bloody head off. Okay?

Keith I wouldn't want to be leader, I don't know how to be leader, I'm just a blank sheet of paper...

*(**Graham** reaches up and grabs him by the throat.)*

Graham I told you to draw your sword.

(They both face each other, with their swords ready.)

On guard.

Keith Very well. Have at thee, varlet.

Graham ...I beg your pardon?

Keith I have to get into character.

Graham Right. For that, you *deserve* to die.

*(And they begin to fight. **Keith** is always on the defensive, not wanting to hurt **Graham**. **Graham** is less experienced, but blind fury and desperation give him considerable power. He hacks away at **Keith** every which way, backing him all over the stage.)*

Keith Now, I don't want to hurt you, Graham... Graham? ...Graham!

*(And they lock swords. They don't seem to notice that between them on the grass sits the sleeping **Reg**.)*

This has all been a misunderstanding. Why don't we talk it over a pint in the pub?

Reg *(waking)* Oh, hello? Am I missing something interesting?

*(And, looking up at the swordplay above him, he gives a scream. Which surprises both **Graham** and **Keith**, who scream as well, jump apart, and break the deadlock.*

*(The fight resumes. **Reg** scampers over towards **Barbara** for safety, who helps him to his feet.*

*(And we hear the tuneful ring of **Graham**'s mobile phone. He tries to ignore it, but it gets all the more shrill and insistent.)*

Graham Oh, damn. Excuse me.

(And he lowers his sword, pulls out an aerial from behind his ear. Mobile phones, evidently, have got about as small as they can.)

This isn't a good time, Mr Franklin... Wizzy's done *what*?... God. Well, seal off all the areas and stop it spreading... I'll deal with it when I get home.

(He pushes behind his ear, there is a beep. He lowers the aerial and broods for a moment.)

Keith *(hesitantly)* Graham?

Graham What, sorry?

Keith Have at thee, varlet?

Graham Oh yes.

(And the fighting resumes in earnest.)

*(Attracted by the sound, enter **Chloe** and **Stephen**.)*

Chloe What's going on?

*(**Keith** is distracted; **Graham** knocks the sword out of his hand. He advances on him, sword at throat.)*

Graham I'm no good with cats. I'm no good with pots. I'm no good with this whole marriage business.

Keith Now, calm down, Graham...

Graham But I'm not going to lose the one thing I am good at. On your knees.

Keith Graham...

Graham I said, on your knees!

*(And **Keith** obeys.)*

We were a nice happy group before you joined! Fun weekends out for us all. Prepare to die!

Keith Oh, for heaven's sake...

*(And **Graham** raises his sword, leaving his body vulnerable. **Keith** punches him hard in the groin. Winded, **Graham** drops his sword, and doubles over.)*

Chloe Hooray! Well done, Graham!

Reg Our new leader! I always knew you'd fight to be leader at some point. You've wanted it ever since the day you joined.

Graham *(slowly getting up)* Traitors. That's what you are. Traitors. Five hundred years ago they'd have rounded you all up, and hanged you, and drawn you, and quartered you. And they'd have put you on the rack and used thumbscrews as well. A little before the hanging and the quartering.

Chloe Please don't be nasty. I mustn't get all emotional, the doctor says it's bad for my boob...

Graham *(rounding on her, quietly)* And as for you. You're the worst of the lot.

Chloe *(nervously)* I am?

Graham You're even worse than a traitor. You're a *bad historian*. I've been teaching idiots like you all my life. You just don't get it, do you? These battles really happened. Real soldiers fought here, they really died. And every week you show up you insult them, because you just don't care, you've never *cared*, you're a vacant, soulless little prat!

Chloe *(desperately)* Please don't get me upset, I'm real too, well, most of me is...

Graham *(furiously)* Real? You're not real! Look at yourself! You're a freak! The Yorkists would have strung you up and burnt you at the bloody stake!

*(Shocked silence. Even **Graham** realises he may have gone too far. **Chloe** is too frozen to react; then, slowly, she opens her mouth and gives a silent cry. And then we hear a long raspberry as the breast slowly deflates.)*

Chloe *(shocked)* You've bust my boob. You've bust my boob.

Stephen *(quietly, dangerous)* Get out of here.

Graham What?

Stephen Get out of here. Leave us alone. We don't want you as a leader. We don't even want to see you again.

(He picks up the sword nervously.)

I love Chloe. If you're going to bust anyone's boob, then you can try busting mine!

Chloe Oh, Stephen...

Stephen I'm not going to let any harm come to her. Okay, she's not very bright, she might sleep around a bit. But I love her anyway.

Chloe Oh, Stephen!

(And she runs off, upset.)

Stephen See what you've done? I lay down this sword before our new leader.

*(And he gets on the grass in homage to **Keith**.*

(Stunned pause. Then:)

Reg *(delighted)* Our new leader!

(And he gets down on the grass too.)

Graham ...Barbara?

Barbara *(to **Keith**)* May I move in with you? Do you promise to give up all other hobbies but me?

Keith *(startled)* Of course. I'll be whatever you want.

Barbara In that case...

(And she too kneels.)

Our new leader.

*(And **Graham** exits without a word.)*

Barbara Come along, leader. You have to go and command your first battle.

Keith But I really don't want to be leader! I'm just a mediocrity. I'll ruin the whole thing...

*(And they exit. **Reg** and **Stephen** are left.)*

Reg You seem to have made quite an impression on Chloe.

Stephen Well. Maybe.

(He gets up.)

Reg My advice paid off, then. Good, good. I was wondering whether you could do a favour for me in return. I wondered... whether I could borrow Chloe for a while.

*(Short pause. **Stephen** stares at him emotionlessly.)*

I know it's early days for you yet, you probably want to break her in yourself first! Yes. But when the novelty's worn off, maybe. I won't leave you empty handed. You could borrow Sheila. A good woman, in good working order, we could have a little swap. As often as you like. As often as you can.

(He tries to get up. He can't.)

Sure, I know what you're thinking. You're thinking, I know all about sex, thank you very much. And I can see you are, I know the type. But you'll find out. Sex with the same person, it gets very stale. You'll find out. I'm doing you a favour too.

(He tries to get up again.)

Please. You've got to help me. I'm desperate. I miss sex so very much. Good sex, I mean, not that half-hearted parody Sheila offers me. Do you know she's got white scabs growing over her skin? That's not normal, is it? Not normal.

(He tries to get up.)

Could you please help me up?

*(**Stephen** considers this coolly, then lends **Reg** his hand.)*

Thank you. Whew. There you go.

*(And without even dignifying him with another glance, **Stephen** exits.)*

Okay. Don't make up your mind right away. I'm not going anywhere! Nowhere at all.

5 – The Battle of Tewkesbury

14 May 1471 (fourteen months later)

*(Enter **Chloe**, in doublet and hose. Her hair is a natural colour once more. But she looks drained, and she clearly has bad acne – she has also put on some weight. She carries a rucksack, drops it down. Exits.*

(She re-enters, bringing on her sword. She puts it down, exits.)

(She re-enters, pushing a pram. As some gesture towards historical authenticity, it has been decorated with chainmail. She takes a little book out of the rucksack, sighs, sits down.)

*(In the pram, the baby starts crying. **Chloe** gets up.)*

Chloe Oh no, don't cry. Ssh, darling, you mustn't cry. Crying will make your face all ugly.

(We can't see what she is doing inside the pram to comfort the child, but it clearly works.)

There. That's better. Good girl. My good beautiful girl.

*(Enter **Keith**. He wears a moustache, similar to **Graham**'s. He carries on a rucksack and sword of his own.)*

Oh, Keith!

Keith Hello.

Chloe Test me. Test me.

Keith *(putting down his load)* What?

Chloe I've got my exam on Wednesday. Test me on this.

(She gives him the book.)

Any question you like.

Keith All right. 'Your daughter regularly walks home from school. She tells you that a stranger has been stopping her outside the school gates and offering her a lift in his car. Do you give your permission or not?'

(Short pause)

Chloe Well. It depends.

Keith It's only a yes or no answer.

Chloe It depends how strange this stranger is. It could be rather a nice stranger.

Keith There isn't room for an explanation. It wants you to tick a box.

Chloe You can't stop a child from meeting strangers. That's how they stop being strangers and start being friends. Like everyone in this group, you're all my friends, aren't you?

Keith Which box are you ticking? Should she go in the stranger's car? Yes or no.

Chloe Yes then. But a very small tick, because it depends.

Keith No. Sorry.

Chloe Bugger.

Keith That's not the answer they give here.

Chloe What would you do? You understand children.

Keith I teach them all day. Wouldn't say I understood them.

*(Enter **Barbara**. She pulls on a picnic hamper. She is dressed in her armour.)*

Barbara Keith. A hand, please.

*(**Keith** gives **Chloe** back her book.)*

Chloe Thanks.

Keith *(helping **Barbara**)* See, darling, Chloe's here. So that makes three of us.

Barbara Well, darling, we knew Chloe would be here. But three's still hardly enough to call ourselves an army.

Chloe Stephen's coming.

Barbara *(dismissively)* That's highly unlikely. He hasn't been for months.

Chloe No, he'll be here. I asked him to be.

Keith That's four then. A possible four. And Reg might show up...

Barbara Of course he won't show up. He'll hardly be in the mood for waving a sword about, will he?

*(Enter **Reg**, unseen.)*

To tell you the truth, I'm glad Reg isn't coming. Doddering around on the field, he's just not credible as a soldier any more. Really, he's worse than useless. Only good for cannon fodder.

Reg *(cheerily)* Hello, everyone. How are we all?

Barbara Reg.

Reg Hello.

Barbara We thought you weren't coming.

Reg Oh, couldn't miss this. Eh? Not a Tewkesbury.

Keith We just want to say how sorry we are.

Reg I'm sorry?

Keith For your loss.

Reg Well, I don't suppose it was your fault, eh? You had nothing to do with it.

Keith Anything we can do. You know, to help.

Barbara Except we can't put you up. We haven't got the space. And of course we can't help financially.

Keith But any emotional support. You know. You know where to come.

Reg Thank you.

(Short pause)

Well, looks like it's going to be a nice day for it. Eh? I think I'll go and get changed.

(And he exits.)

Keith He seems pretty cheerful.

Barbara *(opening the hamper)* Well, if Reg is here, I'm not sure we have enough sandwiches to go round.

Keith You don't think I should make a speech or something?

Barbara Well. I'm not going to panic. There are plenty of sausage rolls. What?

Keith Do you think a speech would be appropriate? On behalf of us all?

Barbara I'd have thought that would be nice, yes. You're the leader. That's your job.

Keith *(miserably, as he exits)* I'll work something out then. I hate being leader...

*(**Barbara** unpacks the hamper. Sandwiches and sausage rolls, cellophane wrapped on plates. A few flasks of drinks. She spreads out a big white tablecloth.)*

Chloe ...Have we got another picnic then?

Barbara *(distantly)* Yes.

Chloe That's nice. I think your picnics are better than the battles. I do, honestly.

Barbara And no-one ever lifts a finger to help.

(Short pause)

Chloe Barbara.

Barbara ...What?

Chloe Would you do something for me?

Barbara I'm a little busy at the moment, aren't I?

Chloe Would you test me on this?

*(Short pause. **Barbara** sighs, gets up.)*

Barbara All right. Just one question. Just one.

Chloe Thank you.

Barbara I thought we'd already been through all this at the battle of Barnet.

Chloe I failed. This is my retake.

Barbara All right. An easy one. 'You are in the kitchen, preparing a big saucepan of boiling water. Do you let your child sit on the cooker to play with it?'

Chloe Ooh. I know this one.

Barbara Yes?

(Short pause)

Yes or no, Chloe?

Chloe Just a minute...

Barbara She's putting her hand inside, it's getting nearer the water...

Chloe Don't rush me...!

Barbara Splash. Sizzle, sizzle, screams of pain.

Chloe No...!

Barbara *(tossing the book back at her absently, and returning to the picnic)* Too late, your kid's dead. God, you're absolutely hopeless.

Chloe You think I'm going to fail again?

Barbara Of course you're going to fail. You haven't got a hope in hell.

Chloe No. No, I mustn't fail again! They only let you fail once, then they take the baby away from you...

Barbara Well, that's the system.

Chloe It isn't fair. It's not my fault I wasn't born with any maternal instincts.

Barbara *(busying herself with napkins)* I think it's perfectly fair, frankly.

Chloe You do?

Barbara *(rapidly)* Stupid people like you don't deserve babies. Not when cleverer people aren't able to have them. I don't expect you even *tried* for your baby, did you? Probably just rolled over in your sleep into a wet patch, and, bam, you're pregnant...

Chloe Bam?

Barbara Whereas some of us put some real effort in. We try at the right time of the month, we try at the wrong time of the month, we try in the middle of the afternoon. We try lots of different positions which are either painful, or embarrassing, or both, you try lots of different pills and ointments to keep your biological clock ticking, and it's no good at all, it seems to have finally tocked out. So don't talk about what's fair and unfair, you're too bloody young and too bloody thick to have a clue about either. There aren't going to be enough sandwiches. Thank God I brought so many sausage rolls.

(Pause)

Chloe I haven't got to get every single question right. I'm allowed to make a few mistakes. So I might be all right.

Barbara I'm sorry. It's just been, well. Haven't been sleeping recently. Would you like a sausage roll?

Chloe No thanks.

Barbara Go on. I've made far too many. How about Wotsername? In the pram?

Chloe No, she hasn't got any teeth yet...

Barbara Fair enough, you would need teeth. Please have a sausage roll. As brain food.

Chloe Is it? Really? All right then.

(And she takes a sausage roll, returns to her book.

(As an afterthought, **Barbara** *takes one too and munches on it as* **Graham** *enters. He is dressed in armour, and carries a cardboard cat box.)*

Graham Barbara.

Barbara *(mouth full)* Graham.

Graham I brought the cat.

Barbara As I can see, great. Mmm, how is he?

(She takes the box.)

Graham He's fine...

Barbara *(opening it cautiously)* Hello, Wizzy! See, it's your mummy...

(And, puzzled, she opens the box wide open.)

Graham. He isn't moving.

Graham He wouldn't be. I drugged him before we left.

Barbara Oh.

Graham I often drug him, he doesn't squit so much when he's asleep.

Barbara Hello, baby, baby...

Graham He'll be out for hours yet. I'm not going to need the pills again, so I finished the bottle.

Barbara Thank you for taking care of him.

Graham Mr Franklin is heartbroken. Says feeding Wizzy's all he's got to live for. Never mind, I told him. Actually, I'm surprised you didn't want Wizzy earlier...

Barbara Oh. I've only just worked out I need him after all.

Graham Well, that's the last things of yours out of my house. We're as divorced now as we'll ever be.

Barbara Yes. It's a funny feeling, being divorced. I wake up in the morning, and think, 'ooh, I'm a divorcee'. Anything for a buzz.

(Short pause)

Divorcee... I want to make love to you right now...

Graham I want to make love to you too...

Barbara I want to rip off your armour.

Graham I want to take you on the picnic hamper. You divorcee, you.

Barbara Amongst the sausage rolls. Divorcee!

*(They both look across at **Chloe**. And sigh.)*

Better not though.

Graham And how is Keith?

Barbara *(vaguely)* Oh, fine. The usual. He's around somewhere. I imagine... Would you like a sausage roll, by the way? I made too many.

*(She puts down the cat box, and offers **Graham** a plate.)*

Graham Oh, thanks. You always made great sausage rolls. Well! One cat, safely returned. Well. See you on the battlefield, then...

Barbara Yes.

Graham *(eating)* Thanks. It's very nice.

(He hesitates awkwardly. Then he turns to go.)

Barbara Oh, and Graham. Don't let anyone else kill you but me.

Graham You bet. I'll watch out for you.

*(And he exits. **Barbara** watches after him thoughtfully.*

*(Enter **Stephen**.)*

Stephen Hello, Mrs Widthorpe.

Barbara Stephen! Now I really have made far too few sandwiches. They'll never go around now.

Stephen I'm sorry.

Barbara A bit too late for that, isn't it?

(She exits.)

Chloe Stephen. Thanks for coming. I wasn't sure you would.

Stephen Is that the baby then?

Chloe Inside the pram? Yeah, that's the one.

(He looks inside.)

Stephen She's very pretty. What's her name?

Chloe Tanya.

Stephen She's a bit of a funny colour though.

Chloe Oh, no. That's just her lipstick. I ran out of the red she normally wears, had to resort to pink.

Stephen No. It's her skin. Sort of shiny.

Chloe Just perfectly ordinary foundation.

Stephen Makes her look a bit... plastic. Still. She's very pretty.

Chloe Thank you. Aren't you going to say I'm pretty?

Stephen ...I didn't know if it was appropriate...

Chloe I mean, I'm not pretty, I know I'm not. But I miss being told I am.

Stephen You're beautiful. If you like.

Chloe Thanks. Stephen. ...How would you feel about being Tanya's father?

Stephen ...Crikey.

Chloe You could start immediately if you wanted. If that's convenient.

Stephen What about Barry?

Chloe Haven't heard a word from him since Tanya was born. He hasn't given us a penny, nothing. Please, Stephen? She is pretty, isn't she, you said so yourself. And she looks even prettier in some of the dresses I've got for her. And don't those earrings suit her, don't they go well with her jimjams?

Stephen You want me to live with you? Really?

Chloe And she's very well-behaved. Happy kid, never cries.

Stephen No, she's not made a sound.

Chloe Though that could be the lipstick she uses. I think it welds her mouth shut.

Stephen I still love you, Chloe.

Chloe And that's a definite plus too. So, what do you say?

*(**Stephen** kisses **Chloe**.)*

What's that then? A yes, is that a yes?

Stephen Yes!

Chloe Oh, thank God for that. So that means you'll be able to sit the exam on Wednesday.

Stephen Sorry. What exam?

Chloe The Parental Assessment Test. You know the sort of thing. They ask you lots of questions to see whether you're able to raise a child. It was a real worry, I'm hopeless at exams, my brain just seizes up, you know?

Stephen Sorry, so you want me...

Chloe So I want you to take the exam instead! Only one of the parents has to pass. And demonstrate he can support the child financially. You've got a job, haven't you?

Stephen I'm still at Speedy Burger.

Chloe Well, that's all that settled then. Oh, I tell you, I thought they were going to take Tanya away from me, I couldn't cope with that, she's the only pretty thing I've got left. You'll do it, won't you?

Stephen I'd do anything for you. You know that.

Chloe *(throwing the book away)* Don't need this any more then, hooray! You hear that, Tantan? Daddy's going to save you. Thank him, let me prise your lips apart...

(She reaches inside, and does so. The baby begins to cry.)

Okay, that's enough.

(And she closes the baby's mouth once more. Abruptly, the sound cuts off.)

Stephen Let's do this properly then. Let's get married.

Chloe What?

Stephen I've still got the ring, I never threw it away. Isn't that silly, I've kept it with your photos, just in case! Marry me.

Chloe No. I don't think we need to go that far. Just pass the exam, that would be fine.

Stephen Oh. Okay.

Chloe Anyway, it might put Barry off. If I was a wife or something. He'll come back one day, I know it. When Tanya's just a bit older, when he sees her all nicely brought up. You'll help me with that, won't you, Stephen? You'll help me bring Tanya up all nicely? ...You said you'd do anything for me.

Stephen Yes.

Chloe Well. That's perfect, then!

*(Enter **Keith**. **Reg** and **Barbara** follow behind.)*

Keith Stephen! Hello! Great to see you again!

Stephen *(miserably)* Hello.

Keith Well, that makes us a full house then. That's splendid. Bring a sword, did you?

Stephen Yes.

Keith Marvellous. Okay, everyone. If we all just gather around... this lovely spread supplied for us by Barbara. Everybody give her a round of applause.

(As there's half-hearted clapping:)

Barbara You'll have to share the sandwiches.

Keith Great. But before we tuck in, just a few words. Reg's wife's dead, so I've prepared a little something. If we could all quieten down... Reg? Thanks.

(Solemnly:)

Just want to say, Reg... About Sheila... How sorry I am. How sorry we all are. We feel for you in this period of grief. And, erm, mourning. We share your loss. She was a wonderful woman. And I'm sure some comfort can be taken in knowing that she's in a better place. Yes.

Chloe What better place?

Barbara He means heaven.

Keith Yes. Sheila's in heaven now. One presumes. Not that I ever met Sheila. Reg, was Sheila the heaven sort?

Reg Fingers crossed.

Keith Yes. Did anyone here meet Sheila?

Chloe I didn't.

Barbara Not me.

Stephen No.

Keith But I'm sure she'll be missed. And her suffering's over. That's the main thing. Did she suffer, Reg?

Reg I don't know. We weren't talking much by the end.

Keith That's the main thing anyway. ...Great! Battle of Tewkesbury then. I'll just go through the battle plans, help yourselves to refreshments if you like. Now. We're going to need someone to get killed early again. Stephen, are you up for that?

Stephen No.

Keith Sorry?

Stephen No.

Keith But you always... I mean, you always do corpse duty.

Reg I'll do it, if you like.

Keith Now, that wouldn't be fair...

Reg No, I don't mind. It's what Barbara was saying. I'm really not credible as a soldier, not any more. I think I'll make a good corpse.

Barbara *(embarrassed)* Right. Well.

Reg *(cheerfully)* All I ask is, someone helps me on to my feet afterwards. I seem to have problems standing up these days!

Barbara Stephen, aren't you eating?

Stephen No.

Barbara Go on. Have a sausage roll.

Stephen All I eat nowadays are Speedy Burgers. It's all I'm allowed to eat.

Chloe Have a sausage roll, Stephen. For me.

Barbara That's the way. I'm sure they're just as bad for you as what you're used to.

Reg Can I just say. Thank you for this wonderful spread. Going to all this trouble for Sheila, I know she would have appreciated it.

Chloe Oh. Is all this for Sheila?

Reg We didn't have any nibbles after the service. Lots of people came to the funeral, she was a very popular woman. Paid their respects, you know. But no-one came back with me afterwards to the reception. I worked out in the end it was because they didn't like me very much. All of my friends were really Sheila's friends – I think it was only because she stuck with me so long they gave me the benefit of the doubt. I didn't have any friends at work either. They've put out a court order to stop me visiting the office, so they can't be that fond of me. But you all, all of you, you're my real friends. Sheila and I often talk about you. Oh, I know she's dead, but she often comes for a little chat. And I know she'd appreciate you all, putting up with me these years, even though she never met you. Though she was going to sleep with Stephen, I remember, and Keith wanted her body as well, I know. So. Basically, thanks.

(Awkward silence. **Barbara** *raises the plate full of sandwiches. All but* **Stephen** *reach out for one.*

(And enter **Graham.***)*

Graham Look, is there any chance of you coming out to fight soon?

Reg Oh, look! A Lancastrian! Let's throw him in the dungeons!

Graham The battle started ages ago. Since you win it, you might want to be there.

Keith We're nearly ready. I've just got to fill them all in on the historical background...

Graham Oh, for heaven's sake. Okay, everyone, pay attention.

(And, unquestioningly, everyone does.)

Keith Oh. Okay...

Graham Right. Very simply. By this stage, the war had got very nasty indeed. No more of your little skirmishes, these battles are the real thing. Take Towton, do you remember that one? Thirty thousand dead. The bloodiest battle on English soil. And it allowed the Yorkists at last to put their leader on the throne, King Edward. But the Lancastrians weren't defeated yet. They rallied round, deposed Edward, and made their leader, Henry, king instead.

Chloe I bet Edward wouldn't have liked that.

Graham No, he didn't. And here at Tewkesbury he made the Lancastrians pay, once and for all. He wiped them out. Finally wiped the whole lot out. All of the family, all of the followers, thousands of them, dead.

(Short pause. Everyone seems sobered by this. Lightly:)

So there you go. That's what you've got to do to me this afternoon. Wipe me out.

Keith *(awkwardly)* Look, Graham, I know we've had our differences. But I feel a bit bad about that.

Graham Oh, don't you worry. A few years down the road, and the Tudors will wipe *you* all out. And then you'll be laughing on the other side of your face. And we'll all be dead, all of us, thank God there'll be an end to it.

Barbara Well. Well, it makes you think. Doesn't it?

Stephen ...No.

Barbara What?

Stephen No. It doesn't make you think. That's the whole point. It's not supposed to make you think. Thirty thousand dead. Sixty thousand, a hundred thousand. So what? They'd all have been dead by now anyway.

Barbara Stephen. I hardly think that's the attitude.

Stephen No, listen. Listen. It was their job. Do you understand? It was their *job*. They went out there, they fought, they got slaughtered. And they got paid for it. And one thing they didn't do, they didn't *think* about it. They weren't paid to think. At least they had a purpose. At least they knew what they were getting paid *for*. At least they weren't working for Speedy Burger.

Keith Erm. I wouldn't have thought that was a fair comparison...

Stephen At Speedy Burger I wear a uniform with a name on. But it isn't even my name. They've already got a Stephen, they can't have two Stephens, I'm called Marvin. Marvin's what's printed on my uniform. God knows what happened to the real Marvin. I think about the millionth time he said 'you want fries with that?' he finally flipped and they had to lock him away somewhere.

Graham Shouldn't we be getting on and fighting the battle?

Stephen They have rules for everything. The exact words you say, how often you should smile. There's a rota for cleaning the lavatory. I go in there twice a day and wipe down the toilet seats. You don't think about it. You're not paid to think about it. Back in the Middle Ages you were chopped to bits on a battlefield, nowadays you work for Speedy Burger. But back then, you were either a soldier or a peasant. Back then, being hacked to death on a field was a good career move. But I spent three years at university, and I'm cleaning toilets, I wipe them down and flush it away and write my initials on the rota, and they're not even my initials, they're Marvin's bloody initials. And I know that in five hundred years there won't be a bunch of idiots like us dressed in Speedy Burger uniforms re-enacting the whole bloody thing. So I say, sod the thirty thousand. Sod them all.

(And he suddenly grips his stomach in pain. He begins to sway, losing his balance.)

Oh God...

Chloe What is it?

Stephen I only eat Speedy Burgers. I'm not able to. They put something addictive in the special sauce. It's got so my stomach actually rejects any food which isn't a Speedy Burger. Your sausage roll, Mrs Widthorpe, it's the first real food I've had for weeks...

Barbara Thank you very much...

*(And **Stephen** suddenly stiffens, stumbles a moment, then freezes again, his face contorted in a rictus. And he falls into a dead faint on to the cat box. It is all but crushed underneath him.)*

Chloe Stephen!

Barbara Wizzy!

Chloe *(turning him over)* Stephen! Stephen, are you all right?

Barbara Never mind about him, what about my cat?

Chloe Stephen! Please don't die...!

Keith Let me look. I know a bit of First Aid. It used to be a hobby of mine.

Graham *(at the box, about to lift it up)* I would look away if I were you, darling. This may not be a pretty sight.

Barbara No, I'm all right. I have to see.

*(He squeezes **Barbara**'s hand in support, then gingerly raises the bit of cardboard.*

(And there is a loud yowl from underneath. Delighted:)

Wizzy! You're alive!

(And Wizzy rushes across the stage and out the exit. A fast moving piece of fur.)

No, not that way! That's the battlefield!

Graham Oh my God! He'll be cut to pieces!

*(And he rushes off after the cat. **Barbara** stands anxiously at the exit. **Reg** cheerfully joins her.)*

Barbara He's heading straight into the main action! I can't look!

Reg I can. ...Two soldiers swordfighting. Here comes the cat. And he's tripped up the Yorkist. I think he's fallen on to the cat! No, wait, there he is. The cat's fine. Now he's tripped up the Lancastrian. And off he goes! Straight towards the cavalry. Watch out for that horse...!

Barbara No...

Reg ...And through the legs. The horse has thrown the rider... He's jolly useful, that cat, isn't he? We should have had him join the group ages ago.

(He smiles benignly, then walks back to the picnic. Resumes eating.)

Chloe Don't die, Stephen, please. I need you for the exam on Wednesday...

*(And the baby begins to wail. **Chloe** anxiously goes to the pram.)*

No, Tanya, not now! Don't cry, you don't want to cry, it'll make you ugly. Your eyes will run and your mouth will swell, and you'll look all ugly, just like Mummy. You don't want to be ugly like Mummy, do you?

(And she applies lipstick. The baby begins to sound as if it's being gagged, then is silent.

*(All the while, **Keith** has been trying all sorts of first aid on **Stephen** – thumping his chest, mouth to mouth, attempting the Heimlich manoeuver. All demonstrating he doesn't really have a clue what he is doing. At length, **Stephen** groans.)*

Keith I think he'll be all right.

Chloe *(bending over him)* Stephen! Can you hear me? Are you going to live?

Stephen Ughhhh....

Chloe Come on, wake up. We better get you home. I'm going to take you home.

Stephen *(feebly)* You're going to take me home?

Chloe That's right. Get you well again. Keith, could you give me a hand?

Keith *(lifting the groggy **Stephen** to his feet)* Of course...

Chloe That's it.

Stephen *(feebly)* I love you, Chloe...

Chloe I know...

Stephen Do anything for you. Anything at all...

Chloe Just get well by Wednesday. That'd be a start.

*(As she leads him off, to **Keith**)*

Could you bring the pram?

Keith Sure.

(He takes the pram, glances inside. Double takes, revolted.)

My God...

(And hurries offstage with it.)

Reg Well. Sheila. That was exciting, wasn't it? Much more exciting than when I was in charge... I think you're right! I think I was a pretty useless leader. Have a sausage roll, Sheila. My love.

*(Re-enter **Graham**, exhausted.)*

Graham I'm sorry. I couldn't catch him.

Barbara My hero.

Graham He'll be on the other side of Tewkesbury by now. I don't think we'll ever see him again.

Barbara It doesn't matter. I'm not sure I need him after all. Not any more.

(And she looks at him, gives a seductive growl.

*(**Graham** looks surprised, then grins in boyish delight.*

*(They run at each other. There is a dull clang when armour hits armour. They try to reach each other's mouths, but **Graham** is too short and **Barbara**'s breastplate gets in the way. He jumps up, and she catches him, and they kiss each other hungrily.*

*(**Reg**, finishing his sausage roll, licks his fingers appreciatively.)*

Reg Mmm. Delicious.

6 – The Battle of Bosworth

22 August 1485 (fifteen months later)

*(**Keith** and **Graham** stand on the stage together, looking down at the grass critically.)*

Graham Well. Actually. I'm quite impressed.

Keith Yes.

Graham Not bad. Not bad at all.

*(Short pause. Then **Keith** starts jumping up and down.)*

Keith It's got great spring.

Graham Has it?

Keith Oh yes. Give it a go.

*(**Graham** jumps up and down with him.)*

Graham Oh yes! I see what you mean...

Keith Good spring, isn't it?

Graham Yes. You can really feel it...

Keith ...Springing you upwards.

Graham Yes.

(And they come to a halt.)

What's it made of, would you think?

Keith I don't know. Some kind of plastic, I expect.

Graham *(stooping)* Looks great. Much better than real grass. Ow. Bit sharp though.

Keith Is it?

Graham Better take care to die face upwards, I think.

Keith Living history, isn't it? Living history. They should do this to every battlefield. Dig it up, and build a whopping great dome over it. Preserve it for posterity, this will.

Graham They'd never do it, Keith. The other battles, they're just small fry. This is the big one. Bosworth. Where it all ends.

Keith I suppose you're right.

Graham People are only interested in the endings, mate. It doesn't matter how you got there. It's *where* you end up that's important. The rest, it's just details.

Keith Well. Maybe.

Graham And quite right too. Look where I've ended up, for instance. When you first met me, a few years ago, I was utterly miserable. And now I've never been happier in my whole life.

Keith How's your teaching going?

Graham *(cheerfully)* Oh, badly. I was so bad at pottery they took it off the syllabus. Then they put me on to woodwork, and they've just scrapped that too. They're giving me mathematics next. I'm hoping I can destroy that one as well.

Keith That's nice.

Graham How's *your* teaching going?

Keith *(sighing)* It turns out I'm actually rather good at it. I only began part-time, as you know, to keep Barbara happy. Now I'm taking five classes a day. The children say I really make a difference.

Graham What have they got you teaching?

Keith Everything. It's all those hobbies I took, they've given me far too much information. It's horrible, Graham. Every morning I wake up in a cold sweat, knowing all those kids will be hanging on my every word. I don't want to make a difference, I don't need that sort of responsibility.

Graham The trick is just to stop caring. That's what I did.

Keith I'm trying. But however hard I try, they still end up learning something. I wish I was inept like you, Graham.

Graham Well, perhaps I can give you some pointers. Would that help?

Keith You'd really do that for me?

Graham Tell you what. Why don't you come over one evening, we could talk about it over a meal. See if I can't sort you out.

Keith Thank you, that would be great...

Graham But I'm warning you. I'm not a very good teacher.

Keith *(shaking his hand)* That's okay, I'm a very good pupil. I'm a blank sheet of paper, just a blank sheet of paper. If you could make me mediocre again, it'd be such a weight off my mind.

*(Enter **Barbara**.)*

Barbara The simulation swords should be ready soon. They're just sorting some out for us.

Graham Great.

Keith Graham and I were just saying, darling. It's all very impressive, isn't it?

Barbara I miss the sky.

Keith Sorry?

Barbara I miss the sky.

Keith But you don't need sky. There isn't any sky required at the battle of Bosworth.

*(He shares the joke with **Graham**.)*

Barbara There's no logic to it, Keith, I just miss it, that's all. I picked you up a commemorative T-shirt from the battle gift shop.

Keith Oh. Thanks.

Barbara Why don't you go and try it on? I want to have a private chat with Graham.

Keith Sure, okay. See you in a bit.

*(He raises his eyebrows at **Graham** again, jokingly. **Graham** smiles back. **Keith** exits.)*

Graham Nice man.

*(And he and **Barbara** kiss.)*

So. Do you think you can get away from him this evening?

Barbara I'd imagine so. Why?

Graham It's Bosworth! You know. Without fail, on the anniversary of Bosworth, we'd always, you know.

Barbara But we're always you-knowing.

Graham I know...

Barbara I haven't you-knowed so much in my entire life.

Graham Do you think Keith suspects something?

Barbara God. I hope so. I drop enough hints. Pretending to talk in my sleep, moaning, Graham, Graham, take me, Graham. But he never rises to it. It's like trying to provoke a sponge.

Graham What on earth are you doing that for?

Barbara Just trying to put a bit of danger back into it all. What we've got, I'm just so bored of the whole thing.

Graham I'm sorry. I've been reading up on sex, I got a book from the library. I thought I was getting quite good at it.

Barbara It isn't the sex itself, it's everything around the sex. I don't wake up any more thinking, 'ooh, I'm having an affair'. I'm not really, Keith and I barely touch any more, he's too busy with his teaching and his battle plans. Instead I wake up and think, 'I'm sleeping with the man I was married to for eleven years'. Where's the excitement in that?

*(**Graham** makes to kiss her.)*

No. Don't. You just don't make me feel guilty like you used to. And sex is no good without the guilt. I'm sorry.

Graham ...I don't know what to suggest.

Barbara Well, I've got an idea. Something that will make me feel really bad about myself. But you'll have to trust me.

Graham I trust you, Barbara. In fact. I love you.

Barbara What?

Graham I love you.

(Short pause)

Barbara I didn't ask for that. I'm not even sure I want it.

(And she exits.

*(Enter **Chloe**. She looks paler and more tired than before. Her acne has worsened, leaving large crusty scars on her face. Her hair has greyed prematurely.)*

Graham *(brightening)* Here she is! Here's the girl I want to see!

Chloe Hello, Mr Widthorpe.

Graham Yes. Well, where is she?

Chloe The studio said I couldn't bring Tanya to a public event. The insurance wouldn't cover it.

Graham *(disappointed)* Oh. That's a shame. I've never met a celebrity before. Stephen's looking after her, is he?

Chloe *(thinly)* The insurance certainly wouldn't cover *that*. No, I left him to park the car.

Graham I saw Tanya on the telly last night.

Chloe *(wearily)* You would have done. She's on the telly every night.

Graham It was an ad I hadn't seen before. Selling nappies. I thought, I know her! Well, almost. She was very good.

Chloe Tanya's the cover girl this month for *Cosmopolitan, Elle* and *Infant Monthly*. Every time I go into a newsagent's, her face stares out at me.

Graham She was even better than in that last ad she did. The one for sanitary towels.

Chloe I always felt she was a bit miscast in that one. Still.

Graham You must be very proud. She's the most famous baby model since, well... whenever.

Chloe The studios are trying to work out a sitcom vehicle for her. The problem is, they can't think of many situations a two year old baby would get into. But they've got good scriptwriters.

Graham I'd love to have an autograph. Do you think she could do that? I know she couldn't write much, just an X would be great.

*(Enter **Stephen**. His acne is rather fresher than **Chloe's**.)*

Oh, hello. Stephen. How are you?

Stephen *(automatically)* I'm very well, thank you, sir. And I hope *you* have a nice day.

Graham What?

Stephen Sorry. Force of habit.

Graham You're still working at Speedy Burger then?

Chloe *(dryly)* Yes.

Graham I thought you'd have given it up. Tanya must be raking the money in...

Stephen I couldn't desert Speedy Burger. It's not a job. It's a vocation.

Graham ...I see.

Stephen They feed me, they clothe me, they gave me a new name. And there's no scientific proof that our food is addictive, a panel of nutritionalists recently agreed. So a meal at Speedy Burger is still a meal for all the family to enjoy.

Chloe *(brooding)* I could have been Tanya. I had what she has. I think I'll get her tattooed. 'Mummy Forever'. Just so she remembers what her fame cost. Just so I'll get a credit.

Graham *(awkwardly)* Right. Yes.

*(And he backs away from them both involuntarily. He is clearly relieved as **Barbara** enters. She is carrying five light sabres, the plastic illuminated staffs seen in* Star Wars.*)*

Barbara This is what they want us to fight with. Not swords, but these sticks.

Stephen Light sabres! Yes!

Barbara The tourist board thinks they'll be more exciting to watch. They light up in the dark, apparently.

Stephen And they make a great noise too! Woosh! Listen to that! Woosh!

(He demonstrates the electronic sound effect the toy makes to a nonplussed audience.)

Graham I suppose it will keep the kids happy...

Stephen Absolutely! With these light sabres, this battle will be a battle the whole family can enjoy.

Barbara So long as you're happy.

*(Enter **Reg**. He is dressed as a World War I pilot, all goggles and scarf. He looks a bit like Biggles. Everyone stares at him; **Stephen** lets his light sabre droop.)*

Reg Hello, everyone! Not too late, am I?

*(**Barbara** steps forward.)*

Hello, Sheila.

Barbara I'm not Sheila. What are you dressed like that for?

Reg I couldn't find my kit. So I went along to a costume shop, told them I was fighting in a war. Only I couldn't remember which war it was. Don't you like it, Sheila?

Barbara I'm not Sheila. I'm Barbara. What are you doing here? We told you we didn't want you to come any more. You're no use to us, Reg.

Reg Does that mean I have to go home? Can't I stay and fight a little bit?

Barbara All right. But you can't have a sword. There aren't enough to go round. You'll have to chop about with your arm.

Reg I can do that.

Barbara And you'll have to die early. As quickly and unobtrusively as possible. Not having you alive spoiling it for the rest of us.

Reg That's great, that's fine. You don't know what it means to me, just to take part. Thank you, Sheila.

Barbara It's *Barbara*. Sheila's dead.

Reg Oh yes.

*(She exits. **Reg** sits down on the grass. Smiles, stares off into the distance.*

*(**Graham** waves his sabre around distractedly. **Stephen** and **Chloe** are giving theirs a full practice.)*

Stephen This is going to be great. Whoosh. Come on, Chloe. Put a bit of oomph into it.

Chloe Whoosh.

Stephen You can be more aggressive than this. Come on, really attack me!

Chloe You Lancastrian bastard.

Stephen Better. But we're fighting the Tudors now.

Chloe You Tudor bastard then.

Stephen It is a bit confusing, I know. But not to worry, they'll massacre the lot of us shortly.

Graham Are you all right, Reg?

Reg Oh yes. I was just talking to Sheila. You know, in my head.

Graham Oh. Do a lot of that, do you?

Reg She's always there, bless her. Never leaves me alone. I was just saying to her, this grass seems sharper than normal!

Graham Yes, it's plastic...

Reg And she said I was a senile old git who couldn't tell my arse from my elbow. Which hurt me, in fact, because in all the years I knew her she never once said arse.

Graham I'm sorry.

Reg *(surprised)* You're being very nice to me. I never liked you, did I?

Graham I don't think so, no. Not very much.

Reg *(not unkindly)* Well. I'm sorry, but I think it's a little too late for me to start liking you now.

*(**Graham** nods, pats **Reg** sympathetically on the back, then exits.)*

*(**Chloe** and **Stephen** are still fighting their* Star Wars *duel.)*

Stephen Whoosh! That was a good one.

Chloe Stephen, I need to talk to you...

Stephen Nastier than that! Hit me with everything you've got!

Chloe Barry's come back. I want you out of my house within the week.

Stephen Yes, that's the sort of thing. Really hurt me.

Chloe *(lowering her sabre)* Stephen.

(Short pause)

I've been wanting to tell you, but you're never there any more. Always out high on Speedy Burgers till gone midnight.

Stephen I told you, I'm clean. I've given up that stuff.

Chloe Oh, please, when you come in I can smell it on your breath. You hide sesame seed buns all over the house where you think I won't find them. Face up to it, Stephen. You're a junk food junkie.

Stephen *(whining a little)* The patches they gave me don't work. I still can't beat the cravings... All right. I'll get help. I promise. I'll get better...

Chloe But this isn't about you. It's about Barry. I've waited so long, and at last he wants me back.

*(**Stephen** begins to prod **Chloe** sulkily with his light sabre.)*

Prodding me with your light sabre won't do any good.

Stephen Makes me feel better.

Chloe Had enough?

Stephen One more. ...You don't really think Barry wants you for you.

Chloe What do you mean?

Stephen You do. God. You are so bloody stupid. He wants Tanya. Tanya's making millions. He wants the money.

Chloe No. He said he loved me. He said he's always loved me, he wants things back the way they were...

Stephen How could he love you? Have you looked at yourself in a mirror? Have you seen how ugly you are?

Chloe ...I'm not ugly.

Stephen You're repulsive. You're the ugliest woman I've ever seen. I can hardly bear to look at you, I'm afraid if I touch you bits will flake off. And you're stupid, and you're dull. What could he want with *you*? He wants the money, Chloe, surely you can see that? Nobody in their right mind would love you. Except me, Chloe, I love you, I'll do anything you ask, you know that...

Chloe *(forced calm)* I know you love me. And I know Barry doesn't. But I don't want you. I want Barry.

*(Pause. And **Stephen** turns away, miserably.)*

*(For a moment, **Chloe** does nothing, standing frozen. Then, gently, she begins to cry.)*

*(**Stephen** sits on the grass and opens his bag. He takes out the first in a series of wrapped burgers. He begins to chew on one morosely.)*

*(**Reg**, distracted by **Chloe**'s tears, looks around. With difficulty, he gets up and goes to her.)*

Reg ...Sheila?

Chloe Go away.

Reg Sheila?

Chloe I'm not Sheila, please...

Reg Please, Sheila, please don't cry, please, Sheila.

Chloe *(facing him)* Leave me alone, why can't you leave me alone...

Reg *(reacting to her face)* It *is* you. Oh, Sheila. Oh, my love. You're so beautiful.

Chloe I'm not beautiful.

Reg Oh, you are. You're as you used to be. Before our fights. Before our indifference. Oh, Sheila, I love you. Is it really you?

Chloe ...Yes. Yes, it is.

Reg Oh, Sheila. At last.

(Short pause. Then, painfully, he gets down on to his knees.)

Chloe No, what are you doing?

Reg I'm sorry. I'm sorry.

(And he begins to weep softly.)

Chloe Reg, no, get up...

Reg Oh, Sheila. I'm so sorry. Please forgive me.

Chloe Reg, come on...

Reg I didn't want to hurt you. I wanted to be a good husband. But I didn't know how to. You see? I didn't know how to.

Chloe Reg, it's all right...

Reg No, it's not all right. All the years I wasted. Forgive me. Forgive me.

Chloe I forgive you.

Reg I love you, Sheila, I miss you so much. Please forgive me...

(And he cries freely. No sound.)

Chloe I forgive you. Please. ...Please.

(And she helps him to his feet. He can't look at her. But she gently lifts his face towards her, and smiles. As she dries his tears:)

Ssh. Ssh now.

Reg *(crying done)* And you'll leave me alone now? You won't be in my head any more?

Chloe No.

Reg Promise?

Chloe I promise.

*(**Reg** smiles, nods.)*

Am I really beautiful?

Reg Oh yes. You're the most beautiful woman I ever knew. You always were.

*(**Chloe** smiles, kisses him on the cheek.*

*(Re-enter **Barbara**, **Graham** following.)*

Barbara Okay. If I could have your attention, please. Before we start, I know our leader would like to say a few words. I give you our leader.

*(She applauds. Everybody duly follows, as **Keith** enters. Over his doublet he wears a T-shirt. On it are the words, 'I Got Killed at the Battle of*

Bosworth'.*)*

Keith *(gently)* Great. Thanks, everyone. Well, this is where it ends. Thirty years of conflict will soon be over. We fought to restore the rightful heir to the throne, to support the Yorkist claim over the Lancastrian usurpers. And we did it too! And today all that we achieved is going to be destroyed by an invasion from the Welsh. Well, that's life. Well done, anyway. And when you go out there to die, remember, you can die with pride.

*(Applause. **Barbara** holds up her hand for silence.)*

Barbara Just before we go off to our deaths, I'd like to make an announcement of my own. Concerning Keith and myself. You have all seen the ups and downs of our relationship during the battles we've fought together. In a small way, you've not just been our footsoldiers, you've been our friends as well.

Keith Oh God. You're going to dump me, aren't you?

*(But **Barbara** gets down upon one knee.)*

Barbara Keith. Would you do me the honour of becoming my husband? Will you marry me?

(Short pause)

Keith *(amazed)* My God. Why? Yes. I mean, yes. God. Wow.

*(And everybody applauds. **Barbara** gets to her feet. **Keith** makes to kiss her, but she turns it into a peck on the cheek.)*

Graham *(warmly, to **Barbara**)* Many congratulations.

Barbara And *now* we're having an affair.

(And she gives him a passionate and undisguised kiss on the mouth.)

Keith We'll go out this evening, Barbara. We'll celebrate!

Barbara Not tonight. I'm otherwise engaged.

(And as the applause dies down:)

Keith Well. I don't know what to say. I must be the happiest man alive. Wow. ...Quite frankly, going out there now to be butchered in front of the tourist board takes the edge off it a bit.

Stephen *(unexpectedly)* Speaking for myself. I'm tired of always losing. I'm sick of it.

(And he throws away his burger with disgust.

(Pause)

Keith What are you suggesting?

Stephen *(shrugging)* Let's win instead.

Reg He's right.

Barbara What?

Reg I don't want to die. Not yet, not now. Marvin here is absolutely right.

*(He moves to join him. Then **Chloe** does too.)*

Barbara Where are you going?

Chloe My life, it really isn't that great. If I can't make things work out right *here*... what chance have I got out there?

Barbara Stop this, all of you. This isn't what the tourist board wants at all. There are some very important people in the tourist board. Tell them, Keith. Oh, don't bother, you're useless. Tell them, Graham.

*(Short pause. Then **Graham** moves too. **Barbara** stops him.)*

No, Graham. This is ridiculous.

Graham Well, if you can't beat them.

Barbara But what about history?

Stephen History's done us no favours. So let's change it.

Graham He's got a point.

*(And he has joined them. **Keith** moves too.)*

Barbara Keith! Back here. Now.

Keith Darling, you know what I'm like. I'm very easily influenced. I'm just a blank sheet of paper. ...Maybe that's all history is.

*(And they all face **Barbara**.)*

Barbara This is insane. You can't expect me to agree to this.

(Short pause)

All right, I admit, this isn't how I imagined the future either. The twenty-first century, by now I thought we'd all be living on the moon. Instead, I'm in a small flat in Burnley. But we can't change anything like this. Not like this.

(Short pause)

ALL: Why not?

(Short pause)

Barbara The tourist board will have a fit.

(And she runs and joins them, laughing.)

Let's do it!

Keith All right, everyone. Let's go out there and fight. And in spite of what we've been taught. In spite of what we *know*. Let's do the impossible. Let's go out there and win! Light sabres at the ready...

*(Everyone lifts up their sabres. Except for **Reg**, who cheerfully chops with his arm.)*

ALL: Charge!

(They freeze in a spotlight. We hear horses braying, swords clashing, men dying. And cheers of jubilation and victory.

(Blackout.)

Inappropriate Behaviour

(2001)

OPENED AT THE STEPHEN JOSEPH THEATRE, SCARBOROUGH,
ON 8TH JUNE 2001, WITH THE FOLLOWING CAST:
JEREMY JASON BAUGHAN
HELEN CATE DEBENHAM-TAYLOR
DIRECTED BY FRANK MOOREY

IT WAS FIRST BROADCAST ON BBC RADIO FOUR
ON 17TH AUGUST 2002, WITH THE FOLLOWING CAST:
JEREMY MARTIN JARVIS
HELEN ROSALIND AYRES
DIRECTED BY MARTIN JARVIS

Act One

1 – The Wedding (1)

(The set is very simple. There is a large table, and access to a door. A hatstand may be used to facilitate costume change – but as the scenes move on and the years pass, these changes should be kept to a minimum.

*(It is the reception of a wedding. We hear pop music in the background. **Jeremy**, perhaps in his early thirties, is smartly dressed. He stands, eating buffet items from a paper plate – and watching the events a little awkwardly. He is approached by **Helen**, mid to late twenties, in a party dress.)*

Helen I've been watching you.

Jeremy Oh. Have you?

Helen I've been keeping my eye on you.

Jeremy Oh. Gosh. Well, thank you. I expect.

Helen And you're not dancing. You can't deny you're not dancing, are you?

Jeremy No.

Helen You can't deny it.

Jeremy No, you've got me there.

Helen Everybody's dancing. Look, over there. Even my mother is dancing. Look.

Jeremy Is that one your mother...?

Helen ...Launching herself across the floor like a dying whale, yes.

Jeremy Gosh.

Helen Which I admit isn't much incentive for you to join in, but you see, it's proof, everyone's dancing. Or in my mother's case, cavorting. Everyone but you.

Jeremy You've been keeping your eye on me.

Helen I have.

Jeremy Yes. Well, the truth is, I'm just not very good at it.

Helen What's that got to do with it? I'm an appalling dancer.

Jeremy Really?

Helen Yes, you should see me. Really embarrassingly awful. Two left feet. No, worse than that, one left foot and a crutch.

Jeremy The only dance I know is the waltz. The waltz, you see. I don't know anything else.

Helen You don't need to *know* anything. You just jig up and down a bit.

Jeremy My wife taught me how to waltz, you see. It's where we met, dancing classes, I thought I'd give it a go. I kept kicking her in the shins. Week after week, I'd come back, I didn't get any better, just kept, you know... kicking her in the shins! Yes. She only married me to get me to stop.

*(He laughs shortly. **Helen** looks at him, puzzled.)*

Helen ...Yes. All I'm saying is, I hate dancing, but I still have to do it. All those people out there, they hate dancing too. Do you think my mother doesn't know she looks like a dying whale? Of course she does, it's obvious she's like a dying whale, but she's still doing it. She's still joining in. So why won't you?

(Short pause)

All right. Well, I've done my job. Dad told me to make sure everyone was dancing. I've done the best I could, haven't I?

Jeremy You did very well...

Helen 'I haven't spent all that bloody money on a bloody DJ just to have people not dancing.' That's what he said. But that's fine. Suit yourself. It's not your wedding, it's mine. But it doesn't matter. Suit yourself.

(She walks away. Short pause)

Jeremy Oh dear.

(He practises awkwardly. Rather self-conscious bopping and swaying of hips. He looks around, embarrassed, and tries to make the actions look like he was doing something else. He withdraws back into himself.

*(And re-enter **Helen**, who stands apart, looking at him. Immediately he resumes.)*

Ah. I've changed my mind...

Helen Sorry, can I just ask you...

Jeremy It's all right, I'm dancing, look...

Helen No, it doesn't matter, really...

Jeremy Oh yes, you see, I'm having fun, who would have thought it...?

Helen No, no. Please. Don't. Please.

Jeremy ...Okay.

Helen I need to ask you, and please tell me honestly. Was I rude just now?

Jeremy Well...

Helen Back then. To you. Was I? I was, wasn't I?

Jeremy I wouldn't say you were rude exactly...

Helen I can see I was, it's written all over your face...

Jeremy More what I would call impolite. Not as bad as rude.

Helen It's not good enough. Sorry. I told myself not to do this. I said, Helen, getting drunk and being rude to complete strangers was all part of single life. You'll have to cut that out now you're a married woman.

Jeremy Not even very impolite, just a tad abrupt.

Helen I've been doing everything I promised I wouldn't. Getting weepy and telling the bridesmaids how lovely they look. Pretending to laugh at the best man's speech. Trying to make sure everyone's having a good time, God, why does it matter, if you want to stand at the back of the hall looking miserable why should I care...?

Jeremy I'm not miserable. This is simply the way my face is, it hangs downwards...

Helen There you are, you see, I'm being rude again. The thing is, I'm a bit drunk.

Jeremy Yes.

Helen And it's not even my fault. I've only had a couple of glasses of champagne. But I'm drinking on an empty stomach.

Jeremy Oh, I understand. Not able to keep your food down, eh?

Helen What?

Jeremy Wedding day nerves. My wife was just the same. When we got married, she couldn't stop throwing up. And she felt decidedly queasy throughout the honeymoon.

Helen No, no, it's nothing like that...

Jeremy In fact, come to think of it, it was the best part of a year until she got her appetite at all. It took that long for her stomach to adjust to married life.

Helen No. It's simply there's nothing here I can eat.

Jeremy Oh.

Helen The caterers got it wrong. There's hardly a vegetarian option at all. Well, a bit of salad. I can hardly fill up on salad, can I?

Jeremy What a nuisance.

Helen Oh, that's just the tip of the iceberg. The whole day has been a disaster, quite frankly. Standing out in the pouring rain for nearly an hour of photographs that'll never develop properly. My father's been telling everyone he wishes I'd been a boy so he wouldn't have had to pay for everything. The DJ seems to have only brought three or four records with him – I tell you, if I hear 'Mull of Kintyre' one more time I'm going to scream.

Jeremy Its charms do fade somewhat on repeat listening.

Helen But all that's nothing to the wedding itself. That was just ghastly.

Jeremy Oh. I thought it came off rather well...

Helen God, no, it was *awful*. Where did they get that vicar from? Droning on and on with that ponderous voice, I wanted to say, for God's sake, cut to the chase here, any just cause or impediment, right, no, good, you're married, let's get out of here.

Jeremy *(awkwardly)* Ah. Oh.

Helen I'd always wondered, ever since I was a little girl, how I'd feel getting married. At the actual crunch, proud, excited, scared as hell, any of those. I never thought I'd be bored out of my mind.

Jeremy He probably just wanted to get it right. Give you the best start he could...

Helen I can't wait for this day to be over. On the scale of bad days it's right down there with taking my O-levels and having my wisdom teeth pulled out. Everyone's having a rotten time, they all want to go home. Look at them.

Jeremy *(out into the audience)* Yes, well, they're probably all a bit tired...

Helen And yet they're all being so bloody *nice*. If one more person comes and tells me how beautiful I looked as I walked up the aisle... You, for instance, what did you think?

Jeremy Me?

Helen I don't know you, you don't know me. So be honest. Walking up the aisle. Did I look beautiful? Or like an enormous marshmallow?

Jeremy You looked fine, really.

Helen Yes, but fine in what way? Fine as a beautiful bride, or fine as a marshmallow?

Jeremy I suppose veering more towards the marshmallow side of fine, really.

Helen You see? That's what I want. That's all I want. People being honest and telling me how big a mistake this whole thing has been.

(Short pause)

Jeremy You don't mean getting married itself was a mistake?

Helen I don't know. I think I might. I don't know.

Jeremy No.

Helen Don't listen to me. I'm drunk. That's what it is. Too much champagne, not enough nut roast.

Jeremy Because it's perfectly normal to have doubts...

Helen But getting married makes perfect sense, doesn't it? Doesn't it? Andrew and I have been living together for years already. My mother's been nagging me to marry, his mother's been nagging him, we thought this was the best way to shut them up.

Jeremy So long as you love each other, then all is fine. And I'm sure you do, don't you?

Helen But watching Andrew today. He's actually *enjoying* this. When people say to him how handsome he looked, he loves it! And if we can't agree on how our miserable our wedding day was, how do I know we've really anything in common at all?

Jeremy Maybe it isn't so bad. Maybe he's just pretending not to notice how miserable the wedding is.

Helen No, he really means it. I looked into his eyes when the vicar pronounced us man and wife, and he had tears in his eyes. And it was at that moment I realised how incompatible we were. ...I'm sorry, I shouldn't say this, for all I know you're Andrew's uncle or something...

Jeremy No, no...

Helen But you're obviously one of Andrew's guests, I'm sorry, you shouldn't hear this. I told myself, doubting that I love Andrew is all part of single life...

Jeremy I don't know Andrew at all.

Helen *(suspiciously)* Really? Then why are you here? If you don't know Andrew and you don't know me...

Jeremy Well. I suppose it's my job.

Helen *(ashen)* Oh my God. You're the caterer, aren't you?

Jeremy No.

Helen And here I am, being rude about your lack of vegetarian options.

Jeremy No, honestly, it's all right. I'm not the caterer. I'm the vicar.

(Short pause)

Helen But that's much worse.

Jeremy Oh. I suppose it is.

Helen Do forgive me. I didn't recognise you without the dog collar...

Jeremy No, sure, even my wife says the dog collar is the most distinctive thing about me...

Helen This is terrible, I'm so sorry...

Jeremy And you're right, I am useless doing weddings. It's my face, you see, hanging downwards like it does. It's a funeral face, I'm really a lot better at funerals.

Helen I promised I wouldn't be rude again, and I've just spent the last five minutes insulting a vicar. The day just can't get any worse.

(And Mull of Kintyre *starts to play. She bursts into tears.* **Jeremy** *looks around awkwardly.)*

Jeremy Oh dear... no, don't do that...

Helen I can't help it! Has anyone noticed?

Jeremy Erm. Well, yes.

Helen Oh God. Try to reassure them...

(**Jeremy** *steps forward, smiles broadly. He gives a little wave and a shrug.)*

Jeremy They don't look very convinced...

Helen What am I going to do?

Jeremy Perhaps if you stopped crying...

Helen Got to look happy. Got to enjoy myself. Dance with me!

Jeremy But I told you, all I can do is the waltz!

Helen It's easy! Please! Just do as I do!

(*And through her tears she does some elementary disco dancing.* **Jeremy** *awkwardly joins in.*)

I'm so sorry, I'm such a mess...

Jeremy No, that's okay, really...

Helen Try swinging from side to side a bit more...

Jeremy Oh, right.

Helen That's it. I'm just not sure I can deal with being married after all.

Jeremy Honestly, it happens to all of us...

Helen Mmm, and turn round as well.

Jeremy Like this?

Helen And again.

Jeremy Right. Everyone gets scared at the idea of being with someone for the rest of their lives...

Helen Try to move with the rhythm of the music. What, everyone gets scared?

Jeremy Yes, I think so. I know I did...

Helen You're getting the rhythm, good...

Jeremy I still am scared most of the time. Really, have I got the rhythm?

Helen Yes, it looks as if you're enjoying yourself now...

Jeremy Does it? Oh good.

Helen Yes.

Jeremy Because I'm not.

Helen On the one hand, I was quite happy the way things were. We did the shopping together, we shared the bills, we made love every Friday night. Not passionate, but regular.

Jeremy Yes, I see...

Helen I'm not sure I want that to change simply because we're married.

Jeremy I understand...

Helen No, you're losing the rhythm again, you're getting too slow...

Jeremy Ah, force of habit.

Helen Are they still watching me?

Jeremy I haven't dared look.

Helen And yet, part of me thinks. I'm a wife now. I have a husband. Something *ought* to change. I should wake up tomorrow morning feeling different. I should wake up tomorrow *being* different.

Jeremy Yes, I see that too...

Helen Or else what's the point? If it's just going to be the same. Twirl again. That's good.

Jeremy Thanks.

Helen You see, in the one hand I'm scared marriage will change everything. And on the other I'm scared it won't. So I lose either way.

Jeremy Well, yes...

Helen Sway a bit more.

Jeremy Sorry, it's hard to sway and give advice at the same time. You see, from the other point of view, you could say you *win* either way. Am I swaying enough now?

Helen Yes, that swaying is fine. How do you mean?

Jeremy If nothing changes, then you know where you are. And if everything does, it makes it all worthwhile.

Helen Oh yes. Actually, that's rather a good way of looking at it.

Jeremy Thanks. Anything I can do.

Helen I've stopped crying now.

Jeremy Does that mean I can stop dancing?

Helen Yes.

Jeremy Thank goodness.

(*They stop. So does the music, shortly afterwards. Short pause*)

Helen I'm sorry, you know. That I said you were boring.

Jeremy That's okay. I did say your dress made you look like a marshmallow.

Helen You're not boring. You're actually very sweet. You just take a bit of getting used to.

Jeremy Thank you.

Helen You're welcome.

Jeremy Yes.

Helen Yes.

Jeremy Yes.

(Short pause)

And you didn't look like a marshmallow. You were beautiful. Really.

(Pause)

Helen I'd better go and mingle with the other guests.

Jeremy Oh, yes. Absolutely.

Helen The caterer must be lurking around here somewhere. See if I can't be rude to him. Joke.

Jeremy Have a good life, Helen.

*(She nods. Then turns and drifts away. Another song begins to play. **Jeremy** hesitates, then cautiously starts to dance again. He laughs at himself, and stops.*

(And the pop music becomes more choral, as we go into:)

2 – The Christening

(We are outside in the cold, in front of a church door.)

Helen I just wanted to say. Thank you for the service, vicar.

Jeremy Oh. You're very welcome.

Helen And sorry about Paul biting you like that.

Jeremy Don't worry about it.

Helen I just wanted to say that.

Jeremy A lot of babies bite when they're being christened. Everybody staring at them, the water on the forehead, some strange chap dressed in funny robes. It's an occupational hazard.

Helen He's reached that stage where he just likes to hurt everybody he can as much as possible.

Jeremy Mind you, when most babies bite me all I feel is gums and spit. Nothing quite as sharp as little Paul had to offer.

Helen You'd never guess he was only two months, would you? Not with a set of fangs like that. The doctors say he's very dentally advanced.

Jeremy Mmm. You must be very proud.

Helen Well, I think I'll wait until Paul can walk or talk or find a cure for cancer before I get too excited.

(Short pause)

You don't recognise me, do you? You married us nearly two years ago.

Jeremy Oh, yes...

Helen I saw you standing there in the church, you know, holding Paul over the font. And I thought, I know him!

Jeremy No, I remember you...

Helen I know him, I thought, as he chomped down on your finger. Really? You recognise me?

Jeremy Oh yes. How have you been, Helen?

Helen All the hundreds of brides you must have married. Thousands even. I was sure you wouldn't recognise me.

Jeremy I didn't think you'd recognise me either. Even wearing the dog collar.

Helen I wasn't going to say anything. In case you'd forgotten.

Jeremy Nor was I. I was sure you would have.

Helen *(laughing)* Well, there you are. Aren't we both silly?

(Short pause. They both shiver a bit in the cold, blow on their hands and rub them. Smile at each other.)

Well.

Jeremy Yes.

Helen So, how have you been?

Jeremy Oh. You know.

Helen Yes!

Jeremy You've been busy, I see?

Helen *(frowning slightly)* In what way, sorry?

Jeremy Well. The baby.

Helen Oh. Yes, sorry. I see what you mean.

Jeremy Little Paul.

Helen Yes! Well, I haven't been that busy, actually. It was only one night's work.

Jeremy Sure.

Helen Not a lot of effort required. I'm sure you've been a lot busier.

(Short pause)

Jeremy Still. You must be very proud.

Helen Yes, we must be. I mean, yes, we are.

Jeremy Just to think, when I last saw you. You were all nervous about being married.

Helen Yes.

Jeremy Do you remember that? That you were all nervous?

Helen Yes.

Jeremy And here you are now. With an addition to the family. You see how things work out?

Helen Mmm.

Jeremy They always work out, don't they? Things. I mean, in the end.

(Short pause)

Helen It was the dog's fault, you know.

Jeremy What's the dog's fault, sorry?

Helen Paul. The dog was very poorly, you see. We took him to the vet's, he said he only had a few months to live. Well, fair enough, we'd had our money's worth. But it meant Andrew and I had to decide whether simply to replace the dog, or to invest in something, you know. A little more permanent.

Jeremy Oh, I see. And Paul is...

Helen More permanent. We hope. And it kept my mum happy, and Andrew's, both were dying to be grandmothers.

Jeremy And the dog? I mean, I suppose by now he's...

Helen No, no, that's the thing. He's still hanging on. Incredible, really, he's lost his liver as far as we can tell, he's lost his kidneys, he's lost his eyesight, we have to hold his head in his dinner bowl or he'd never find it. Nature's giving him all these hints, but he's just not taking them.

Jeremy Incredible.

Helen It's a bit annoying, really. If I'd known the dog would still be kicking, I wouldn't have had Paul. But the vet was quite certain Spike wouldn't outlive the year.

Jeremy Well.

Helen Whereas it's turned out Spike has outlived the vet. Or so I read in the local paper.

Jeremy God works in mysterious ways.

Helen Yes.

Jeremy Spike's clearly a survivor.

Helen Oh, I think he's on his way out now. I get the feeling Paul resents the competition, and attacks the dog whenever we're not looking. I keep finding teeth marks all over Spike's body.

Jeremy No, that isn't good, is it...?

Helen Of course Andrew won't hear a word against his son, of course not, he thinks Spike is doing it to himself. And I say, look, Andrew, look where the bite marks *are*, it's physically impossible for Spike to reach that, he'd break his neck trying.

Jeremy I'm sure it's just a phase Paul will grow out of.

Helen It's only a matter of time before Paul clamps down on something really vulnerable, and then that's it, we've got a dead dog on our hands.

Jeremy ...Yes. But I dare say you must take great comfort in looking at your son, and thinking of all the years of happiness he'll bring you. To see him and know that someone exists who would have no life without you, that you have created him, that he's yours and nothing can ever take that away.

Helen Well, no, not really.

Jeremy My wife and I have been trying for so long, I think all she ever wanted was a child, not even really a husband, just someone she could call her own...

Helen *(barely listening, interrupting)* I'm just waiting for Paul to get a personality, I think. Something recognisably human, something other than simple evil-minded viciousness. That'd be nice.

Jeremy *(quietly)* I'm sure it'll happen soon.

Helen I bloody hope so.

(Short pause)

Anyway. I just wanted to say. Thanks for the christening. I was dead set against it, actually. But I was wrong. It was lovely.

Jeremy What was the problem?

Helen Well, I don't believe in God. And Andrew doesn't believe in God. I don't especially want my son believing in God. But my mother and his mother, they got talking, no, we've got to get this done. So. Not that they believe in God either, I mean, who does? But they wanted a day out.

Jeremy I see.

Helen I said, if we're going to indoctrinate the baby into a religion, why Christianity, let's shop around first, Buddhism, Shinto, let's see what they've got to offer. But Andrew told me I was being silly. He always says I'm being silly.

Jeremy I'm glad you enjoyed it anyway.

Helen I did! Watching you up there, and you did it so beautifully, it was lovely...

Jeremy *(shyly)* Thanks...

Helen ...I could almost believe it all actually meant something and wasn't part of some stupid superstition. I'm telling you. It almost made me wish it could happen to me. I'm telling you!

Jeremy Haven't you ever been christened, then? Not as a baby?

Helen No. My parents never quite got round to it. You know, with the divorce and everything.

Jeremy Well. Would you like to rectify that?

Helen What? Just like that?

Jeremy Yes. I mean, if you wanted to.

Helen You could do that. Christen me right here and now?

Jeremy If you'd like it. Obviously, only if you'd like it.

Helen It's very strange, but you know, I think I would? I think I'd find it a bit reassuring. I won't have to do anything, will I? Start praying or going to church, nothing religious like that?

Jeremy *(sighing)* Well, most people don't...

Helen Okay. Yes, then. I think that would be really really exciting. Thanks.

*(**Jeremy** tries to open the door.)*

Jeremy Oh. Sorry, the church door is locked...

Helen What?

Jeremy The verger's locked the door. I told him I'd finished, you see...

Helen Does that mean I can't get christened? I was really looking forward to it.

Jeremy You can always come back some other time...

Helen Oh, no. No, I don't think so. If I can't get christened on the spur of the moment, I'm not sure I want to get christened at all. It's now or never.

Jeremy I need the water, you see. I need the holy water in the font.

Helen *(reaching for her handbag)* I've got some water. If that's any good to you.

Jeremy Really?

Helen Mmm. Some mineral water. Here.

Jeremy Well, yes. I suppose we could make do. That's what the Lord would have done.

Helen It's sparkling with a twist of lemon. Do you think God will mind?

Jeremy He's suffered worse indignities, I think.

(He takes the bottle. It opens with a hiss. And sprinkles her forehead with water.)

Ready?

Helen *(steeling herself)* I'm ready.

Jeremy What's your full name?

Helen Helen Anne McAden.

Jeremy Helen Anne. I baptise thee in the name of the Father, and of the Son, and of the Holy Ghost. Amen.

(He ceremoniously dips his finger in. He marks a cross on her forehead and winces as he does so.)

Helen *(softly)* Amen.

Jeremy Fight valiantly under the banner of Christ against sin, the world, and the devil, and continue his faithful soldier and servant till the end of your life.

(Short pause)

Helen ...Is that it then?

Jeremy Well, that's the essentials. Welcome to the club.

Helen Thank you. Your finger was very cold.

Jeremy Oh. Sorry...

Helen No. It was nice. It was nice... I thought I saw you wince a bit...

Jeremy My finger's still pretty sore. I think all the fizzy water attacked it...

Helen You used the same finger that Paul bit?

Jeremy I always use this finger for baptism. It's my baptism finger.

Helen Let me see it, what he's done to it... Ow. I'm sorry. He's made a bit of a mess there.

Jeremy I doubt it's as bad as it looks. Or feels.

Helen It's a shame. Because I was thinking, as you baptised me, that you had a nice finger.

Jeremy Oh.

Helen I mean, you still do. I mean, it'll heal. Yes. You've got a nice finger.

Jeremy Well. You've got a nice forehead.

(Short pause. He clears his throat. More formally:)

Helen Anne. We welcome you into the Lord's family. We are children of the same Heavenly Father, we are inheritors together of the Kingdom of God. Here's your Highland Spring back.

Helen Thank you. Thank you very much.

Jeremy Jeremy. Jeremy Reginald.

Helen Thank you, Jeremy.

Jeremy Jeremy Reginald Wilberforce. At your service.

(She smiles at him. He smiles back awkwardly. Then she leaves.)

3 – The Nativity Play

*(Enter **Helen** hastily through the door. As she enters we hear from behind it children singing – cut off as the door closes again. She fumbles desperately in her handbag.)*

Helen *(muttering)* Come on, come on...

(And she finds what she is looking for. A nicotine inhalator. She takes it and sucks on it deeply. Then visibly relaxes, sinking against the door.)

Oh, that's better...

*(Enter **Jeremy**, after her. The door bangs into her gently as he enters; she glares at him for a moment.)*

Jeremy *(softly)* Hello! I thought it was you!

Helen Oh. Hello!

Jeremy Helen McAden! That's it, isn't it?

Helen The vicar. Erm. Gerald.

Jeremy *(without offence, cheerfully)* Jeremy.

Helen Jeremy. Yes.

Jeremy Helen Anne McAden. Well. It is good to see you again. I saw you leaving at the back, and Helen Anne McAden, it just popped into my head...

Helen *(interrupting slightly)* Are you enjoying the nativity play?

Jeremy Oh yes. I mean, the children are doing very well, aren't they?

Helen Yes.

Jeremy Under the circumstances. I mean, I don't quite know why it has to be such a lengthy retelling of the story...

Helen No. I mean, it's a fairly straightforward plot, isn't it? Son of God born in stable.

Jeremy I've seen *King Lear*'s which are shorter. But it's all part of Christmas, isn't it? Wouldn't be Christmas without sitting through the school nativity play.

Helen Is your child in it this year?

Jeremy I thought I... No, Eunice and I didn't... I mean, couldn't.

Helen So you're here in your vicar capacity then. Representing God, making sure the kids say nothing libellous.

Jeremy *(laughing politely)* Yes, that's right. No, I know quite a few of the cast. Joseph I know. And Third Angel. They're both in the church choir. And I teach the donkey at Sunday school. In a way, they're sort of like my real children. You know. In a way.

Helen That's nice.

Jeremy I mean, I know they don't like me very much. They've got a nickname for me. Boring Bastard.

Helen Almost exactly like having real children then.

Jeremy But I like to be supportive. And your son...

Helen *(abruptly)* Yes.

Jeremy Is he in...

Helen *(abruptly)* Yes.

Jeremy Yes. Well. That's nice.

*(Short pause. **Helen** takes a deep puff on her inhalator.)*

I was in a nativity play once. They put me down as one of the Wise Men.

Helen *(vaguely, going back to the door)* That's nice for you.

Jeremy Except it wasn't, really. The teacher had an idea it should be an all-singing, all-dancing part. I can carry a tune, but I'm really not a dancer at all. Even now, the only one I can do is the waltz.

Helen *(looking through the door, worriedly)* Paul's not on yet. But it's only a matter of time...

Jeremy My wife taught me. That's how we met, you know. I kept on kicking her shins! Every week there I'd be, kicking her shins.

*(**Helen** turns away from the door. She is obviously very worried, and takes another blast on the inhalator.)*

I'm sorry. I didn't know you smoked.

Helen I don't.

Jeremy I never had you down as a smoker.

Helen I'm not smoking. I'm inhaling.

Jeremy Mind you, it doesn't bother me, you go ahead. It's never been my bag, smoking. But my wife, she smokes forty a day. At least. She jokes about it, she says she needs it for her nerves being married to me!

We laugh about that. She'd like to give up, I think. Yes. Is it hard giving up?

Helen I don't know. I've never started.

Jeremy Oh. But isn't that the idea of those things?

Helen Smoking's very bad for you. Gives you cancer and things. No, when I decided I'd take up nicotine, I went straight to the inhalator. It gives you the buzz you need without any of the health risks.

Jeremy Oh, I see. Clever.

Helen Smoking's very out of fashion. All the girls at the office, we're all on these. Eleven o'clock and half past three, we all gather in the kitchen for our inhalator break.

Jeremy Gosh. Well. Good for you.

Helen Mind you, I'm not addicted. I'm just a social inhaler. But I was sitting there during the play, that bit where angel Gabriel was telling Mary she was going to have a baby and explaining in detail what that was going to entail...

Jeremy I think it was a mistake letting the biology teacher direct this...

Helen And I got a sudden craving. So, here I am. Sorry, I'm being rude. Would you like a puff?

Jeremy No, that's fine.

Helen It isn't bad for you, it isn't remotely harmful at all. No? Okay.

(And she takes a particularly deep puff, which leaves her quite breathless.)

Sorry. I'm a little on edge at the moment. Let me take a peep. Oh, God, Paul's on, he's actually on...

Jeremy *(joining her to look)* Ah. Bless. Which one is he?

Helen He's one of the sheep. Do you see him?

Jeremy Bless.

Helen The one with the horns and the fangs. I tried to tell him sheep don't have horns and fangs, but he doesn't listen to me. He doesn't like sheep, they're boring.

Jeremy Well, I agree it's not a terribly interesting part...

Helen He wanted to play Jesus. Mummy, he said, I want to play Jesus. But Paul, I said, nicely, trying to be reasonable, no-one plays Jesus. You can't have a little boy playing Jesus, it'd probably be blasphemous. They use a little doll instead, that's why Jesus is played by Barbie with her hair pulled out. But he stamped his foot, and shouted, I want to be Jesus! I want to be the Son of God!

Jeremy Oh dear.

Helen I want to be in the centre of the stage, with all the lights on, with everybody kneeling down in front of me. I want it to be *my* birthday, and everyone to worship me forever and ever.

Jeremy He always was a very forceful little chap. I can still feel those teeth marks...

Helen *(wistfully)* Oh, biting. Oh, I do miss biting. I'd *pay* to be bitten by him now. Do you have children, Jeremy?

Jeremy No, no, I said...

Helen Wise man. Good choice.

Jeremy It wasn't so much a choice, actually...

Helen Having a baby sounds okay in theory, but you've no idea what sort of person you've got breeding inside.

Jeremy My wife said we had to stop trying. What is it? I said. Don't you want children? Don't you like the idea?

Helen At the end of nine months, anyone could pop out. It's a gamble no-one should risk.

Jeremy Oh, I'd want children, she said. I just wouldn't want them with *you*. Not with you, Jeremy.

Helen A gamble I lost. He's a horrible little bastard.

Jeremy She can be so cruel when she's drinking.

Helen You did the right thing, Jeremy. I envy you. I really do.

Jeremy Would you mind... if I took a puff on your inhaler thing? After all?

Helen *(surprised)* No. Of course not...

(She wipes it, hands it to him. He takes an experimental puff.)

Jeremy Well. That's pretty foul.

Helen Yes. But you don't notice once the addiction kicks in. I tell you, I need it. I need something to get me through my days.

Jeremy Oh.

(Short pause)

Helen ...It's Andrew, you see. It's Andrew. He keeps looking at other women.

Jeremy Ah. And when you say looking...

Helen I mean, really looking. Staring, practically. Any woman at all, it doesn't seem to bother him, in the supermarket, in the pub, Paul's teachers at school. He's even been looking at my mother.

Jeremy Oh dear. That isn't good, is it?

Helen Mind you, there's a lot of her to look at. She's noticed, she phoned me up, she said, Helen, I think Andrew's been looking at me. And I have to deny it, of course, I can't tell my own mother my own husband is looking at her. I tell her it isn't true, but she knows it, and I know it, and he knows it, quite obviously, we all know he's looking at her.

Jeremy Is he still at the looking stage? Or has he begun touching yet?

Helen Oh no. Andrew keeps his hands to himself.

Jeremy Well, and I don't mean in any way to be trivialising this, obviously what he's doing is *wrong*, a husband shouldn't be looking, especially not looking at your mother, but he is a man. Isn't he? And men do look.

Helen No, you don't understand.

Jeremy Even I have been known to do it. Look, that is. I can't help it sometimes. Don't get me wrong, I don't do it often, I wouldn't regard myself as a habitual looker, but I've done it, we've all done it, men are drawn to looking, it's what we do. But if he's not actually touching...

Helen No, that's just it. I want him to be touching. A bit of looking would be fine if I thought he'd move on to the touching eventually. But looking's all he's good for. For God's sake, I wish he'd come right out with it and have a full-blown affair.

(Short pause)

Jeremy Ah.

Helen I've suggested it to him. I know you find so-and-so attractive, you can't take your eyes off her, well, it's okay, I don't mind. Go for it.

Jeremy No, you've lost me now.

Helen But he's such a wimp of a man. Other men would be at it like a shot, they'd be bonking away to their heart's content. But not Andrew, oh no, he just lies there in bed crying and telling me to stop saying such things. He's so dull that looking is about as unfaithful as he can get. I wonder. If you could have a word with him...

Jeremy I really don't think so.

Helen No, you're right. It's a hopeless case. He's never going to leave me, he's never going to set me free, unless he starts touching as well as looking, but at the end of the day, when it comes down to it, I married a looker. Someone who just looks, someone who watches life go by. And hasn't got the guts to do anything about it.

Jeremy Isn't it just possible... I don't know... That he loves you and wants to be with you?

Helen Why? I'm nothing special. Am I? I mean. I'm nothing special.

Jeremy *(coughing)* I'm sure there are a lot of men. Out there. Who could find you something special. Including him. Probably.

Helen Typical. Not only do I marry a man without guts, but he hasn't any taste either.

(Short pause)

Jeremy *(gently)* I think he's got taste...

(Short pause)

Helen A few weeks ago, on Friday night, after we made love. Because we still make love on Fridays, regular as clockwork, come hell or high water, at half past nine he'll stand there by the bed with that silly little grin of his. And I said to him, timing it for those few seconds just *after* he rolled off and just *before* he fell asleep, I said, Andrew, I'd like a divorce. And there was this silence, and I thought, no, I was too late after all, he already *has* fallen asleep, next week I'll have to tell him whilst he's still up there. But then he said, very quietly, 'But what about our son? We have to think about our son.' Not Paul, you understand, 'our son', as if he's a lifetime responsibility or something. And I wanted to tell him that I *was* thinking about our son, that was the whole point, I wanted Andrew to take custody of him, I wanted Andrew to take Paul away with him and I'd never see either of them again. But I couldn't say that, of course. I had to pretend it was just a joke. Some post-coital tease I'd read about in *Cosmopolitan*. And now every Friday when we make love, he grunts and rolls over and says 'let's get a divorce' in a tone of voice he obviously thinks is seductive, and I just want to slap him around the face, if only it were true, if only it were bloody true. If he could just run off with somebody else, he even finds my mother more attractive than me, if only he could stop being a looker and start being a doer.

(Short pause)

Jeremy Oh. Oh dear.

Helen God, I need some more nicotine...

Jeremy Here.

Helen No. Something stronger than that.

(And under the above she rummages in her handbag, and produces a pack of patches. She sticks a couple on to her arm.)

Jeremy Look, I don't want to pry. But I feel partly responsible. I mean, I was the one who married you to him. I'm not saying it was specifically my fault. In fact, if I think about it, it had nothing to do with me at all. If I think about it, I *am* prying. I'm sorry. Forget I said anything.

Helen *(struggling with the sticky label)* Come on, you bastard...

Jeremy It's just that. I don't know. If I were single. Which I'm not. And you were single. I mean, at the same time. And we're not. Well. *I'd* look. At you. I would. I mean. And not in a *bad* way. Just look. You know. Very happily. I just wanted you to... Well. Not that you should. No. Not at all. Ever, in fact.

(After applying her second patch she has stopped still and listened to this. Silence. She turns to look at him slowly. Then we hear a sudden roar of commotion from behind the door.)

Helen What's that?

Jeremy I'm sure it's nothing important...

Helen *(looking through the door)* Oh my God. Oh no. Paul!

Jeremy What is it? Oh, my dear lord.

Helen He's taken his costume off. Why has he taken his costume off?

Jeremy He's going to the manger. One of the Wise Men, look, he's going to stop him...

(A distant cry of pain over the hubbub.)

Helen No-one stops Paul from doing what he wants.

Jeremy The baby Jesus! What's he doing to the baby Jesus?

Helen Paul! Put Jesus down this instant!

Jeremy *(ashen)* He's pulled his head off. He's pulled Jesus' head off!

Helen *(walking away from the door, shivering)* I'll have to go on stage and get him. And they'll all know I'm his mother. They'll all know.

Jeremy He's got into the manger. No-one can pull him out...

Helen But they know already, don't they? They *all* know. I'm Paul's mummy. I'm the mummy of the monster. Oh God, please, I just want them all to go away, Paul, his father, the school counsellors...

*(**Jeremy** goes to her. She doesn't see him approach. He makes to put his arms around her, hesitantly. As they touch, she flinches.)*

No. You're right. I'm ready. I'll go. I'll get it over with. I'll go.

Jeremy I'll come with you.

Helen Why? He's not *your* son, is he? He's not your son.

Jeremy No.

Helen *(vaguely, as she walks to the doorway, steeling herself)* You haven't got a son. Lucky bastard...

Jeremy About what I said...

Helen Yes, thank you for that...

Jeremy I don't think... you listened to it properly.

Helen *(looking directly back at him)* Yes. I did.

(Short pause. She breathes in deeply.)

Here goes nothing.

(And she walks through the door. The hubbub grows louder; some jeering.)

Jeremy *(softly)* No. No, you didn't.

(And absently he takes a puff on the inhalator. He winces.)

4 – The Funeral

*(The cast put black coats over what they're wearing. **Jeremy** approaches **Helen**.)*

Jeremy *(gently)* Sometimes, at the end of the service. Usually at the *very* end, when most of the mourners have gone home or on to the wake or wherever. The widow will come up to me and say thank you. And tell me that she knows how much her husband would have enjoyed the funeral.

Helen *(dully)* Really?

Jeremy Yes. I mean, part of you wants to reply, I really don't think he would have, you know. We have just stuffed his body in a box and set fire to it. But it's something they feel they have to say. Like they can't move on without it.

Helen *(quietly)* Do you expect that from me?

Jeremy I don't know. I don't know what I expect from you, Helen.

Helen He probably would have enjoyed it. That's the silly thing. Andrew was always pathetically grateful whenever I gave him any attention.

(Short pause)

Jeremy Oddly enough, the men never do it. Or very rarely. I bury their wives, cremate them, whatever. Then they just leave. They don't want to speak to me. They have nothing to say.

(Short pause)

Are you all right?

(Short pause)

Helen I hope we did the right thing. Cremating him like that.

Jeremy Well.

Helen It's not something we'd discussed. Whether he'd prefer burial or cremation.

Jeremy Well, you wouldn't.

Helen I expect we'd have got round to it sooner or later. Probably when we reached something approaching middle age.

(Short pause)

It's typical. I thought over the years Andrew and I had discussed everything we could ever find to talk about. Over and over again. I thought I knew his opinion on absolutely bloody everything. It's taken him to die to realise we still had some conversational gambit we hadn't tried.

Jeremy Cremation is best. Most people opt for cremation nowadays.

Helen I think he'd have preferred it. Knowing Andrew, he wouldn't have wanted his remains taking up much room.

Jeremy It's definitely the one I'm going for.

Helen What happens about the ashes? Will they get sent to me, or do I have to pick them up from somewhere?

Jeremy We'll sort something out.

Helen Okay.

(Short pause)

Jeremy Paul seemed to be bearing up well.

Helen Oh, he was very cheerful. He got the day off school.

Jeremy Very well-behaved. Didn't bite or kick anyone.

Helen He was fascinated. He's never seen anyone cremated before. I think he was a little disappointed there wasn't a little window, so he could actually see it burn, but I'm sure his imagination made up for it.

Jeremy He's in a better place, you know.

Helen He's gone to his grandmother's for the reception.

Jeremy No, Andrew.

Helen Oh.

Jeremy He's gone to a better place.

Helen Right. Thanks.

(Short pause)

You really believe that, don't you?

Jeremy Yes.

Helen You really believe in God.

Jeremy Yes.

Helen You really believe God loves you?

Jeremy Yes.

Helen That's nice.

(Short pause)

Jeremy It's hard to explain. I mean, my life isn't perfect. I'm not always happy. In fact, quite often, well, most of the time, actually, I really feel pretty miserable. And it would be easy to turn round to God, to say to him, when it comes down to it, you've got it in for me, haven't you? But the way I think about it, I sort of liken my relationship with God to the relationship with my wife. Yes, they're both difficult, a bit stand-offish. You can talk to them until you're blue in the face, and you can never be sure if either are listening to you, whether they've forgotten you exist, shut you out altogether. And sometimes you cry out to them, please. Please just give me a reason to go on believing in you, to have some faith that you care whether I live or die. Just some sign, Eunice, just a little word, I say to her. Anything. And some days, out of the blue, she'll suddenly smile at me, she'll say something kind, she'll surprise me with a touch, even a kiss, and I know I was right not to lose hope. She *does* love me really, she *does*. And I was right to hold on regardless.

Helen But you can sometimes feel that God doesn't love you at all?

Jeremy *(softly)* Or worse. That he once did, but has forgotten how to now, for a long long time...

(Short pause)

Helen Andrew didn't even believe in God.

Jeremy No, I know.

Helen So how could he be in a better place? Isn't that one of the conditions?

Jeremy Oh, I'm sure God takes all sorts of things into consideration. Just believing in God a hundred years ago would have been fine, you're into heaven, no problem, but nowadays he'd hardly be getting anyone at all, would he?

Helen I suppose not.

Jeremy I'd be very surprised if God hasn't adjusted to the times.

Helen *(slowly, even fearfully)* So, even if you don't believe in him, you think there's a chance God will take notice of you anyway?

Jeremy Oh yes. Bound to. He's got to keep himself busy somehow, hasn't he?

Helen Oh dear.

Jeremy What's the matter?

Helen I killed Andrew.

(Short pause)

Jeremy He was knocked down by a bus.

Helen Yes.

Jeremy You're not a bus driver.

Helen I'm a secretary for a camping equipment firm.

Jeremy Well then.

Helen But I asked God for this. Don't you see? I'd wake up in the morning, and see Andrew's head on the pillow next to mine. And his face would look so calm, and he'd have a little smile on his face, Andrew's the only person I've ever met whose natural composure was smiling...

Jeremy Yes...

Helen And I'd think, I wish you'd just die, Andrew. I'll never divorce you, I couldn't, it would break your heart. So I wish you'd simply die instead. Much less awkward for both of us. I'd lie there, with him snoring gently in my ear, and I'd work out the ideal scenario. At first I wasn't too fussy, any death would do, I'd have been quite happy if he'd die then and there and never wake up again. But then I'd think about what it would mean to have him cold and rigid inches away from me, and I changed my mind. So I began to run through fatal diseases he could contract, see what would be first: pretty quick, and second: pretty painless. Because I didn't want him to suffer, he's always been a good father to Paul.

Jeremy *(uncomfortably)* Yes, that's something...

Helen But no diseases are *that* quick. I checked, I got lots of medical books out of the library. So I thought a good, decent, horribly life-destroying accident would do the trick instead.

Jeremy Being run over by a bus.

Helen Yes, I liked a bus because it's so big and red and comforting, isn't it? There's something reassuring about a London bus, I think it would be quite a nice way to go.

Jeremy I suppose so...

Helen And they're bloody big as well. Get squashed by one of those, you won't get up again.

Jeremy And, having made your selection... you prayed to God.

Helen Yes. 'Dear God, it's Helen, please knock Andrew down with a bus.' I never expected it would actually *happen*...

Jeremy Well, no, you wouldn't...

Helen If I'd known I was *really* talking to God, I'd have been a lot more formal about the whole thing. Oh, Jeremy. I really don't want to have killed my husband...

Jeremy Well, you didn't. Of course you didn't.

Helen But how can you be sure?

Jeremy Because God doesn't answer prayers like that.

Helen He does in the Bible. He's always turning people into pillars of salt and things.

Jeremy Sometimes I don't think God answers prayers at all. Listen. This was just this last Saturday. And Eunice asked me to do the week's shopping, she'd do it usually but she... didn't feel up to it. She takes the shopping very seriously does Eunice, draws up a huge list, cross referenced and everything...

Helen I don't see the point you're making...

Jeremy *(surprisingly firmly)* No, listen. Just listen. So I drove off to the supermarket, took the list with me. And there were some very tricky things to find, kiwi fruit, things like that, but I was doing well, I found them. I allowed myself to think it was all going to be okay, I'd be home within the hour and Eunice would be so proud of me, she might even smile...

Helen No, I don't understand...

Jeremy It was the baked beans and frankfurters which stumped me. I didn't think they'd be hard to find, when I saw them on the list I thought, fine, baked bean tins with frankfurters inside, everyone loves those, don't they? And I wasn't even that worried at first. I thought, okay, I'll just drive to another supermarket, get them somewhere else instead. But wherever I went it was the same. There wasn't a tin to be had for love nor money...

Helen I've never bought baked beans with frankfurters.

Jeremy And I knew what would happen when I got home. Just before I left Eunice said to me, 'you can't do anything right. I bet you won't even be able to do the shopping. You're hardly a man at all. You were never a man. Never.' And I knew I had to find those beans and furters, I just had to, to prove I had a reason for going home at all. And so I prayed. I know you're not meant to, but I did. Please, God. Please, just one tin. Please, before the shops shut.

Helen Jeremy...

Jeremy *(sharply)* Listen.

(Short pause. More gently:)

On the scale of things, I don't think it was much to ask. When I got home, tinless, furterless. Before I even got my coat off, the first thing she said to me, she said, 'And did you get the beans and furters? Did you get them?' And I knew. I knew it had been a test. A test of my manhood.

Helen *(softly)* My God.

Jeremy And I had failed her. And God had failed me. I've asked for nothing from him, not all these years. Not even the son we wanted, that might have made a difference. But that tin of beans and chipolata sausages could have been the turning point. If I could have held my Tesco's bag high, and said, 'Yes, my love! Yes! I have your groceries!' And she'd have fallen in my arms, I know she would have done, she would have loved me again, everything would have been okay, everything could have been as it used to be. She'd have *believed* in me. I've served God all my life. Not that well, perhaps, but to the best of my ability. If he couldn't get a tin of baked beans for me, why would he kill a man for *you*?

(Short pause)

I'm sorry, I'm so sorry...

Helen No, it's okay...

Jeremy I'm sorry. I used to be so good at funerals. Everyone said my face hung in just the right direction.

Helen It was a good funeral. Andrew would have enjoyed it. I knew Andrew would have enjoyed it.

(She hugs him briefly.)

Jeremy I'm never going to see her again, am I? *My* Eunice. The Eunice I fell in love with.

Helen I don't know.

Jeremy It's dead. What was all that love for, if it was just going to die?

Where did all that love go?

(Short pause)

Helen   *(softly)* Maybe... Maybe it went to a better place.

(They stare at each other in silence. Then, music and into:)

5 – The Jumble Sale

*(**Jeremy** stands behind a table, selling small sponge cakes. His face falls when **Helen** enters and walks to him excitedly.)*

Helen Good news! Do you want to hear my good news?

Jeremy I thought you said you weren't coming.

Helen Shall I tell you my good news? Would you like to hear it?

Jeremy I thought that was the whole point of last night's phone call.

Helen Look at what I'm wearing. Look.

Jeremy Very nice.

Helen It's a crucifix, you see? I'm wearing a crucifix. I've become a Christian!

Jeremy I think there's a little more to it than that.

Helen Silly! I mean, I'm wearing it since I became one. It's nice, isn't it?

Jeremy As crucifix jewellery goes, it's smashing.

Helen Well, I want to show off about it. I'm very proud to be a Christian. I decided last night. I thought, something's missing from my life, I've known that for a while.

Jeremy Was this before or after the phone call in which you said you wouldn't be here today?

Helen After. So I got the Bible down and had a look through, and do you know, it's a gripping read. You have to skim, but bits of it are fantastic. I spent half the night riveted to it. And first thing this morning I contacted God and told him I was ready to devote my life to him.

Jeremy Well, you have been working hard.

Helen It's not that any of it's particularly difficult. I thought it'd be a hard read, but it's mostly very clear. It's all about love. It all revolves around love. Love thy neighbour. Don't love idols in the shape of golden bulls.

Jeremy I'm glad you've cracked Christianity so quickly. It takes some of us ages to sort out.

Helen Love a lot, but stick to people rather than objects. That's my sort of religion. Do you like the earrings too, look, they're in the shape of crosses.

Jeremy Would you like to buy a sponge cake?

Helen I'm sorry?

Jeremy Well, that's what I'm doing here. This is the sponge cake stall.

Helen Yes.

Jeremy Raising money so we can save the steeple. It's falling down, you know. Are you going to buy one or not?

Helen How much are they?

Jeremy Fifty pee.

Helen No thanks.

Jeremy Perhaps you'd like to go to another stall and buy something else instead? All the proceeds are going to a good cause. You're going to need the steeple now you're a Christian.

(Short pause)

Helen Why aren't you pleased? I thought you'd be pleased.

Jeremy Where's it going to stop, Helen? You phone me three or four times a day. You sit at the back of all my services and wave at me. Even the funerals, you're the only one waving and smiling at funerals. Now you become a Christian.

Helen You think I've become a Christian for you?

Jeremy Well, haven't you?

Helen …Yes.

Jeremy I don't know. I just think that that may be for the wrong reason.

Helen You think that everybody becomes a Christian because they believe in God? I know my Bible. You think they weren't saying, okay, okay, I'll convert, I'll convert, now hurry and pass round the loaves and fishes.'

Jeremy Eunice will think I'm having an affair with you. Which wouldn't be so bad if I actually were.

Helen Eunice doesn't care. She's having an affair of her own. You told me she is.

Jeremy That's not the point.

Helen I thought this was your job. You know, to convert people.

Jeremy Good lord, no. That's not *my* job.

Helen Well. I just thought.

Jeremy No, well, I should be helping, but as far as I'm concerned, I've got my work cut out looking after the Christians I've already got, thank you very much. My job is to make sure they don't all start using other churches instead, the bishop was very clear in his latest report, our job is to ensure some sense of customer loyalty. It's all market forces these days.

Helen I wanted to make a commitment to something. I wanted to make a commitment to you.

Jeremy Mmm.

Helen I can get to see you much more often now we'll be praising the Lord together. Now I'm born again.

Jeremy But, you see, I can't stand born again Christians. I really can't. When I've been a Christian all my life, brought up for it, going to Sunday school every week, being lectured by my parents whenever I did something wrong that God was watching me. Being a Christian wasn't fun, it was a long hard bloody struggle, half the time being scared out of your wits by what it all meant, being bored to death the other half.

Helen Well, yes...

Jeremy And then there are these born agains, these Johnny-come-latelys, and it's all a big party for them. They've been Christians less than a week and they're out there preaching and clapping and speaking in tongues, and just having *fun*. Happy clappys who can't stop grinning because Jesus loves them, he loves *them* when they've put in so little time and effort and I can't feel he loves *me* when I've given him my whole sodding life.

Helen I'm sorry.

Jeremy Shut up. Why do you keep hanging round me, Helen? What's in it for you?

Helen Well. I thought. Friendship. I thought.

Jeremy But you don't know me. You barely know the first thing about me.

Helen That's not my fault. You never offer very much, do you? You're a good listener. You've always listened to me.

Jeremy That's because you never stop talking. It's hard to get a word in edgeways.

Helen Oh. I thought we were friends...

Jeremy I've lost my faith. I think.

(Short pause)

You see, you're right. You put no thought into it, but you're right. It is all about love. I used to believe that's what God was. Love. Taught it from the lectern, God, love, same thing. It's got to the point I want to hit Eunice, that's what she's reduced me to, the sort of man who wants to hit people. And I don't believe in love. Not any more. She's hardly subtle about her affair, he sends her flowers and she leaves them in vases all over the bloody house. I'd try to send her flowers too, you know, try to compete, but we haven't got any vases left...

(Idly he begins to tear apart the sponge cakes in his hands. Lots of cream and jam.)

He hardly knows her, this Johnny-come-lately who's taking her away when I've put all the work in all these years, I've had to work at this for years, and he's made her happier than I ever did in a matter of weeks. What am I doing to these sponge cakes, I've got to sell them...

Helen It's all right, they're only sponge cakes. Look. I'll help you. Look.

(And she starts tearing up the cakes as well.)

Jeremy They probably drink red wine and eat chocolates in bed and *dance*, they probably dance. She taught me how to dance, you know, I kept kicking her in the shins. I was no good at it, but I loved her, you see, I went back every week, I had to see her, had to dance with her again. Couldn't stop kicking her though. And she said eventually, look, I'll marry you, if you could just bloody *stop*, I've bruises all over my legs, I'll marry you if you just leave me *alone*. I don't believe in love, not any more, and I don't believe in God. Love and God. They're both dead.

Helen ...I love you.

Jeremy Yes. I love you too.

(Short pause. Then they reach across the table to each other and kiss passionately.)

No – what are we doing?

Helen We're kissing.

Jeremy Yes, I know *what* it is, we shouldn't do this...

Helen But it feels so good...

(And to kiss better she sits on the table, crushing the last of the cakes.)

Jeremy Oh God. Do you know the last time I was kissed like this?

Helen No, when?

Jeremy That's just it. I can't remember. All the women on the tombola are watching us.

Helen Let them. It's only a tombola, it's only a bloody tombola...

Jeremy Oh God.

(And they kiss again. She climbs off the table and they hug.)

Helen Let's run away together!

Jeremy What? Just like that?

Helen Why not? Let's do something impulsive! Let's just get in the car and go. Let's go straight up the M1 and find a new life for ourselves.

Jeremy What's up the M1?

Helen Or down the M1. It's up to you. I'll let you decide the direction, it's your choice.

Jeremy But we can't just go. I've got a wife.

Helen Whom you don't love.

Jeremy You've got a kid.

Helen Yes, but let's face it, he's a pretty nasty kid, isn't he? Stealing money from my purse and nicotine inhalers from my handbag.

Jeremy He's only fourteen...

Helen As far as I'm concerned, if he's old enough to shave and shoplift, he can fend for himself.

Jeremy I can't just go. I've got to sell the sponge cakes for the steeple restoration fund...

Helen You don't even believe in God any more...!

Jeremy No, I know. But it is a very nice steeple...

Helen Okay. How about this then. I'll buy the sponge cakes. I'll buy them all.

Jeremy What?

Helen No, come on. You'll have nothing left to sell. You can come with me.

Jeremy You can't want the sponge cakes. You've sat on half of them. You can't want to eat them...

Helen Of course I don't want to eat them, you idiot! I want to eat you!

(Short pause. Both are rather shocked by this revelation. Quietly:)

I want to eat you, Jeremy. I want to eat you all up. Both for main course and dessert. I want us to get in the car, find some nice hotel off the M1, northwards or southwards, it doesn't matter, I want to take you to bed, and we can eat each other up, every last scrap of us, for the rest of our lives.

(Short pause)

Jeremy Gosh. I mean. Gosh.

Helen I've got money. Look. I've got money. Here. I'll pay for your cakes. I'll pay for whatever you've got to offer.

(He takes the money dumbly, looks at it. Short pause)

Jeremy *(softly)* Or I could just not sell them to you. The management reserves the right to refuse service. Yes.

Helen ...What? Why?

Jeremy I don't want to love you. I don't want it all over again. To put my faith in somebody and then watch it get eaten away. It happened with Eunice. It happened with God. It happened with the English cricket team. It'll happen with you.

Helen It won't. I promise.

Jeremy Of course it will. In all the years I've known you, I've never heard you say a kind word about anybody. I've never heard a single expression of love, not for your husband, not for your son, not for yourself. Why should I be any different? You don't really love me at all, do you?

(Short pause)

Helen I'd try. I'd try very hard.

Jeremy But it would be cruel, wouldn't it? Because I do love you. Have done for years.

(Short pause)

Helen I want to love.

(Short pause)

I do.

(Short pause)

I thought with Andrew gone, things might change. You know, that the boss would stop brushing past me accidentally in the lift and instead give me a no holds barred hug. Now that I was free to be loved again.

Jeremy I certainly hope that you can find love with someone, Helen.

Helen Not a chance. Not now I'm a widow. A widow sounds so... old. People take care not to swear in front of me, they'll be giving up their seats for me on the bus next. And my boss would rather wait for the next lift going down, thank you very much. I'm only thirty-nine, for God's sake. My husband doesn't follow the Green Cross Code, he winds up dead, I wind up an OAP.

Jeremy I'm sorry. Really.

Helen I shall never have sex again. If only I'd known that I'd have taken more trouble to enjoy it at the time. We're not going to have an affair, are we?

Jeremy No.

Helen ...Not even a little one?

Jeremy *(sighing)* No.

Helen No. But I shall stay a Christian. If it's all the same to you.

Jeremy Please don't love God the way you love me. I'm not sure the poor chap could take it.

Helen And I'll see you in church on Sunday.

Jeremy You don't have to do that.

Helen No. I will. And I'll wave to you from the back, as I always do.

Jeremy *(smiling)* You really mustn't, you know...

Helen Why not? We're friends, aren't we?

Jeremy No.

Helen No. Well. We will be. From now on.

Jeremy All right.

Helen Good.

Jeremy And if we *are* friends. Perhaps... I can wave back. Just a little.

(He demonstrates.)

Helen That's the idea.

(Short pause)

I probably do love you, you know. I probably do.

Jeremy Yes.

(And she leaves. He practises the wave again, smiles. Then, cheerily:)

Come and get your sponge souffle here! Sponge souffle. Only fifty pee a scoop.

435

6 – The Wedding (2)

(This is the only time that the actors should appear noticeably older. A whitening of the hair should suffice.

*(**Jeremy** is in position as in scene one, holding a paper plate of buffet food. He is approached by **Helen**.)*

Helen I thought I'd better warn you.

Jeremy Hello...

Helen I overheard the bride talking. There's going to be music soon.

Jeremy Oh dear.

Helen And she wants everyone dancing.

Jeremy I don't like dancing.

Helen No.

Jeremy I'm not very good at it.

Helen I know.

Jeremy *(putting his plate on to the table)* Well, it's been a great day. A great day, no denying that. But maybe this is my cue to leave.

Helen Yes. Perhaps that would be best.

Jeremy Don't want to stick out like a sore thumb.

Helen Well, it was good to see you again.

Jeremy And you. It's been a long time.

Helen It has.

Jeremy I'm sorry we didn't get the chance to speak much.

Helen *(defensively)* We said hello in the church.

Jeremy No, I know.

Helen And we said hello after the service. That's two hellos.

Jeremy No, I wasn't complaining. Really, we spoke a lot. You're looking well.

Helen Thank you. As are you.

Jeremy Oh, I don't think so! I don't think I am. But thank you. Thank you anyway!

(Short pause)

I feel well.

(Short pause)

Helen Well. Thanks for coming.

Jeremy My pleasure.

Helen It was quite a surprise.

Jeremy Well, it's a special occasion, isn't it? I couldn't have missed it.

Helen I'm sure Paul was very grateful.

Jeremy Oh, I don't suppose he even noticed.

Helen Maybe not.

Jeremy I'm sure it didn't mean that much to him.

Helen No.

Jeremy But it meant a lot to me. Who would have thought it? Looking so smart, up there at the altar.

Helen A big day. His first wedding.

Jeremy Let's hope there'll be many more of them.

Helen Oh. There will. He's got another one in a fortnight.

Jeremy Gosh. A fortnight.

Helen And another, I think, in March.

Jeremy Well. That is impressive. Good for him.

(Short pause)

I must say. He did a better job on his first wedding than I did on my hundredth.

Helen Oh, I'm sure that isn't true.

Jeremy No, no, it is. He really looked the part up there. He's got the right face for weddings, his face hangs in the right direction.

Helen Yes. He's got an upwards-hanging face.

Jeremy We'll see how he does with funerals! That'll be the clincher. It's funny, I never really imagined your son becoming a man of the cloth.

Helen His congregation think the world of him.

Jeremy I can imagine.

Helen Though sometimes I look up at him, during a sermon, singing a hymn. With that beatific smile of his. And I think that somewhere beneath it is the evil little brat that used to set fire to things.

Jeremy He turned out well in the end.

Helen I suppose so.

Jeremy His father would have been very proud.

Helen Oh yes. Mind you, Andrew was proud of him whenever the police would let him off with just a caution. It didn't take much to impress Andrew.

Jeremy Everything turned out well.

Helen He married me, after all.

Jeremy They always work out, don't they? Things. I mean, in the end.

(Short pause)

Helen Do you miss this?

Jeremy What?

Helen The church. Being a vicar.

Jeremy Oh. No. No, I don't think so.

Helen Believing in God.

Jeremy Not often.

Helen Good.

Jeremy I'll never preach again. Paul's the way forward now. With his crucifix tattoos and his hymns set to rap music. That's the way ahead, I suppose.

Helen It's very popular.

Jeremy He did a grand job today. Up there, what he said, it was lovely. I could almost believe it all meant something.

(Short pause)

Helen I was very sad when you left the church.

Jeremy You used to wave at me.

Helen Yes.

Jeremy When I left, I thought you'd stop going. But you didn't.

Helen No. Well. I'd found God, hadn't I?

Jeremy I thought you'd follow me.

Helen I found God.

(Short pause)

I'm so sorry.

Jeremy What for?

Helen You know. I'm just very very sorry.

(Short pause)

I've missed you.

Jeremy Yes.

Helen I've missed your friendship.

(Short pause)

Have you missed mine?

*(Short pause. **Jeremy** takes out an inhalator, and sucks on it deeply.)*

Do you hear much from Eunice?

Jeremy Oh yes. Quite regularly.

Helen That's good.

Jeremy There's always a Christmas card. She never forgets.

Helen That's nice.

Jeremy I'd like to send her one back, but I don't know her address. But I look at the postcode each year, and every time it's different. So she's obviously happy, moving round a lot.

Helen Good for her.

Jeremy And every year the cards she sends get bigger and bigger. So she obviously misses me more and more. I expect one year a card will arrive which will give her phone number. Maybe even this year. Who knows? How about you? Is there anyone special in your life?

Helen No. Not especially special.

(Short pause)

Do you ever think back? To us, I mean? To what might have been?

Jeremy *(cautiously)* No.

Helen No. Nor do I.

(Pause)

Jeremy I suppose I'd best be off then.

Helen Yes.

Jeremy Before the dancing starts.

Helen Yes.

(Pause. Neither makes a move.)

When I think back. Which I never do. We did the right thing. You were right, I was wrong. You were right, no question of that. I thought I loved you. I wanted to love you. But I didn't love you, did I? Or we'd be together now. Nothing would have stopped us.

Jeremy No.

Helen You were right, I was wrong. I used to wave to you in church. And sometimes you'd wave back, just when you felt brave enough. But you weren't brave enough *often* enough. I have no regrets. When I look back, and I *never* look back, I have no regrets at all.

Jeremy No, quite. Absolutely. Nor me. ...But sometimes...

Helen *(eagerly)* Yes?

Jeremy You know the story of how Eunice and I met? Of how she taught me to waltz.

Helen Oh yes. Yes, I do.

Jeremy It was a good story. I sometimes think *we* could have had a story like that. About how *we* danced, at your wedding. We *did* dance, didn't we?

Helen Yes.

Jeremy That would have made another good story. I could have told people. That that's how *we* met, fell in love. If we had.

Helen But you've no regrets.

Jeremy Oh no. Not if you haven't.

(Short pause)

You haven't, have you?

(And the music begins to play. It's loud and strident, some futuristic rap metal cacophony.)

Helen It's started. They'll find us soon, ask us why we're not dancing.

Jeremy How can you dance to this? It hasn't even got a rhythm...

Helen I think that's the idea. You just do your own thing.

Jeremy Everybody just does their own thing these days.

Helen *(opening her arms)* Well. Shall we?

Jeremy ...But the only dance I know is the waltz.

Helen Yes, I know.

Jeremy I'm very bad at it. I'll probably damage your shins.

Helen I can't do it at all. Maybe we'll both be so bad it'll cancel the other's badness out. Maybe, together, in spite of everything, we can be good.

(She opens her arms again.)

Come on, Jeremy. After all these years. Let's find what our thing *is*.

*(And he takes her hands. And they dance the waltz. It's a little ungainly at first – but they are doing it with the wrong music. But as they begin to enjoy themselves, we hear the techno din segue into a classical waltz. And when it comes to an end, **Jeremy** bows to **Helen,** who curtseys in return. And they hold this position, and smile at the other.*

(Blackout.)

Shaw Cornered
(2001)

OPENED AT SHAW'S CORNER, AYOT ST LAWRENCE,
ON 14TH JULY 2001, WITH THE FOLLOWING CAST:
SHAW ROGER RINGROSE
ALL OTHER CHARACTERS PLAYED BY CHRIS MYLES AND SASHA WADDELL
DIRECTED BY MICHAEL FRIEND

IT WAS LATER REVIVED AT THE HABITAT CENTRE, DELHI,
ON 9TH DECEMBER 2007, WITH THE FOLLOWING CAST:
SHAW ROGER RINGROSE
ALL OTHER CHARACTERS PLAYED BY CHRIS MYLES AND JANE GODDARD
DIRECTED BY ROBERT SHEARMAN

Act One

*(The garden at Shaw's Corner. A single chair sits on the grass. An elderly **Bernard Shaw** sits in it, sleeping.*

*(Enter a man, who stands by him and looks down at him doubtfully. He is smartly dressed, and formal in appearance – but is, in fact, a **Germ**.)*

Germ Mr Shaw? Mr Shaw, sir?

*(**Shaw** doesn't stir. Short pause)*

Mr Shaw? Are you asleep, Mr Shaw? Or have you finally died?

(Short pause)

I do hope you haven't died. Not just yet. I did so want to speak to you first. Mr Shaw? Could you let me know which it is, sir, sleep or death? Tell you what. If you're only sleeping, wake up now and say hello. And if you're dead, I don't know. How about you slump forward with your tongue lolling out of your mouth?

Shaw *(without opening an eye)* What is the meaning of this?

Germ So you're asleep after all! I'm so pleased.

Shaw *(looking at him)* I *was* asleep. It is hard to sleep with a strange man shouting in my ear. Impossible, even! Who the devil are you?

Germ There are a few questions I'd like to ask you.

Shaw And what are you doing in my garden? Mrs Laden! Mrs Laden!

Germ She can't hear you.

Shaw You'd best be careful, sir. You don't want to cross Mrs Laden. She's quite the most ferocious woman I've ever met.

Germ Mrs Laden isn't coming.

Shaw You should hear the way she shouts at me if I don't drink her soup. She'll soon put paid to the likes of you.

Germ *(firmly, gently)* I said. Mrs Laden. Isn't. Coming.

(Short pause)

Shaw Who are you? Are you a BBC journalist?

Germ I need to ask you a couple of questions.

Shaw I'm utterly besieged by BBC journalists these days. What's the matter with you all?

Germ I won't take long.

Shaw I've nothing to say to you. All the things I had worth saying are to be found in my plays, or in my essays to my plays, or in my essays to other people's plays. I suggest you get thee to a library, young man.

Germ I shall not leave here.

Shaw What? How dare you.

Germ I shall not leave here until you've answered my questions.

Shaw Well, I shan't talk. You'll just have to stay there then.

*(The **Germ** idly walks about the garden for a few paces. **Shaw** watches him warily.)*

Germ *(at last, gently)* Mr Shaw...

Shaw I will not be cornered in my own garden! Reporters popping out all over the place, asking my opinion of the economy or the foreign policy or the colour of Mr Atlee's boots! Not because they think I have anything worth saying, but because I'm old.

Germ Calm down, Mr Shaw...

Shaw I will not calm down. Because I'm old, I say. Because this ridiculous body of mine refuses to give up the ghost and run down when it should, when it ought to have run down and stopped years ago. I will not talk to you, sir! Mrs Laden!

Germ I was merely going to suggest. That if you won't talk to me, you might at least consent to take a walk with me around the garden.

Shaw I beg your pardon?

Germ It's quite marvellous, isn't it? Come, Mr Shaw. Get up and take a walk with me.

Shaw Don't be absurd. A single pin is holding my legs together since the operation. I barely have the strength to eat, let alone walk. I'm dying. Do you hear me, I'm dying. And I'm in constant pain.

Germ Are you in pain at the moment?

Shaw *(surprised)* What? No.

Germ No.

(Short pause)

Take a walk with me round the garden. And I'll ask you a couple of questions. Just a couple, no more. And then I promise you. It will be the last interview you'll ever give.

Shaw You can't promise that. I tell you, they come every day. Mrs Laden is usually able to beat them off, but...

Germ I promise you. Please. Take my hand.

(*Shaw* considers, then takes it. He rises.)

Steady. Not too fast.

Shaw I never thought I'd move again so easily.

Germ You never thought you'd give another interview either. And yet here we are.

(Short pause)

Only two questions. Only two.

(Short pause)

Shaw (softly) What is it you want to know?

Germ Are you afraid of death?

Shaw No. Not any more.

(Short pause)

I'm sorry. Were you wanting something more profound? ...I don't know when I stopped being frightened of death. About the time I realised I had no place with the living any longer. When most of the people I knew or cared for had the good fortune to move on long ago. And all the rest come to me to say their final farewells. Always with such awkwardness, I know my hanging on embarrasses them. Every time I fall asleep there's someone at my side telling me to wake up. All the time I'm awake there's someone telling me I should rest and get some sleep. I'm a waste of all the food they make me eat, I'm a waste of all their effort to keep me breathing, keep one day following the next, plodding on, plod, plod, plod. I'm tired of it all, all the plodding. I'm tired of the days if there's nothing to achieve in them, if there's nothing more remarkable I can do than swallow a bit of soup and maybe breathe just a little bit longer.

(Short pause)

Is that any more helpful? I know how the BBC appreciate a good quote. Well. And your last question?

Germ Are you now ready to die?

(Short pause)

I'm here to help you, Mr Shaw.

Shaw You're planning to kill me?

Germ I'm not planning it, sir, I don't need a plan. I'm already doing it.

Shaw Is there really much point? Every time I shut my eyes for a nap I say goodbye to the world. Just in case. Exactly what have I done to so antagonise the BBC that they'd send a journalist to my house to assassinate me?

Germ You said I was a BBC journalist. I never said I was a BBC journalist.

Shaw I have to say. You *look* like a BBC journalist.

Germ I can't help that, sir. It was the way I was made.

Shaw Who are you?

Germ I'm a Germ.

(Short pause)

There. That's surprised you, hasn't it?

Shaw You're a big disappointment to me, young man. I've half a mind to go and sit down again and ignore you after all.

Germ Oh, I'm sorry, sir. I'm disappointed you're disappointed.

Shaw Do you know how many people have come to me over the years to tell me they're characters in my plays?

Germ Oh, a fair few, I'd imagine. What with you being so famous and all.

Shaw I had a woman last year telling me she was Catherine the Great. Not *the* Catherine the Great, she wanted me to understand, *my* Catherine the Great. There is a difference.

Germ And you think that's what I am? Someone acting out a Germ?

Shaw It's original, I grant you. Normally they'll try Captain Shotover or Henry Higgins.

Germ All us Germs were terribly impressed when you wrote *Too True to be Good*. We've never had proper representation in literature, we feel. You really were a marvel, Mr Shaw. Your writing predicted the rise of socialism, female emancipation, and the dangers of fascism. And big talking Germs.

Shaw Big talking Germs which look like BBC journalists.

Germm *(smiling)* Ah, no, you didn't predict that bit. But good on you for trying anyway. 'In substance, it seems to be made of a luminous jelly with a visible skeleton of short black rods'.

Shaw You remember the stage directions I wrote?

Germ Not an easy thing to forget, Mr Shaw. Quite a few Germs were very offended. Called it slander.

Shaw Oh dear.

Germ Not me though. No, I'm just honoured to meet you at last. Really, I'm such a fan.

Shaw Indeed?

Germ I'm so proud. Excited, too! I've never got to kill anyone literary before. I was so pleased when I was given this assignment. A cousin of mine was on the G K Chesterton project years ago. And I've got a friend who's doing minor works of disrepair on W Somerset Maugham's gut. But they're nothing to Bernard Shaw. To delivering the actual, final, terminal, killing blow to the author of *Mrs Warren's Profession..* I'm chuffed. That's what I am.

Shaw How fortunate for me. I am to be killed by a Germ of discernment.

Germ *(pleased, embarrassed)* Well.

Shaw I'm hallucinating, aren't I?

Germ Well, I'm not an expert. I'm just a Germ. But I'd have thought that was a reasonable guess, yes.

Shaw Before she died, my wife hallucinated. She saw strangers when there was no-one to be seen.

Germ The brain does all sorts of funny things when it's on its last legs. So to speak.

Shaw It's typical. Charlotte was surrounded by actual people. I get a Germ.

Germ Not just any old Germ. I'm the Germ which kills you.

Shaw So you said.

Germ Just doing my job. Something had to get you in the end. All the other lads, they've been trying to wear you down for ages. But to no avail.

Shaw Ninety-four years. It does seem a very long time.

Germ Must be because you didn't smoke, you ate vegetarian food, and practised sexual abstinence.

Shaw Yes.

Germ Bet it felt like ninety-four years as well. Hadn't you considered, well. Just dying sooner? They say that no artist produces anything truly great after the age of forty-five. Fifty tops.

Shaw I don't think that's true.

Germ Oh, come on. You haven't written anything halfway decent in years. You're not going to tell me you can look at *Buoyant Billions* or *King Charles' Golden Days* with any sort of pride, are you?

Shaw I know a lot of people who enjoyed them.

Germ The other Germs and me, when we discuss literature. Which we do often, considering there's not much to talk about, being a Germ. We don't think you wrote anything good after *Pygmalion*.

Shaw When I want the opinion of Germs, I'll ask for it.

Germ I know some Germs who don't think you wrote anything good *before Pygmalion* either. I know a streptococcus who's very vocal on that subject.

Shaw Everyone's a critic.

Germ Not me though, sir. I really like some of your early stuff. *Arms and the Man* is good for a giggle. And *Candida*, that's just lovely. Could bring tears to a Germ's eyes, that could.

Shaw I don't care. Can we get back to the matter in hand? You were about to kill me, you said.

Germ *(sniffing)* Hey, I'm just a Germ. But I know what I like. Very well, Mr Shaw. So are you now ready to die?

Shaw If I'm going to die, what better place to do it than in my own garden?

Germ Oh, Mr Shaw. You're not in your garden. It's a cold night in November. You're safely tucked up in bed. Well, not so safely, as it happens.

Shaw So all of this is just a dream?

Germ Oh, no, nothing as simple as that. It's really happening. It's just not happening... here.

Shaw I don't understand a word of that.

Germ No. Well. Now you know how most of us felt during Act Three of *Man and Superman.* I thought that the garden would be the most peaceful place for this little chat of ours. You always liked this garden, didn't you?

Shaw What will you do to me?

Germ First of all, the breathing will stop. Just suddenly. As if the body has forgotten how. As if the body never knew in the first place.

Shaw Yes.

Germ Can you feel it?

Shaw Yes.

Germ Don't fight it, Bernard. It's all right. There's no pain. And then the heart slows. And slows. And then doesn't beat any more.

Shaw Am I dead yet?

Germ Not quite. The brain is the last to go.

Shaw Ah yes, the brain.

(Pause. Eventually the **Germ** *checks his watch impatiently.)*

Germ It's taking quite a while. But then you always were a cerebral fellow, weren't you, Mr Shaw?

Shaw Sorry...

Germ Still, not much longer now. And... there.

Shaw And now I'm truly dead? Really?

Germ Dead as a doornail. Welcome to the club.

Shaw That wasn't difficult.

Germ Oh, it wasn't. Any fool knows how to die. Knowing *when* to die, that's another matter.

Shaw I mean it was surprisingly painless.

Germ Death always is, Mr Shaw. It's the body's attempts to fight it which causes all the problems.

(Short pause)

Shaw So. What happens now?

Germ Well, frankly, you've been a long, hard job, Mr Shaw. Ninety-four years, I could do with a nice holiday. Somewhere warm and sunny, I think. Yes, I'll go and nestle somewhere within a Spaniard.

Shaw No. I mean, for me.

Germ Well, I don't know, Mr Shaw. You're dead. What do you think should happen?

Shaw Is there an afterlife?

Germ Don't ask me. I'm a Germ, not a priest. Do you believe in one?

Shaw I think so. I wrote about it once or twice.

Germ Well, I'll keep my fingers crossed for you then. If you'll excuse me, Mr Shaw. It was good to meet you at last, I was quite a fan. But you are now dead and everything, and quite frankly, talking to you gives me the creeps.

Shaw Isn't that a problem in your line of work?

Germ Occupational hazard. Still, the money's good.

Shaw Wait. What do I do now?

Germ *(stopping)* ...If you'll take my advice. You'll do nothing. Fifty-four plays, seven novels, and reams upon reams of essays and criticism. Don't you think it's just time to take a rest?

(He exits.

*(**Shaw** stands still for a few seconds, then experimentally stretches out his arms.)*

Shaw No pain. No pain at all. Wait. Wait.

(And he raises his arm above his head.)

That ought to be agony. I can't remember how long it's been since I could do that. This is wonderful. And the other arm...? I can *stretch*. I can stretch again! ...No pain in my legs either. I can bounce. Oh, I can hop! I can jump up and down!

(Ecstatically, he does so.)

I don't even feel tired. I could go on forever!

(Then he stops. With a frown, he touches his arm. Looks a bit panicked. Touches his face, his head. Pulls his hair.)

I can't feel *anything*. Anything at all. Well, that takes the edge off it a bit. But still. I suppose in death one must take the rough with the smooth.

(Short pause. And then, almost as an afterthought, he jumps up in the air a few more times, an expression of utter joy on his face.)

Hooray!

*(Unseen by him, enter the **DEVIL** behind. She watches him curiously.)*

Devil Excuse me. Mr Shaw?

Shaw Oh, good lord. How embarrassing.

Devil Not at all. I'm sorry to interrupt such a display. You were clearly having the time of your death.

Shaw No, I assure you, it was more a scientific examination of the dexterity of my limbs.

Devil Oh, there's no need to explain. To be honest, it's a refreshing change. When most people face up to their demise, they fall on the floor and curl up into little balls and wail and things.

Shaw So it's true then? I am dead.

Devil Oh yes. Have you been dead long, by the way?

Shaw Just a couple of minutes, I think.

Devil I'm so sorry to have kept you waiting. It's unforgivable. I always try to greet our celebrities personally. Especially you, one of the greatest intellects of the modern age.

Shaw I take it that this is some sort of afterlife?

Devil Which is precisely what I mean, Mr Shaw. Nothing gets past you.

Shaw And can I ask... It sounds silly, I expect...

Devil No, go on. You fire away.

Shaw If this is the afterlife, have I gone upwards? Or am I, well. Down there.

Devil *(laughing, not unkindly)* Well, let me introduce myself. I am the Devil. And I am the keeper of Hell.

Shaw Oh. I see.

Devil You're not too disappointed, I hope?

Shaw *(sighing)* No. No, of course not. I don't think I could really have expected to be sitting on the right hand side of God. Not after all these years my writing has been prodding him and provoking him.

Devil You've been damned a long time, I'm afraid, Bernard.

Shaw What was it I did? Anything specific?

Devil You wrote *Back to Methuselah.*

Shaw Ah. Now I understand. One of my greatest works, I think. What was it that was the problem? Was it my insistence at questioning the tenets of faith at the most fundamental level? Or was it that my decision to portray Biblical characters on stage was inherently blasphemous?

Devil Well. It was more to do with its length, really.

Shaw Its length?

Devil *Back to Methuselah* is very very long, Mr Shaw. It's easily a five hour evening. And that's without an interval, and with all the actors speaking terribly fast.

Shaw You're telling me I'm damned because my play was too *long*? Is that it?

Devil It hurts people's bottoms, Mr Shaw, sitting in the theatre for that long. I'm sure you understand.

Shaw It was nothing I said *within* the play? Not my ideas, my attacks on religious doctrine? Just how many words I used?

Devil Maybe if you'd used fewer words, those ideas might have had more impact. I'm just an ordinary punter, Mr Shaw. But I have to tell you I've never been able to sit through it till the end. So whatever ideas you're proposing after the first hour and a half, no matter how heretical, are lost on me.

Shaw Well. I'm shocked.

Devil I'm not a critic. I'm Beelzebub, not Sheridan Morley. But didn't it occur to you when you wrote it, say, halfway through. You know. To *stop*?

Shaw Well, I would hardly have expected the Devil to appreciate my work.

Devil Oh, don't take it like that. You dead artists are all so touchy. I'm not here to criticise.

Shaw I'd have thought that was precisely what you were here for.

Devil Oh, no. No, absolutely not. You've got the wrong end of the stick. There's no punishment in Hell. No torture. No torment. Nobody wants your repentance or your improvement.

(Short pause)

Shaw Then what *do* you want?

Devil It's not so much what *I* want. It's for your benefit, really.

Shaw Tell me.

Devil Really. It's nothing much. Nothing painful. Nothing that isn't yours to give.

Shaw Well?

Devil From you, Mr Shaw. I think something literary would be apt. I think I'll have a play.

Shaw I must tell you, madam, even if I could overcome my scruples sufficiently to accept a commission from the Devil, I've sworn I will never write again. I am dead. I have nothing left to say.

Devil You misunderstand me. Never mind.

Shaw Perhaps you think you can persuade me when you take me to Hell itself. But you don't know George Bernard Shaw. When he says he's resolute, he means it. Are we... Are we going to Hell soon?

Devil I'm sorry. I thought you realised. We're already there.

(Short pause. **Shaw** *looks around him.)*

Shaw Hell is my garden?

Devil Yes. Why not? It's a nice day. And the flowers are blooming.

Shaw It's just not quite what I was expecting.

Devil *(idly smelling a flower)* On the contrary. It's exactly what you were expecting. I've read *Don Juan in Hell.* You wanted somewhere reasonably genteel where everyone could stand around being terribly clever. Where the sound of eternity isn't so much the wails of the damned as the echo of witty three page monologues. Not exactly a Manichean view of Hell, just a very very talkative one.

Shaw You've read *Don Juan in Hell*?

Devil Read it? I've memorised it. I love it. It always makes me laugh. Admittedly, maybe not for the right reasons. I always love it when artists die. It's why I make sure I always welcome them. They have such a *creative* view of the old place. Most people want fire and brimstone – we provide it, but where's the challenge?

Shaw So you try to accommodate everyone's expectations? That's very generous of you.

Devil We had such fun with all those medieval painters. All those lovely lurid colours, marvellous. Hieronymous Bosch thought Hell would be giant orange pincushions. The boys had such fun coming up with that.

Shaw How terrible for him.

Devil Not at all. I think he's very happy there, in his big surreal fresco.
Hell is a *friend* to artists. Look at all the great painters. They all depict
Heaven the same way. Angels on clouds, trumpets blowing in every
direction, everyone haloed so it looks like they've got gold dinner plates
nailed to their heads. Paradise stifles the imagination. But then, let them
loose on Hell, and that imagination runs wild! All the great writers,
musicians, all the painters, they all *claimed* they were working for God.
That their art was to celebrate him, magnify him. But God doesn't need
art. And it's only as they keep an eye on Hell that they give any sense to
their Sistine Chapels, their requiems, their *Pilgrims Progress*es. Even, I
suppose, their *Don Juan in Hell*s.

Shaw I have never claimed I was writing for the glory of God. I was
writing for the glory of Man.

Devil An aphorism! You're so *good* at those! It sounds lovely, Bernard,
but I know it isn't true. You didn't like Man.

Shaw I was writing for the potential of Man. Championing the
underdog, supporting the working classes.

Devil You were writing for yourself. Be honest.

Shaw No.

Devil Of course you were. Don't think I'm criticising. You put yourself
up above the common herd. And why shouldn't you? All artists do.
No piece of art worth the price of admission hasn't been conceived in
anything less than arrogance. The arrogance that it's *worth* an admission
price in the first place, and that the common herd might actually want
to pay it.

Shaw I certainly did not write for my own sake. I'd have been quite
happy if I had stopped writing years ago, and everyone had simply left
me alone.

Devil Have it your own way. For my point of view, I'm delighted. Only
the arrogance of a true artist could conceive a Hell which is your own
garden in Hertfordshire, where the awful dread host of damnation is
content to bandy aphorisms and tautologies.

Shaw If the urge to create art is fundamentally to reflect the Devil, then
why did God give us the urge in the first place?

Devil Oh, I wouldn't worry about God. Truth to tell, he doesn't care for
art much. He doesn't have much of an attention span. It's always caused
no end of trouble. The whole planet is a rushed job, you know – he only

took seven days.

Shaw But surely if God exists, then that artistic impulse must have come from him? The desire to write to compose, to paint...

Devil To be honest, I think all God wanted man to do was to build him temples. And nothing fancy either, none of your spires or curlicues. Just something functional which would keep the rain off. No, the urge of the artist comes from somewhere else altogether. Mind you, I can't take all the credit. Oh, go on then, yes, I can. You artistic types are far better off here in Hell than you would be in Heaven. God's tastes are so banal and passé. All pastel colours, chipboard and easy listening music. Ugh.

Shaw That sounds like the sort of punishment and torture I'd have expected down here.

Devil Oh, I do wish you wouldn't go on about punishment. That's really not the idea at all. Hell isn't meant to be a retribution for your life. It's just an explanation of it, with all the distractions removed.

Shaw I don't really understand.

Devil All will become clear. Well, that's the point! Death is life, with all the questions answered. No inequality, no ambition. Everybody at last levelled out.

Shaw But... that sounds perfect. That's not a Hell. That's a Utopia!

Devil Do you think so?

Shaw It's all my socialist ideals, made whole and real! It's what all my plays have been wanting to achieve!

Devil And, of course, there are no ideals either.

(Short pause)

There is no longer any point to your plays. All their idealism here has no purpose.

(Short pause)

Shaw You said Hell was a friend to the artist.

Devil On the other side, yes. But the afterlife needs no art, Bernard. It just *is*. It requires no depiction of it, or contemplation of it. And all your life's work means that to us.

(And she snaps her fingers.)

Shaw You're telling me that art is redundant?

Devil   Yes! Isn't it marvellous, Bernard? I thought you'd be pleased, you who argued for years that art had to have a social conscience. All those years you spent attacking the ills of mankind... Well, there are no ills left for you to attack.

Shaw   Yes... That is good news. Isn't it?

Devil   You were a famous man, Mr Shaw. But your life has become as meaningless as the common herd's you worked to rise above, to entertain, and to judge. You're the same as everybody else. Just another corpse who never really had enough fun. Many congratulations.

*(She offers him her hand. **Shaw** shakes it dumbly.)*

Shaw   But they'll still perform my plays, won't they? The people who are still alive. I might be dead, but my work still lives. Surely?

Devil   *(shrugging)* Maybe. Who cares? I'm telling you. From this side of the fence, with eternity staring you in the face every morning, posterity seems a very naive concept.

Shaw   *(clutching at straws)* But wait. You told me. You told me you wanted to commission me.

Devil   No, not exactly...

Shaw   You said you wanted a play from me! You do, don't you?

Devil   I do.

Shaw   Then I do have some purpose! Thank God. And though it goes against all my principles, I said I'd never write another, you're a lucky woman. Because I will write again. Just one more play. For you.

*(Enter **Shakespeare**. He is dressed as the stereotype, in doublet and ruff.)*

Shakespeare   Gadzooks! Surely it isn't! But it is!

Devil   And pat, see who comes, like the catastrophe of the old comedy.

*(**Shakespeare** strides over to the somewhat alarmed **Shaw**, and shakes his hand energetically.)*

Shakespeare   George Bernard Shaw. As I live and breathe. Which, of course, I don't! But then, neither do you!

Devil   Allow me to introduce a fellow playwright.

Shaw   *(dazed)* William Shakespeare?

Shakespeare   No need for introductions! We're old friends!

Devil   You've already met?

Shakespeare Not exactly. But when someone has been as free with my work and reputation as dear Bernard has been over the years, I feel we're practically brothers. After all, the man would hardly be so forward otherwise!

Shaw I assure you, sir nothing personal was ever intended...

Shakespeare Platitudinous fudge. I think that's how you described my work.

Shaw Just harmless literary debate, nothing more.

Shakespeare Oh, my dear fellow, you mustn't think I'm offended! Not a bit of it. The sycophancy which my writing gets even down here in Hell is enough to bore the doublet and hose off me. I've been waiting years for you to die, simply so we could have a good old natter about things.

Shaw And certainly *Shakes versus Shav* was just an idle bit of fun.

Shakespeare Of course it was! That was the puppet play, wasn't it? With you and me as Punch and Judy? Very amusing. I dare say had I ever stooped to write a self-aggrandising literary in-joke in the form of a seaside pantomime, I'd have not written it half as well.

Shaw *(dryly)* I'm pleased you take it in good heart.

Shakespeare *(playfully)* Not at all.

(He mimes hitting him over the head.)

Thwap! That's the way to do it.

Devil The writers in Hell always get on *so* well. They come to realise after a few centuries or so that they're all exactly the same.

Shakespeare *(suddenly serious)* No, the only thing I ever had any problems with was your rewriting the fifth act of *Cymbeline*.

Shaw Oh dear.

Shakespeare *(cold, suppressed rage)* If I had half a mind to get angry about it, I'd suggest that taking *Cymbeline* apart because it had melodramatics would be tantamount to criticising *Pygmalion* because it had phonetics. That's what it was *about*. Do you hear?

Shaw *(startled)* Oh. Erm. Yes.

Shakespeare *(suddenly and disconcertingly cheerful again)* I had a good glower about that for a decade or so. Not that I cared. I don't care about any of it. Just for something to *do*.

Shaw It was just a bit of a joke.

Shakespeare Oh, don't worry. I rewrote the last act of *Major Barbara*, just to get my own back.

Devil I was just explaining to Mr Shaw that I wanted a play from him.

Shakespeare Ah, discussing the admission fee, were you? Jolly good. Well, don't let me get in the way.

Devil Thank you.

Shakespeare Though if you'll take my advice, Bernard, you'll give her *Saint Joan*. I never liked that one. I thought you let off that French strumpet much too easily.

Shaw How can I write *Saint Joan*? I've already written it, haven't I?

Devil I didn't say anything about *writing* a play.

Shakespeare Just *giving* her one.

Devil Everyone who comes here has to give me something. One small achievement. A little chunk of their lives. And then I erase it.

Shaw You want to *erase* one of my plays?

Shakespeare That's the idea.

Shaw When you say 'erase'...?

Devil I mean, it will never have existed. We change history. Just a little. Say you do decide to sacrifice *Saint Joan*. You'll have spent 1924 doing something else.

Shakespeare Water ski-ing, perhaps.

Shaw You want to destroy my work?

Shakespeare No, she wants you to destroy your work. You get to choose what. The choice is the difficult bit.

Shaw What possible reason could you have for such barbarism? What good will it do you?

Devil It won't do me any good. It's not for my welfare. It's for yours.

Shaw Oh, really? And how do you propose hacking away at my life's work will help me in the slightest?

Devil Because it *is* your life's work. Your *life*'s work. And you're not alive any more. It's easier to move on once you accept it's not worth preserving. And you will need to move on, Bernard. You will. You can't go through the eternity of death with the few accomplishments of life hanging around your neck. So, down to business. The sooner we get this sorted out, the sooner we can all compose ourselves for infinity. Bernard Shaw. Which play would you most like to destroy?

Shaw None of them.

Devil How about *Jitta's Atonement*? That one went a bit pear-shaped, didn't it?

Shaw No.

Devil Okay. You want to keep *Jitta*. Fair enough. *Augustus Does His Bit* did nothing for me. Did it do anything for you?

Shaw I won't erase it.

Devil *(sighing)* Well, something a little shorter. *Passion, Poison and Petrifaction*. Nobody would miss that. I don't expect you can even remember writing it!

Shaw Just barely. But I won't get rid of it.

Devil *(impatiently)* Oh, come on, Mr Shaw. Help me out here. How about just a little piece of a play? The odd line here or there? Tell him, William.

Shakespeare You might as well, Bernard. After all, I sacrificed *Voltemand the Great*, didn't I?

Shaw I've never heard of *Voltemand the Great*.

Shakespeare Precisely.

Devil And that *was* great, was *Voltemand*. A blood and thunder swashbuckler with savage duels and identical twins and poisoned handkerchiefs. I'm not asking you to erase anything half as good as *Voltemand the Great*. Just some piddling *O'Flaherty of the VC,* or a *Simpleton of the Unexpected Isles*. Come on, what do you say?

(Short pause)

Shakespeare He's not budging, is he?

Devil You artists, always so bloody stubborn. But you'll come round eventually. Charles Dickens was dead set against it at first, but in time he could see the fun in losing the solution to *The Mystery of Edwin Drood*. Once Thomas Hardy got into the swing of burning his novels, it was as much as I could do to stop him throwing the whole lot on to the fire.

Shaw I will not sacrifice one word. Not one syllable. Do you understand me?

Devil I never have this problem with bricklayers. When I ask them to wipe a few bricks from their life. Or bakers, when they're required to reject the odd loaf or two. Why are you writers always so precious about what you produce?

Shaw Perhaps because we're better than bricklayers and bakers. Nothing they produce is meant to last for posterity.

Devil And you call yourself a champion of the working classes. I'm disappointed in you.

Shaw No, I didn't mean it like that...

Devil You're just an aesthete, like all the other writers.

Shaw The plays I write are *for* the working classes. From the ideas I propound, they'll be able to lay their bricks or bake their bread more prosperously.

Devil The truth is, in Hell you pay for your ambition on Earth. If you wanted nothing more than to bake loaves of bread, then it costs you little to erase a few of them. If you set yourself up to be more than that, to *mean* more than that, it's going to be tougher to give it up. Truly great men have greater need to humble themselves. Napoleon was most put out when he had to sacrifice his conquest of Great Britain, and end up imprisoned on St Elba instead.

(Short pause)

Well, whatever. When you make up your mind, Mr Shaw, you'll give me a shout, won't you? It's 1950 already. Before I know it, it'll be 1956, and I should be setting into Bertold Brecht. Are you coming, William?

Shakespeare No. I think I'll stay with Shaw a little longer.

Devil Yes, of course. I'm sure you have much to discuss. Both being men of the theatre. Erm. Both having names which start with 'Sh'. I'll leave you.

Shaw Thank you.

Devil *(sighing)* I know it might not sound likely, Mr Shaw. But you will come to feel comfortable down here. In time. Well, as comfortable as you *can* feel, when you can't feel anything. And before you know it, you'll be so used to death that you'll forget you ever lived at all.

Shaw *(coldly)* Goodbye.

Devil ...Yes.

(As she leaves:)

Later, William.

Shakespeare You bet.

(Short pause. The two men look at each other, both a little awkwardly now.)

So. Men of theatre, eh?

(Short pause)

Shaw I always wanted to say. Whatever my problems with your work. Platitudes, fudge, whatever. I think no-one will ever write a better tragedy than *King Lear.*

Shakespeare Thank you.

Shaw Though I find its nihilism reprehensible. And the blinding of Gloucester vulgar in the extreme. And I don't like the ending.

Shakespeare And for my part, I always enjoyed the abridged version of your collected letters.

(Short pause)

Shaw Is there a theatre in Hell?

Shakespeare Not as such. Though there are the same exorbitant bar prices and long queues for the toilet in the interval.

Shaw I see.

Shakespeare But it's not all bad. We may not get theatre, but we do get satellite television.

(Short pause)

Shaw Do you miss theatre?

(Short pause)

Shakespeare *(slowly)* I don't think about it. Often.

(Short pause)

I love theatre. But there you go. I expect you do too. Well, obviously you must.

Shaw Yes.

Shakespeare The smell of the greasepaint. The roar of the crowd.

Shaw Yes... Actually, I'm not all that keen on the smell of greasepaint. If I liked greasepaint stench, I'd have not worked in the theatre, I'd have worked in a beautician's. And to be honest, I'm not too taken with the roar of the crowd either.

Shakespeare Then what's it all for, Bernard? If not to communicate with the audience. If not for the roar of the crowd...

Shaw But I do enjoy communicating with the audience. Of course I do. I just don't necessarily want them *roaring.*

Shakespeare I see. You'd rather hear the murmur of thoughtful contemplation, than any evidence that they're actually enjoying themselves?

Shaw If my audience started roaring, I'd have them expelled from the auditorium.

Shakespeare Even from *Androcles and the Lion*?

Shaw Especially from *Androcles and the Lion*. No roaring allowed.

Shakespeare When I wrote, I always had to be conscious of the groundlings. Not able to afford seats, grouped together at the front of the stage, in front of the action. Wanting sometimes to be *part* of the action, heckling, booing, joining in.

Shaw We don't have groundlings in my day and age. Just the social divide between those compelled to buy ice-cream at the interval, and those who don't. That's enough.

Shakespeare But that's the whole point. You have to appeal to the groundling spirit. I always felt that no performance of *Julius Caesar* had truly worked unless someone in the crowd had tried to warn him he was about to be stabbed. 'Watch out, Julius, he's behind you!'

Shaw Terrible.

Shakespeare Not at all.. If they could get *that* involved, lose themselves that completely...

Shaw I think it is to my utter relief that no-one in the audience has ever tried to influence the action of *Caesar and Cleopatra.*

Shakespeare That's because there's precious little action in *Caesar and Cleopatra* to influence. So why love theatre? If not for the audience, who is it for?

(Short pause)

Shaw What I love... Theatre. Theatre is the only place in the world where you can start a reasonable discussion about morality, about the failings of the world, about the *need* to reform... And do it in such a way that the words actually get heard. If you put the same debates in a novel, you've no guarantee that the reader isn't going to skip a bit, or put it down on his bedside table and go to sleep. But in the theatre you can *control* them, they're sat there and they've no means of escape. Not without embarrassing themselves, and even the ice-cream eaters would rather sit through a treatise on philosophy than draw attention to themselves by leaving before the interval. You can encapsulate so much, an entire world of politics and debate and dramatic action, yes, however you may roll your eyes, I tell you there's more honest dramatic action in a character opening their minds to a new philosophy than there is in one being run through with a sword... You can do all of that, a whole world of change and hope, in just one short evening's entertainment. Three thousand years of civilisation honed down into three hours of pure theatre.

Shakespeare Not that *Back to Methuselah is* three hours. I think you're pushing it a bit there.

Shaw Because at its greatest, theatre has the capacity to *change*. If I can change the opinions of Major Barbara, of Henry Higgins, of John Tanner, surely I can change those of the audience too? Even just a little bit? Because without change it's all meaningless. It's like *Hamlet*, eight corpses lying on the stage. Did they learn anything? Did they change?

Shakespeare Yes.

Shaw Possibly. But they're all dead. So what good does it do? No play is worth a bean unless it tries to set up a debate of some sort, unless it tackles an issue that needs tackling. Whenever you try to get philosophical, I just want to laugh. *Hamlet.* To be or not to be. Well, how profound. Shall I kill myself? Or not? Simply staggering.

Shakespeare If you had written the speech, no doubt it would have taken an hour to recite.

Shaw Well, of course. You can't deal with an issue like that so peremptorily. It makes a nonsense of it.

Shakespeare And yet it's quite a popular speech, I gather.

Shaw If your concern was for the groundlings, why did you never write a play which addressed their social concerns?

Shakespeare No man pays a groat's admission to the theatre so they can be sympathised with, or pitied. My concern for the groundling was that I should give them a bit of pleasure. You know? Something to break up the hours shovelling dung. Something that just might make the day worth living.

Shaw When you could have done as I did. And tried to make their whole lives worth living.

Shakespeare You do drama no favours by insisting it all has a social mission. *King Lear* would not be a better play if it were about the problems facing the elderly. Look. I see nothing wrong with philosophising and sophistry. So long as it doesn't get in the way of entertainment.

Shaw I see nothing wrong with entertainment. So long as it doesn't get in the way of the sophistry.

Shakespeare And that's why you'll never be as popular as I am.

Shaw True. And it's why I wouldn't want to be.

(Short pause)

What's all this for? Are you trying to persuade me to erase my work?

Shakespeare Not a bit of it. It makes no difference to me. Sooner or later you'll give in. Everyone does. When I first came here, Geoffrey Chaucer was still resisting. He'd been resisting for over two hundred years. But even he realised in the end that never having written *The Sheepshagger's Tale* wasn't going to upset the balance of world literature that much.

Shaw How did *you* do it? Could you have destroyed an *Othello*, or a *Macbeth*?

Shakespeare Oh, please. I wish I could destroy *Macbeth*. Anything to never have to hear 'Is this a dagger I see before me' again.

Shaw That won't happen to me.

Shakespeare Of course it will. You'll grow to loathe the plays that are popular. And resent the ones that aren't.

Shaw Just because you don't respect your work, doesn't mean I should disrespect mine.

Shakespeare Oh, don't get me wrong. I respect my work all right. And I respect yours too, of course.

Shaw Oh. Thank you.

Shakespeare I just don't like either very much. I'm sick to death of mine, and bored to tears by yours. If I had ever tried to stage *Caesar and Cleopatra* at court, they'd have cut my head off.

Shaw Why? What's wrong with it? It's very historically accurate, you know. Far more so than your Cleopatra effort.

Shakespeare But the audience don't want historical truth. They want dramatic truth. A beginning, a middle, and an end. Strictly in that order, with lots of action along the way. It's the only truth *worth* believing in.

Shaw Typically, as always, you underestimate them.

Shakespeare No, Bernard, I think you underestimate them. And their capacity to recognise the simple *rightness* of a good story well told.

Shaw But when you saw my Cleopatra. History's Cleopatra. Finally emerging from the inaccuracies and gross vulgarity of yours, didn't you see anything in that at all?

Shakespeare Oh come on! All that emerged was the standard Shavian naïf. Just a silly little girl to be re-educated by the great GBS. She's just a prototype Eliza Dolittle, with Caesar as her Higgins.

Shaw I'll have you know I studied the period for ages! From the original source Latin! My Cleopatra is as close to the real Cleopatra as any Cleopatra can get!

Shakespeare Well. Let's ask her.

*(He claps his hands. And **Cleopatra** enters. She takes up a position centre stage, and stands there, statuesque.)*

Here you are. Cleopatra. Queen of the Nile. Last pharaoh of the Ptolemy dynasty. And five hundred lines of blank verse.

Shaw She looks just like the Devil.

Shakespeare Everyone looks the same here. You'll get used to it.

Shaw But is she the real Cleopatra?

Shakespeare She's the only one that *matters*. You do us wrong, when you say our plays should reflect truth. We *create* the truth, you and I. That's what's art's all about, making the truth shinier and more memorable. Look at her.

Shaw I am. And she's as bogus as your argument.

Shakespeare Not true. The Cleopatra you want rotted into dust two millennia ago. No-one remembers her. The real Cleopatra is the someone I made, a goddess and woman rolled into one. Which do you think is better? Which one do you think will do the world greater good? The savage who bedded and murdered her own brothers? Or the personification of overwhelming love?

Shaw Whatever you think, the original Cleopatra deserves her story told too.

Shakespeare I created a testament to femininity that will replay through the ages. And you created a silly teenager.

Cleopatra Actually, I have to admit, I quite fancy the idea of being a silly teenager.

Shakespeare What? What did you say?

Cleopatra I mean, really. Being an icon of world literature is such a strain on the nerves. I'd much prefer Bernard's take than yours.

Shaw I always wanted to find the real person behind the history, you see.

Cleopatra And I think you did a marvellous job, honey.

Shakespeare So what about me then?

Cleopatra Oh, don't look so sad, William. You did your best, I know. But to be honest, I'm sick to death of sitting on burnished thrones on barges. They weren't made for comfort. I'm tired of being statuesque. I want to have a little fun.

(She stretches out her arms.)

Oh, that *feels* better.

Shakespeare And this is the thanks I get. The hours I put into you, making you live. With my wife Anne knocking on the door, saying, please, Will, please come to bed...

Cleopatra You should have gone. I see posterity hasn't remembered *her.* She might have been more grateful. Go. Begone.

*(**Shakespeare** opens his mouth to speak. Then closes it, and exits.)*

Shaw You've upset him.

Cleopatra He'll get over it. He's not used to criticism, that's all. All those RSC productions and O-level questions have gone to his head. It's nice to meet you at last.

Shaw Oh. Well. Thank you.

Cleopatra Shakespeare made me very beautiful. Did you intend me to be beautiful in your play too?

Shaw Well. Erm. Yes.

Cleopatra Oh, that's good. I do like being beautiful.

(She reaches out and strokes his cheek.)

Shaw *(nervously)* Unhand me, madam. Don't you know you're in my *Three Plays for Puritans*?

Cleopatra I tried reading that. But since you made me such a silly, I found it hard to understand.

Shaw Oh yes.

Cleopatra In Act Three of Shakespeare's play I fight the battle of Actium. In Act Three of yours I'm out shopping for carpets.

Shaw I'm sorry. It's not quite as grand...!

Cleopatra Oh, I don't mind. I like shopping. Much more fun than naval warfare.

Shaw Do you think I did a good job? With you, I mean? Was my research thorough enough? Would you say... you were Historically Accurate?

Cleopatra Well, I'm sure I don't know.

Shaw Don't know! But you were there!

Cleopatra But it's such a long time ago. You just forget. Everyone here, we're not the real Cleopatras, the real Mark Antonys. We're the way people remember us. You know. In the living world. Shakespeare's idea of me as tragic heroine is so famous that's all anyone knows, so that's now what I *am*.

Shaw But that's terrible.

Cleopatra And now you've come along, and made me historically accurate. I'm myself again! My own woman. And now history will remember the real *me* instead! Just as soon as your play becomes more popular than Shakespeare's. Will that happen soon, do you think?

Shaw *(awkwardly)* Well. Let's hope. Fingers crossed, hmm?

Cleopatra Such a relief.

Shaw I can imagine.

Cleopatra I hope you get as lucky. When someone writes a play about you.

Shaw ...No-one would write a play about me.

Cleopatra But assuming they did. How would you feel if someone, I don't know, say fifty years from now, made you a character for the stage? Played by an actor years too young, and with a false beard? What would you think of that?

(Short pause)

Shaw *(quietly)* I always kept such a tight control on my life. I created a cartoon version of me, just for the media. The irascible GBS, wit, critic and mocker of the establishment. Just so that no-one would know the real me.

Cleopatra But perhaps it's too late. Here you are in Hell, and just like me, you'll only exist the way people remember. I wonder, Bernard Shaw. What will posterity make of *you*?

(Short pause)

I can show you someone who knows you, Bernard. Before history gets its claws into you. Someone who knows you, no-one ever knew you better.

(And she stands back from him. Takes off her headdress, lets it fall to the ground. Lets her hair hang loose – and looks at him defiantly.)

Shaw *(softly)* Charlotte. My wife. Charlotte. Charlotte.

(Short pause)

Charlotte? My dear?

(Short pause)

Have you nothing to say to me?

Charlotte You took your time getting here.

Shaw Yes. I'm sorry...

Charlotte Six years. Six years I've waited.

Shaw Yes. I know. I did want to die, but my body wouldn't let me...

Charlotte Other husbands pass over much more quickly. They die for grief. Can you imagine that? They actually die for grief.

Shaw My body simply wouldn't let me go.

Charlotte *(sighing)* Ordinary husbands. But you were never an ordinary husband, were you, Bernard? I expected nothing else from you.

(Short pause)

Shaw You're looking well.

Charlotte Thank you.

Shaw Death suits you.

Charlotte Does it?

Shaw Yes. When you died, Charlotte, when you finally... I had never seen you look so beautiful...

Charlotte I look as you remember me, Bernard. Nothing more.

Shaw Oh. Yes, of course.

Charlotte Is this how you remembered me? When you closed your eyes in the night, when you dreamed of your dead wife, is this what you saw?

Shaw Yes.

Charlotte I'm so tired of being remembered. I want to be forgotten. I want you to forget all about me.

Shaw Oh, Charlotte...

Charlotte I've wanted so many things from you, Bernard. Over the years so many different things. But all I want now is to be forgotten entirely.

(Short pause)

Shaw I didn't expect to find you here. I thought you'd be in the other place...

Charlotte Oh no. You keep me down here.

Shaw I didn't want you to misunderstand. Why I didn't come looking for you as soon as I arrived. Why I've been talking to other people instead.

Charlotte Well.

Shaw I spoke to a Germ. And to the devil. Then William Shakespeare and Queen Cleopatra.

Charlotte All of them characters in your plays.

Shaw Well, I suppose they are, yes.

Charlotte Some wives would find that a little arrogant. But I was married to a writer, I'm used to it. I have no illusions, Bernard. That's one of the wonderful things about death. It strips away all your illusions. Wonderful and terrifying.

(Short pause)

Did you ever love me?

Shaw What? Yes, of course I did.

Charlotte Forgive me for asking. I just never knew for sure.

Shaw You're my wife.

Charlotte Six years with no illusions can make a dead wife curious. If you love me. If you loved me, ever. Would you set me free?

Shaw How can I do that?

Charlotte Haven't you realised yet, Bernard? We're only in Hell for as long as we're remembered on Earth. Once we've been forgotten... we move on. Just vanish. Nobody knows where. Some say it's to Heaven. I don't care whether it's Heaven, I don't care where I vanish *to*, I'm happy just to vanish, quite frankly.

Shaw Is that what Hell is? Just a collection of old memories?

Charlotte I shan't vanish until there's not one person alive who can recall the name Charlotte Shaw. We weren't *meant* to be famous, you see, Bernard. That isn't what life's for. It's to be enjoyed, and then we move on. We all have to let go, and move on.

Shaw But what of posterity...?

Charlotte Oh, Bernard. All your life you worked for posterity. It's a trap, my dear. For us both. As long as people stage your plays and write your biographies, they'll remember me too. And they'll keep me in Hell.

Shaw What are you asking of me?

Charlotte You know.

Shaw Yes.

Charlotte The Devil has asked you for one of your plays. Is that right?

Shaw Yes.

Charlotte I beg you, my dear. Give her them *all*. Erase them forever, and we can both vanish into obscurity together.

(Short pause)

Shaw You know I can't do that.

Charlotte I know.

(Short pause)

So long as you're aware. Your life-long desire for reputation and celebrity. It's not just you who suffers.

Shaw ...I understand.

Charlotte Oh, Bernard. Why couldn't you have been an ordinary man, with ordinary ambitions?

(Short pause)

You never loved me.

(Short pause)

Why did you marry me, Bernard?

Shaw I don't know.

Charlotte I became your secretary. I learned how to read your shorthand, I typed for you, I collated your scripts and prepared them for publication.

Shaw I know you did.

Charlotte Even put up with your vegetarian cooking. It's my fault. I made myself indispensable to you. But isn't that what you wrote about? The folly of intelligent women?

Shaw I did love you. Charlotte. I did love you. I know I did.

Charlotte Not a passionate love.

Shaw ...No.

Charlotte But indispensable. Nonetheless.

(Short pause)

Shaw I wish I had loved you… passionately. I wish I had kissed you. I wish I had wanted to kiss you.

(Short pause)

I wish… you had had the sort of face... I would have wanted to kiss.

Charlotte I'm just another character you created, Bernard. Just as much as Cleopatra.

Shaw That's not true.

Charlotte But isn't it? You wrote your Cleopatra play as we were getting married. On our honeymoon you were revising the dialogue. Aren't I just that silly girl you created? Whom you could tutor, whose head you could fill with your ideas and speeches?

Shaw I love you.

Charlotte But the silly girl grew up. She stopped being a secretary, and became a wife. And you found other secretaries.

Shaw I told you not to love me.

Charlotte And you knew I'd love you all the more for it. Please. Set me free.

(*Shaw* approaches her. She looks at him warily. And he kisses her softly on the lips. Puts his arms around her, and holds her. Silence. Then, gently:)

Shaw I can't.

Charlotte You won't.

Shaw No.

Charlotte They're only words. Only a bunch of words.

Shaw No. They're my life.

(Short pause. She disentangles from him.)

But I do love you. I do. I did. I do.

Charlotte Words. Just words.

(Silence. Then, enter **Shakespeare**, cheerily. He carries with him a box, inside which are two fencing swords.)

Shakespeare Hello! Are you busy? Oh, it's all right. I can see that you're not!

Shaw Leave us, sir. I am talking to my wife.

Shakespeare Which is precisely my point. Remember, I had one of them myself. Give me a choice between spending time with my words or with my wife, I'd choose my words any day. Wouldn't you, Bernard?

Charlotte Yes. He would.

Shakespeare Words are so hard to master. To coax them in the right direction, to get them to do what you want. But at least you *can* get them to do what you want, if you try hard enough, and when you do, oh, the thrill is incredible. I could never get my wife to do what I wanted, not after years of effort.

Shaw I must tell you, Mr Shakespeare, you're a big disappointment to me.

Shakespeare Yes. Anne used to say that to me too. Oh well. Let's hope we made better playwrights than we made husbands, eh, George Bernard? But I hope I shan't disappoint you now. In fact, I have a little treat for you.

Shaw What is it? I ask with due sense of dread.

Shakespeare I told you I had rewritten the last act of *Major Barbara*. Well, here it is! Ta-dah!

(*Charlotte* *approaches* *Shakespeare* *and takes a foil from the box. She makes a few experimental swipes with it.* *Shakespeare* *keeps the other.*)

Charlotte and I have been rehearsing it for you. So that when you finally died, we could offer you some entertainment.

Shaw The last act of *Major Barbara*?

Shakespeare The battle between Andrew Undershaft, arms manufacturer extraordinaire, and his daughter Barbara, formerly of the Salvation Army. A battle which shall be fought as you *should* have written it. To the death, with rapier!

Shaw You're going to turn one of my finest philosophical debates into a fencing duel?

Shakespeare I think you missed a trick there, Bernard. It would have made it much more exciting. Are you ready, Charlotte?

Charlotte (*dramatically*) On guard!

(*And she swipes at his rapier.*)

Shakespeare She's ready. Very well!

(*And the two take up a fencing stance.*)

Charlotte To give into the idea of accepting profit by the sale of arms, or not to give into the idea of accepting profit by the sale of arms. That is the question. But hark! Which man from yonder factory breaks?

Shakespeare Sblood! 'Tis I, Undershaft, thy father and thy sworn enemy.

Charlotte Have at thee, Undershaft!

(*And they fight a few blows.*)

Show me some light through the darkness of this dreadful munitions factory.

Shakespeare No darkness here, no dreadfulness. In your Salvation shelter I saw the misery, cold and hunger of the poor. You gave them but bread and treacle and dreams of heaven.

(*He beats her into a retreating position.*)

Charlotte Forsooth!

Shakespeare Forsooth indeed! I give them thirty shillings a week. They find their own dreams, but I look after the drainage.

Shaw *(sardonically)* Oh, a hit. A very palpable hit.

*(**Charlotte** slashes back, and she regains the upper hand.)*

Charlotte Zounds! And their souls? What of their souls?

Shakespeare A touch, a touch, I do confess it.

Charlotte I know you have a soul for salvation. But if you want to use your cheque to buy it, go on being as wicked as ever.

Shakespeare You're fat and scant of breath! What is all human conduct but the daily and hourly sale of our souls for trifles?

(And they resume fighting in earnest. As they do so:)

Shaw Look, just stop. Stop! This is a travesty of my work!

Shakespeare I want to make power for the world!

Charlotte Egad! I want to make power for the world too, but it must be spiritual power!

*(**Shaw** intercedes by standing between them.)*

Shaw Enough!

Charlotte You shouldn't do that, Bernard. I could have run you through.

Shakespeare It is putting actions to the words. That is all.

Charlotte Just think, dear, how much more exciting your plays might have been if your arguments and debates had made people *bleed*.

*(And she lunges at **Shakespeare**.)*

Shakespeare I am wounded!

(And he stabs at her.)

Charlotte We bleed on both sides.

Shakespeare Alas, poor Major Barbara, I knew her well!

Charlotte Good night, sweet arms manufacturer, and flights of angels sing thee to thy rest!

Shaw Oh, this is preposterous. I'm having nothing to do with it.

(And he walks away from them both sulkily.)

Shakespeare Philosophy and gory swordfights, Bernard. Just think of it.

Shaw You cannot do this to my work. I shan't allow it.

Shakespeare It's no worse than what posterity has done to mine. I've had Romeos and Juliets played as gangster rappers, I've had *Tempest*s set on alien planets. My King Lear has been a samurai, a Nazi, a clown, a pimp. My plays have been interpreted to support every ism going, whether it be feminism, communism, fascism, surrealism, postmodernism or antidisestablishmentarianism.

Charlotte You did say you wanted posterity, didn't you, dear? It means everything's up for grabs.

Shaw My stage directions are always very clear. And my prefaces outline my greater intentions.

Shakespeare Do you think your work will stop evolving? That your children will stop growing now you're dead?

Charlotte Kill those children, Bernard. For both our sakes.

Shaw No!

Shakespeare You're a fool to want posterity. But you're an even bigger fool if you think you can control it.

*(**Shaw** puts his hands over his ears and walks downstage towards the audience. Behind him, **Shakespeare** and **Charlotte** resume their duel half-heartedly.)*

Shaw And now at last I truly understand. This really is Hell.

*(And **Charlotte** stabs **Shakespeare**. He falls to his knees.)*

Shakespeare *(quietly)* O, I am dead. The pointy poniard quite o'ercrows my spirit.

Shaw I have, it seems, abused my wife's love, abused my own potential. Wasted my life. All for a few scraps of plays which I could and should have written better.

*(And **Shakespeare** stabs **Charlotte**. She falls to her knees too.)*

Charlotte Is this the promised end?

(They both die kneeling, holding the other upright.)

Shaw And yet I will not give in. I, Bernard Shaw, who *never* gave in. Because if I did, what would that waste have been for? What point all that abuse? However the world remembers me. However it remembers my work. I *shall* be constant. I *shall* be GBS. Whatever happens! I'm GBS forever!

(Short pause)

The rest is silence.

(Blackout.)

Act Two

(As before, except there are now three garden seats and a small table.

*(Dressed in modern clothing, a middle-aged couple, **Norman** and **Esther**, walk into the garden. **Esther** carries a camera. **Norman** is very enthusiastic – his wife clearly less so.)*

Norman Well. Isn't this just marvellous?

(Short pause)

Esther?

Esther Yes, darling?

Norman Marvellous. Isn't this just simply marvellous?

Esther Yes, darling.

Norman Well, say it, darling. Say it's marvellous.

Esther It's marvellous, darling.

Norman That's the idea. Take a picture of me. You've got the camera? Standing here. No, wait. Like that. ...Perfect. That's one for the collection.

Esther Yes.

Norman We can put it on display with the others.

(Short pause)

You know. Some people. Coming here. Looking round. Like we are. All they'd see is just a garden. You know that, don't you?

Esther It's hard to imagine why.

Norman It is, isn't it? They see the grass. And the flowers. But not the genius therein. You know what I call those people, Esther?

Esther Philistines.

Norman Philistines. That's it. That's it to a tee. Philistines, every last one of them. You can feel it, can't you, Esther? Walking around this place. This is the garden in which *Pygmalion* was conceived. In which *Heartbreak House* was first dreamed up. You can feel it's special, can't you, darling?

Esther Yes, darling.

Norman And that's because you're not a philistine.

(He breathes in deeply, happily.)

Even the pollen count has a definite Shavian twang to it. Take another photo. Of me breathing in. Go on. That's the idea. ...Do you want me to...

Esther No.

Norman Take a picture of...

Esther No.

Norman No. Okay.

(Short pause)

It's overwhelming isn't it? This is where *Saint Joan* was born. Just thinking that gives me goosebumps. Do you think genius can rub off on to a place? I think it can. Shaw's here, darling. Bernard Shaw is alive and well in every blade of grass under our feet. Every... clump of dirt. And I like to think, I don't know. That if I stayed here long enough. That if I got... down on the grass, like this. For years and years and years. That some of that genius might rub off on to *me*.

Esther *(quietly)* I felt that at Haworth.

Norman What?

Esther I felt that at Haworth. All that genius rubbing off. You remember, we went to Haworth.

Norman Yes, I know we went to Haworth...

Esther Where the Brontes lived...

Norman Yes, I know the Brontes lived there, thank you...

Esther All I'm saying is I felt something very powerful there...

Norman We're not talking about the bloody Brontes though. We're talking about bloody Shaw. George bloody Bernard Shaw.

Esther I was just saying.

Norman Well, don't. It's hardly politic. I can well imagine what Shaw would have made of the Brontes.

Esther Why? What did Shaw make of them?

Norman ...I don't know. But I can't imagine he was overly impressed. Remind me to look it up on the internet, darling, when we get home, and we can find out.

(Short pause)

Esther You always get like this when we come here.

Norman No, I don't. Get like what?

Esther You told me you wouldn't get like this. But you always do.

Norman No, I didn't. Like what?

Esther I don't think it's Shaw's genius which rubs off. Just his bad temper.

Norman Rubbish. I'm perfectly happy. This is perfectly marvellous. Isn't it?

Esther Quite why we could never go on a proper family holiday. Quite why it had to be Shaw's Corner every year.

Norman *(smiling)* Well.

Esther The children always complained. Why do we have to go to Shaw's Corner again?

Norman The children loved it here.

Esther Why can't we go to Alton Towers?

Norman I told Barbara on the phone we'd be here today. She sounded really envious.

Esther And we'll never get a family holiday again. Not now the kids are older. They won't want to come on holiday with us any more.

Norman Oh, Dad, that sounds fun. I wish *I* were coming.

Esther Never again. Not even if we went to Alton Towers.

Norman Come on, darling. Come and sit with me here on the grass.

Esther No.

Norman Go on.

Esther I don't want to.

Norman Of course you want to. We're on holiday.

*(And reluctantly **Esther** sits with him. Short pause)*

Do you know when Bernard Shaw moved here?

Esther *(dully)* November 1906.

Norman That's it. And he lived here...

Esther Forty-four years.

Norman That's it, that's it exactly. Well done. Just think. He wrote *Village Wooing* here. And *The Intelligent Woman's Guide to Socialism*.

Esther Mmm.

Norman I find it inspiring.

*(Short pause. **Esther** thinks about this, then frowns in concern.)*

Esther But you don't need to find it inspiring. Do you? You're not doing anything to be inspired for. Are you? Norman?

(Short pause)

Norman?

Norman I've decided to direct another play for PADS.

Esther But not another Shaw. Please tell me it's not another Shaw.

Norman It's the only thing worth directing, darling. You know that. I feel such... a close bond to Shaw.

Esther They won't stand for it. No-one wants to do any more Shaw. They all find it boring.

Norman They'll come round.

Esther You remember what Colin Parker said. On the first night of *Androcles and the Lion.* Looking through the curtains at the empty house. Sweating like a pig in his lion costume. He said, if Norman wants me in any more bloody Shaw, tell him he can stick it where the sun don't shine.

Norman Even Colin Parker will come round.

Esther You promised you wouldn't do a Shaw this year. You promised *me.*

Norman I'm doing *Back to Methuselah.*

Esther Oh God.

Norman I know I've got a great Methuselah in me. I want to give the world my Methuselah. Don't deny me my Methuselah, Esther, don't come between me and my Methuselah.

Esther Don't you think you could find a great *Run For Your Wife* in you? I'm just saying.

Norman Here we are at Shaw's Corner. The home of the greatest literary genius who ever lived...

Esther But, Norman...

Norman Who *ever* lived. And I feel inspired. I shall not rest until the Purley Amateur Dramatics Society has produced every single one of his works. With me at the helm, directing them. And with you as my leading lady. We're keeping Shaw alive, darling, the great GBS alive. If Shaw were able to hear me, just imagine how proud he'd be.

Esther I think he'd turn in his grave.

*(And immediately enter **Shaw**, looking dazed. He stands stock still, then spins round and collapses to the ground.)*

Norman Oh my God!

Esther Well, come on, we've got to help him!

(And they help him to his feet.)

Are you all right?...

Shaw Yes, I just had a funny turn...

Norman Upsadaisy...

Shaw Really, I'm quite all right now...

Esther There you go.

Shaw Thank you. Well.

Norman *(seeing **Shaw**'s face)* ...Oh my good God. Esther!

Esther What?

Norman Come over here a moment!

(She joins him.)

Do you know who that is?

Esther No. Is he somebody from the National Trust?

Norman It's George Bernard Shaw!

Shaw It's very peculiar. I've just been having the strangest dream.

Esther *(looking at him, then back at **Norman**)* No...!

Norman I tell you it is! I've seen enough pictures of him on the back of my Penguins to know a real live Bernard Shaw when I see one!

(And they both look back at him in awe.)

Shaw I must say, I'm glad I've woken up. Better than imagining myself dead for fifty years!

Esther It's like seeing actors off the telly. He's a lot shorter than you'd have thought.

Norman He's been resurrected.

Esther I told him that you'd make him turn in his grave.

Shaw I don't mean to sound ungrateful for your help, but might I ask what you young people are doing in my garden?

(And dumbly they hand over their admission tickets.)

Esther *(feebly)* We paid admission...

*(**Shaw** stares at the tickets, then hands them back without a word. He walks away, lost in thought.)*

Norman Mr Shaw. Sir. May I just say what an honour it is.

(Short pause. He advances towards him.)

Well, I will anyway. Mr Shaw. It's an honour. My name is Norman Trent. One of your greatest admirers and most ardent supporters. And this is my wife, Esther. Say hello to Bernard Shaw, Esther.

Esther Are you all right, Mr Shaw? You had a nasty turn there.

Norman I should also say that I've been a lifelong member of the Shaw Society. I've even contributed to the newsletter. And as artistic director of PADS, that's the Purley Amateur Dramatic Society, I am committed to keeping your work in performance right into the twenty-first century...

Esther Shut up, Norman, I think he looks a little pale. Mr Shaw?

Shaw The twenty-first century?

Esther *(gently)* Yes, It's 2007. You've been dead for absolutely ages.

Norman Fifty-six years, seven months, twelve days.

Esther Norman!

Shaw Fifty years. It felt like fifty years too. Fifty years I've held on.

Esther ...Held on to what, exactly?

Shaw Do you have a book of my complete works?

Norman *(proudly)* We certainly do. We keep it by our bedside. Don't we, darling?

Esther Yes, darling.

Shaw And inside this book... do you still have a drama called *The Six* *of Calais*? Are all five acts of *The Doctor's Dilemma* left intact?

Norman Oh yes. And five very good acts, if I may say so.

Shaw Then I've won. Fifty long years I resisted. They came to me constantly, suggesting countless reasons why I should sacrifice my work. And yet I dug in my heels, I stuck my fingers in my ears and kept my eyes screwed up tight.

Norman *(puzzled, politely)* Good for you, Mr Shaw.

Esther Good for you.

Norman Esther, how about a picture of me with Mr Shaw. I'll just stand alongside him like this. Are you ready?

Shaw And now I'm alive again.

Norman Ready, darling? ...That's great.

Shaw ...I think I need to lie down.

Esther Oh dear.

Shaw Yes. That's what I'll do. I'll have a little sleep and it'll all look better in the morning.

(He turns towards the house.)

Norman But you can't go in there, Mr Shaw!

Shaw What do you mean, sir? It's my house, isn't it? I can go where I like.

Norman I'm not sure the National Trust would see it that way.

Shaw Oh yes... I left them the house in my will...

Esther They might not like it if you mucked up the bed. It might frighten the tourists.

Shaw So much for charitable ventures. I won't make that mistake again. Next time I die, I'll leave it to English Heritage.

Norman Mr Shaw. I was thinking. Esther and I, we have a spare room.

Shaw *(warily)* Oh yes?

Norman If that's any good to you. We'd be happy for you to stay in it for a while.

Esther Norman...

Norman I'd be delighted. Even.

Esther Might I have a word? ...I don't want you offering up our house to strangers!

Norman Bernard's not a stranger! I've read every word he's ever written! I probably know him better than I know you!

Esther ...Very probably.

Norman Mr Shaw. The visitor's car park is just nearby, and then we're straight up the M1. What do you say?

(Short pause)

Shaw You'll understand I'm not in the habit of accepting the solicitations of admirers. I have always prided myself upon being a very private individual. I even tried to turn down the Nobel Prize.

Norman I know. But the bloody Swedes wouldn't listen, would they?

Shaw That said, I'm also not in the habit of coming back from the dead. This seems to be a day to break old habits. So I'll thank you, Mr Trent, Mrs Trent. I'm in your hands.

(Music plays, and lighting shifts as they walk around the garden, up into the house. Then immediately exit again to walk downstage.)

Norman ...And down here, you see, this is our garden.

Esther We like to eat out here in the summer.

Shaw My word.

Norman *(beaming)* I bet it all seems a little familiar to you.

Shaw It's my garden. It's just the same as my garden at Ayot's...

Esther Norman had it designed this way.

Norman I did, Mr Shaw. I wanted it to be *exactly* the same as yours.

Shaw I thought the shrine to me in the library was bad enough, but this...

Norman Flattering, isn't it?

Shaw That isn't quite the word I had in mind.

Norman I thought this way some of your genius might rub off. Just a little. You know, I come out here, and do what you did, I try to think up great thoughts. It inspires me when I'm rehearsing your plays. I'm sure you drew a lot of strength from the arrangement of your garden.

Shaw Well, no. It was just a garden, really.

Norman So some people say. But you know what I call them, Mr Shaw?

Esther Philistines.

Norman Philistines. That's right, darling.

Shaw Oh. Sorry about that.

Norman Mind you, I never actually get any great thoughts. However hard I try. I come out here early in the morning, or late at night, catch the brain unawares, I think, surprise it into producing something meaningful. But I've not had any luck yet. I suppose my thoughts aren't very original. I rarely come up with anything deep, and if I do, it's been done deeper by someone else. But never mind! I'm not discouraged. It's just a matter of practice! Esther knows I'll come up with something brilliant one of these days, don't you, darling?

Esther Mmm.

Norman She's always telling me. She's to me as I'm sure Charlotte was to you.

Shaw Mmm.

Norman But it doesn't matter. The world doesn't need two Bernard Shaws, does it, Mr Shaw? Not with you back from the dead. I dare say, standing here, you're getting quite overcome with great thoughts of your own already. Really really good ones.

(Short pause)

Esther I hope the spare room will be comfortable.

Shaw Oh yes. Thank you.

Esther It used to be Barbara's bedroom, our daughter, that is. That's why there's pink wallpaper.

Shaw No, it's splendid.

Norman I still say you should take *our* room, Mr Shaw. It's much nicer.

Shaw No, I wouldn't hear of it.

Esther Neither would I.

Norman It's just that the spare room is right next door to the toilet. And it has a very loud flush. Takes ages for the cistern to refill.

Esther I'm sure Mr Shaw won't mind.

Norman Well, fair enough. Fair enough. But if the gurgling upsets you, you just come knocking on our door. Any time of the night. And we'll swap.

Esther ...Well. Would anybody like a drink?

Norman A drink, Mr Shaw? Nothing alcoholic in this house, I promise you.

Shaw Thank you.

Norman What have we got, darling?

Esther We've got Diet Coke, Tango Orange, Tango Apple, Sprite, Seven Up...

(Norman beams at Shaw.)

Shaw Could I have a lemonade?

Esther Seven Up or Sprite?

Norman With a hint of grapefruit or not, Mr Shaw?

Shaw I really couldn't care less.

Norman A Seven Up for Mr Shaw, darling. Maybe we'll move on to the Sprites later. And I'll have what Mr Shaw's having.

Esther Right. So that's three Seven Ups then.

Norman Right.

Esther Right. Okay.

(And she exits to the house, leaving Shaw and Norman alone. Long, awkward pause. Norman smiles at Shaw. Shaw smiles and nods back.)

Norman It really is an enormous treat, you know. Having you here.

Shaw Well. Thank you.

Norman No. Not at all.

(Short pause. Then, shyly:)

I just wanted to say... thanks. You know, for everything.

Shaw I'm sorry?

Norman All the years of pleasure you've given me. I can't tell you. Just what a difference it's made. To my life. To all of our lives, you know. Everyone in the world. But to me in particular. Thanks.

Shaw *(embarrassed)* Well. Think nothing of it.

Norman And for Esther too. I have to thank you for Esther.

Shaw Oh?

Norman That's how we met, you see. Doing one of your plays. Back
in the early years of the Purley Amateur Dramatics Society. She was
playing Raina in *Arms and the Man*. I was Bluntschli, and every night I
had to climb in through her bedroom window. And now, all these years
later, I still am. Well, not through the window, I mean. But you know
that.

Shaw Yes.

Norman Anything I can do for you. Ever. You know. I'd like to think of
you as my friend. My best friend. And, obviously, I'd like you to think
of me as your friend as well. Not necessarily your best friend, I wouldn't
presume... Well, no, maybe in time. Maybe in time.

(Short pause)

Where has Esther got to with those Seven Ups?

*(Enter **Esther**, carrying three glasses on a tray.)*

Ah, here she is!

Esther Here she is...!

Shaw Yes.

Norman We were just wondering where you'd got to, darling.

Esther I had to go and open a new bottle, darling.

Shaw I hope you didn't go to any trouble on my account.

Esther No matter. It's all done now.

Shaw It's not as if I even know whether I like Seven Up.

*(They both watch as **Shaw** lifts the glass to his lips – and drinks, rather
self-consciously.)*

Mmm. It's fine.

(Everybody relaxes.)

Norman So. If I can just ask you, Mr Shaw...

Shaw Yes?

Norman I've always wanted to know. What exactly was going through
your head when you wrote *Pygmalion*?

Shaw ...Well, lots of things.

Norman Yes?

Shaw Well. Yes. I mean, it took months to write.

Norman I see.

Shaw Lots of things went through my head in those months.

Norman Fascinating.

(Short pause)

Like what, for example?

Shaw What?

Norman What things? For example.

Shaw Well, I don't know.

Norman No.

Shaw It was a hundred years ago.

Norman Ninety-four years ago.

Shaw Well, there you are.

Norman Yes.

(Short pause)

Esther Norman, will you stop staring at Mr Shaw? You'll put him off his lemonade.

Norman Fascinating. Quite fascinating.

Esther It must be very odd, Mr Shaw, popping back to life like that.

Norman Nonsense, darling. Mr Shaw is a visionary. He takes everything in his stride.

Shaw It is very disconcerting. Tell me. Has much changed since my day?

Esther Well, I wasn't around in your day, Mr Shaw, I really don't know.

Shaw I take it that no-one adopted the phonetic alphabet I suggested?

Esther No, I don't think so.

Norman No. The fools.

Shaw I suppose I should have expected that. How about my Fabian reforms?

Esther *(looking to **Norman** worriedly for confirmation)* Well, not as such.

Norman We got the National Theatre you asked for.

Shaw Oh, that's something. A home in which my plays can be performed.

Esther Yes. They've got *My Fair Lady* on at the moment.

Shaw ...No, that's not one of mine.

Norman It's *Pygmalion*. With songs and dancing.

Shaw It sounds ghastly.

Norman It is. It's a travesty.

Esther Well, I like it. I've always liked Audrey Hepburn. And the songs, well... it helps break up all your talky bits, Mr Shaw.

Shaw Really?

Esther Yes.

Norman Esther...

Shaw What a good idea. Maybe *Major Barbara* would have been improved by a few conjuring tricks here and there. Maybe the odd trapeze artist might have made *Man and Superman* more fun.

Esther Yes. Who knows? Maybe it would.

(Short pause)

Shaw Please tell me. Mr Trent. My plays... they do still *get* performed, don't they?

Norman ...Well, not very often. But you know. From time to time.

(Short pause)

I'm doing my best. I'll revive them all one day, Mr Shaw. You'll see. And you'll be so proud!

*(**Shaw** puts his head in his hands. Short pause)*

Well, I must be going to bed. Back to work tomorrow! Yes. I hope you sleep well, Mr Shaw.

Shaw Thank you.

Norman In spite of the pink wallpaper and the noisy flush. I've left a pad and pencil on the bedside table. You know, just in case you want to write a new play in the night.

Shaw *(with surprising firmness)* I don't write any more.

Norman No. Well. In case you do. I'll be back around five-thirty six-ish, dependent on traffic. I'm sure Esther will take care of you till then, she doesn't do anything in the day. But if you have any problems, here... this is my work number. And this is my mobile number. And this is my secretary's mobile number. In case you need anything at all. Don't hesitate, Mr Shaw.

Shaw I won't. Thank you.

Norman Good night, Mr Shaw. It really is... well, everything I said. Thank you.

(He smiles, then leaves awkwardly. As he does so, absently, without looking:)

...Night, Esther.

Esther Good night...

(Short pause)

You're privileged. Even I don't get the secretary's mobile phone number. Good night, Mr Shaw. I hope you sleep well.

(She turns to go.)

Shaw Mrs Trent... Just a second.

(She stops. Turns back to look at him. Short pause. Uncomfortably:)

I don't quite know how to... I can tell you're not comfortable with my being here...

Esther I hope I haven't been rude...

Shaw No, no. Not at all. I'm just... sensitive to these things.

Esther I'm surprised. From your writing, I didn't think you were sensitive to anything.

Shaw ...Oh. I'm sorry to hear you say that, Mrs Trent.

Esther I'm sorry. That *was* rude.

Shaw Yes.

Esther Yes. Sorry.

(Short pause)

It's just... so odd having you here. After all these years. Norman's never had an affair or anything. He's not the type. He doesn't need another woman. He's got you, hasn't he? The other man.

Shaw ...I can assure you, madam, that I have no romantic inclinations towards your husband in the slightest.

Esther *(laughing)* No, no, of course you don't. I didn't mean that. It's just that you've always been so much a part of our marriage. At first it was quite sweet, it was him, me, and you lurking in the background. But over the years I feel I've been elbowed aside, I've become the third wheel, not you.

Shaw I'm sorry.

Esther Even our children are named after your plays. We've got two, a boy and a girl. Both teens, started university. Norman insisted we call our son Pygmalion.

Shaw Oh dear.

Esther Pygmalion Trent. I ask you. Our daughter's called Barbara.

Shaw That isn't so bad.

Esther Oh, I don't know. Her full name's Majorbarbara.

Shaw Oh.

Esther I've never seen kids who've been so bullied. Children who have had their heads held down toilet bowls longer than the court of human rights would allow. Anyway. So you see. I'm a little bit tired of you. Sick to death, in fact.

Shaw I'm sorry.

Esther Not your fault. Not your fault at all. I suppose you shouldn't have been such a good writer, should you?

Shaw *(quietly)* No.

Esther Not your fault.

(Short pause)

Shaw I can move out in the morning. I will. I don't want to cause any distress. I'm grateful, madam, for your hospitality as it is.

Esther Oh no. Now I've met you. You... you stay as long as you want.

Shaw Thank you. I... appreciate that.

Esther Good. And it's Esther. Not madam.

Shaw If you say so. Esther.

Esther That's it. No, it'll be good to have someone to talk to for once.

(Pause)

Good night then, Mr Shaw. I hope you sleep well. When you do.

*(And she exits via the house. Music. **Shaw** resets the table and chairs, so that they act like a desk – with one person sitting behind a table.*

*(**Simon** enters, wearing glasses, a somewhat oily BBC production assistant. He carries a tray with three glasses, a bottle of mineral water, and ice. He sits down. **Shaw** sits facing him.)*

Simon   I'm sure Ms Clutterbuck won't keep you waiting much longer.

Shaw   No, no, that's fine.

Simon   Can I interest you in a drink, Mr Shaw? I have sparkling mineral water here.

Shaw   Do you have any Seven Up?

Simon   Ah. No.

Shaw   That's a shame. I've grown rather partial to Seven Up.

Simon   I'm sorry about that.

Shaw   No, that's perfectly all right.

*(Enter **Denise**, power dressed, talking on a mobile phone.)*

Denise   Well, call me when you know. No, call me. Call me. Or should I call you?

Simon   Here she is...

*(**Simon** and **Shaw** stand. She walks to them, continues talking, oblivious. She waves to them both to sit down just before she finishes the conversation.)*

Denise   Well, what would you rather? No, what would *you* rather? ...No, it's what you'd rather, yes. Shall I text you? To tell you when to call me. Or you can text me. To see if you can call. ...Yes, that'll be best. Only if you'd rather. Okay. If you'd rather that. ...Okay. Okay. Ciao. Okay. Ciao.

*(And **Shaw** and **Simon** stand up again.)*

George Shaw, a pleasure. I'm sorry to have kept you waiting...

Shaw   That's perfectly all right.

Denise   Casting directors. Ha! They don't know their collective arses from their collective elbows. Please. Sit down. A drink. A drink, can I get you a drink?

*(She sits next to **Simon**, facing **Shaw**.)*

Simon   I've already offered Mr Shaw a drink...

Denise Simon has already offered you a drink. Would you like a sparkling mineral water?

Simon Mr Shaw wanted a Seven Up.

Denise *(frowning)* Well, do we have any Seven Ups?

Shaw It doesn't matter, really...

Simon We have no Seven Ups.

Denise Make a note of that, Simon. We need more Seven Ups. You must think we're so disorganised, Mr Shaw. You must wonder what we think we're playing at.

Shaw It's really not important.

Denise But it's details, isn't it, Mr Shaw. Details are all that matters, when it comes down to it. Denise Clutterbuck, BBC producer. And this is Simon Murgatroyd, BBC production assistant.

(They all shake.)

Shaw Yes, we've met.

Denise Of course you have. Simon, pour me a mineral water, will you? I'm parched.

Simon Certainly, Denise.

Denise And perhaps George here can tell us what he's been up to recently.

Shaw Well, the situation is this. I've been living with friends now for over a week. I thought I could sort myself out, but it seems that I have no money. My estate says that all the royalties incurred by my works belong to them, after my death the money's theirs, and there's no provision made for whether I come back to life again.

Denise Could I have a bit of ice in that, Simon?

Simon Certainly, Denise.

Denise You're a sweet.

Shaw I vowed I'd never write again. But I have to make a living somehow. Now I *am* living, that is. I thought I could write for the theatre again, but it's all changed since my day, it's all musicals now. So I decided to try the BBC instead.

Denise And I'm sure we're glad you did. Aren't we, Simon? But you misunderstand me. When I say what have you been up to recently, I meant writing-wise.

Shaw Well, that's the point...

Denise I don't want writers moaning to me about money. I get enough of that from their agents.

Shaw I haven't written anything. I've been dead.

(Short pause. Then the phone rings.)

Denise Sorry, I have to take this...

Shaw Of course.

(She stands for the call.)

Denise Darling! Mwa. Yes, I got the script. Yes, I've read it. Yes. Yes, now, darling... You know what I'm going to say, aren't you? ...Where's the sex and swearing? ...Come on, darling, this is for *after* the watershed. You know the rules. There's no point in having a watershed if we don't use it. ...Okay. Just put some in somewhere. We don't want all the grannies at home getting confused, wondering where the sex and swearing's got to. Get back to me. I'm in a meeting. Get back to me. Yes, but not an important one. Okay. Okay. Ciao.

(She sits down again.)

Writers. Never learn. No offence. We're big fans of your work, both Simon and I. Aren't we, Simon?

Simon Certainly are, Denise.

Denise We love that *My Fair Lady* of yours. That song, 'Wouldn't it be Loverly?'

Simon *(speaking, not singing)* 'All I want is a room somewhere, far away from the cold night air.'

Denise I think that speaks to all of us, George. That's uniquely universal.

Shaw *(irritated)* There's more to my career than Eliza Dolittle, you know.

Denise Really? Have you written anything else which is famous?

Shaw *Saint Joan. Arms and the Man. Major Barbara. Mrs Warren's Profession.*

Simon So that would be veering towards a no, then.

Denise But it doesn't matter. As it turns out, *My Fair Lady* is exactly the property we're interested in.

Shaw Really?

Denise I think it would adapt into a perfect sitcom.

Simon The ideal six part comedy series for our spring season on BBC1.

Denise What do you say, George?

*(Short pause. **Shaw** looks as if he might argue, then visibly deflates, sighs.)*

Shaw Well. I suppose I could have a look at it. See if it would translate to the television medium...

Denise Don't you worry about that, George. That's what Simon and I are here for. Right, Simon?

Simon Oh, certainly, Denise.

Denise But there's got to be a few changes. First off. Eliza. The whole flower girl business. I don't know about that for a start.

Shaw You don't like it?

Denise Flower girl doesn't say funny to me. Do you know what says funny to me, Simon?

Simon A hairdresser.

Denise Exactly right. Hairdressers are always funny. We haven't produced a hairdresser sitcom in months.

Shaw You want Eliza Dolittle to be a hairdresser.

Denise An upmarket hairdresser, George. None of your spit and sawdust barber's for us.

Simon We leave that to ITV.

Denise Then we can move on to Henry Higgins. Real problems with his job. He's a... What is he?

Shaw He's a professor of phonetics.

Denise Well, we've done a little survey. And there our very few professors of phonetics amongst our target audience. We need something they can more easily identify with.

Shaw *(sourly)* Well, I don't know. How about another hairdresser.

Denise Oh, yes, that's good. You're getting the hang of this. I told you he'd get the hang of this, didn't I, Simon?

Simon You certainly did, Denise. Things are cooking now.

Denise Two hairdressers. Perhaps rival hairdressers. Perhaps husband and wife!

Simon Rival hairdressers who *are* husband and wife!

Denise Each with their own hairdressing salon, across the street from the other!

Simon 'Henry Higgins' Hairdressing Salon'. 'Eliza's Snips for Ladies'.

Denise With comedy neighbours!

Simon And wisecracking children!

Denise I can see it now. We'll call it – *My Hair Lady.*

Simon You're a genius, Denise.

Shaw I'm not sure this is a project I can work on.

Denise Of course you can. We need you, George. To provide the magic ingredient which will make this show stand out.

Simon This isn't just another run of the mill sitcom about two married rival hairdressers, you know.

Denise We need to preserve that spark which makes Eliza Dolittle such an enduring and well-loved character.

Shaw Her progress towards emancipation?

Denise No. Her ability to talk to the animals.

(Short pause)

It was Eliza Dolittle who could talk to the animals, Simon?

Simon That was Doctor Doolittle.

Denise Her father?

Simon Could have been.

Denise She inherited his gift.

Simon Could have done.

Denise Well then. I think we have a hit blockbuster on our hands. What do you think, George? George?

Simon I think he needs a sparkling mineral water.

Denise Is that it, George? Shall Simon pour you a mineral water?

(Short pause. More confidentially, harsher:)

I can see what you're thinking. It's written all over your face. You writers who have come from the theatre, you think you know it all. With your wanting to create art, all your higher aspirations. You think Simon and I are idiots, don't you?

Shaw *(softly)* Yes.

Denise Yes. I have a degree in Russian literature.

Simon And I got a first in medieval European history.

Denise We're not idiots. We're just in an idiotic profession. Don't you think we know that what we produce is shit? Of course it's shit. We have a whole department which produces comedies which aren't funny. They're called shitcoms. But Simon and I produce our shit well. People *like* our shit. Our shit makes them feel comfortable. Twelve million people watch our shit.

Simon They're twelve million very stupid people, we admit. But even stupid people pay the licence fee. They have a right to watch something they enjoy. When they come in from sweeping pavements or selling hamburgers or cleaning toilets, whatever shitty job they do.

Shaw The groundlings.

Denise Do you understand? Even with a full house in the theatre, what, you get an audience of a few hundred. We're talking millions here

Shaw I'd rather reach only a few hundred with something I believed in than twelve million with something I didn't.

Denise You think you're better than that twelve million, don't you?

Shaw Yes.

Denise Yes. We think we are too. You and I, we're exactly the same, George. The only difference is I swallow my pride. And give the morons what they want.

Shaw But if you gave that twelve million something good, something which might enlighten them, nudge them into improving their lives. A little piece of art amidst all the dross...

Denise If you can get the twelve million viewers. And keep them happy. And keep the shareholders happy too, and the merchandising department. *Then* you can produce art.

Shaw I didn't fight the Devil for fifty years to sell my integrity over a glass of sparkling mineral water. ...I just don't think it's something I could do, even if I wanted to... I'm not sure I could tell the right jokes, come up with the right ideas...

(Denise and Simon laugh, not unkindly.)

Denise   Oh, we've heard that before, haven't we, Simon?

Shaw   Certainly have, Denise. I remember Jasper Cartwright saying the same thing.

Denise   And Marion McKinley. And who now hasn't heard of those two?

(Short pause. Then the phone rings.)

Excuse me. ...Darling! Have you done the rewrites already? You've put a sex scene in? ...Mm. ...Mmmmm. I like it. But what about the swearing? Well, what about... yes, what about if she swears *during* the sex? ...Well, I'd certainly swear if someone did that to me. ... Mmm. Yes. Okay. Ciao, darling. Ciao.

*(She hangs up, then directly to **Shaw**)*

Work with us, George. And I promise you. You'll never have to worry about ideas again.

*(Music. **Denise** and **Simon** exit, taking the tray with them. **Shaw** slowly walks downstage centre, looks out to the audience. A spotlight on him – it is night time.*

(He stares fixedly forward – and sighs.

*(At length, enter **Esther** from the house. The actress' hair is down, and she is in a nightdress – worn underneath the power suit from the scene previously. She approaches **Shaw** gently.)*

Esther   Mr Shaw?

Shaw   Oh. Hello, Esther.

Esther   What are you doing out here? It's late.

Shaw   I couldn't think. I needed a think.

Esther   Would you rather I...?

Shaw   No, no. Please. Stay. I can think in company. I used to be good at thinking, could do it any situation.

(Short pause)

Esther   It's a beautiful night.

Shaw Mmm.

(Short pause. **Esther** *produces a pack of cigarettes.)*

Esther I hope you don't mind...

Shaw Oh, no. No, you go ahead.

Esther Thank you.

(She lights a cigarette. Short pause)

Yes, it's a beautiful night. All the stars out. So far away. It could make you feel lonely, a night like this. ...You were very quiet during dinner.

Shaw Was I? I'm sorry.

Esther You hardly touched your nut roast.

Shaw It was delicious. I just wasn't very hungry.

Esther It doesn't matter. Norman never lets nut roast go to waste. He's asleep at the moment.

Shaw I've been trying to write this sitcom pilot for the BBC.

Esther How's it going?

Shaw It isn't, frankly. I'm having problems working out exactly why there'd be talking animals in the hairdresser's to begin with.

Esther Well. We all have problems, don't we?

Shaw Just doesn't seem very hygienic.

(Short pause)

It's hard, starting all over. I never thought I'd write again. I thought I'd already done enough. I go into the local bookshop, it's got a small play section. A couple of mine are there. No-one's ever so much as picked them up. I know. I check. And yet, a shelf along, the TV chefs are selling books like hot cakes.

Esther Norman doesn't know I smoke, you know.

Shaw What? No, no, I didn't either.

Esther I only do it when he's out, and suck lots of mints afterwards. I know he wouldn't approve. He wouldn't approve, because you *didn't* approve. But you don't mind me smoking, do you?

Shaw Really, you can do anything you want...

Esther See, Norman got even that wrong.

Shaw You're every inch the New Woman I wrote about.

Esther New Woman? No. I'm just a nicotine addict.

(She inhales.)

I'm not the vegetarian you think either. When Norman's at work I drive into town and pop into McDonalds. Have myself a guilty cheese quarterpounder. Do you think less of me?

Shaw No.

Esther I don't like Big Macs. Not keen on that special sauce. But the cheese quarterpounders are to die for. You mean it? You don't think less of me?

(Abruptly:)

I tried reading one of your plays. You know, now I know you. I thought I might like them better.

Shaw Oh. Which one?

Esther *Misalliance.*

Shaw Oh, that one.

Esther Still don't, I'm afraid. I did try, though.

(Short pause)

Shaw Well. Thank you for trying...

Esther I don't like smoking, but I need to do it more and more. Now the kids have gone, and the days seem longer. One day he'll come home early and catch me at it. Either mid-cigarette puff or pre-mint suck. But I don't care any more. I'll tell him, I need *something*, don't I, Norman? Something for my lips to touch. This is what loneliness drives you to. Crafty fags and gobbled burgers and trying to read *Misalliance* because you really want to reach out to someone, but don't how to get to know him.

Shaw It's not one of my better plays. I used to like it. But it seems very very old now.

Esther Yes.

(Short pause. Trying again:)

I didn't have time to find a hobby like Norman did. Obsessing over a dead playwright. No, I was too busy trying to raise a family, to look after my children, teach them right from wrong, pack their school lunches every morning, make them tidy their bedrooms. And then one day, oops, without warning they're up and gone, they grew up suddenly without telling you. And I've nothing left, whilst Norman still has George Bernard Shaw. And it seems obvious to me now he made the right choice. He put his love in something which was never going to leave him, to change on him, to become an adult and forget all about Mother's Day. He still has you.

(Short pause)

I wish I could have you. ...In some form or other, anyway. I miss my kids. They used to drive me up the wall, of course. But I miss them more than I ever thought I could. Don't you miss anyone?

(Short pause)

Shaw No.

(Short pause)

Esther You're lucky.

Shaw ...I suppose so. ...I don't know. It's just that sometimes I think it'd be rather good to miss someone. That it's something I'm missing out on. I never cared, I knew I'd have my plays. My *Pygmalion*. My *Major Barbara*.

Esther And you still do. At least your Pygmalion didn't go off to university and leave you behind.

Shaw No. But it's changed, just as yours has. *I* was the one that went away and when I returned, it had changed without me. *Major Barbara* too – I wrote them to be important, to do some good. Now they're in Penguin Classics, respected, of course respected, but not loved, barely performed. Not as I created them. What do you think happens when you put all your love and faith in something you've given birth to – only to find out that all that faith doesn't mean a thing to them?

Esther That's what I worry about. Pygmalion and Majorbarbara will come back to me sooner or later. But they won't be mine any more, will they?

Shaw *Pygmalion* and *Major Barbara* will never again be something I recognise. I can remember what they were like at the beginning, of course...

Esther Oh, so can I! They were so small back then, I could carry them in my arms...

Shaw That rush of excitement I felt shaping them, bringing them to life.

Esther And they were *mine*. No-one else's.

Shaw Only I had seen the words on the paper. I could shape the fate of Eliza Dolittle, Andrew Undershaft. And it was perfect in my head.

Esther I could carry them in my arms all day, and they couldn't get free. No matter how hard they'd struggle.

(Short pause. She begins to weep gently. She pulls herself up, stops.)

I have to let go, don't I?

Shaw Maybe we both do.

Esther All that love I wasted. If I was going to lose them anyway... It makes me wonder what the point of creating Pygmalion or Majorbarbara was in the first place.

Shaw No. My *Pygmalion* and *Major Barbara* are nothing compared to yours.

(Short pause)

They're just... words. My children, they're just words. I could erase them in an instant. ...And I would. I'd destroy my *Pygmalion* and *Major Barbara*, I'd uncreate them. If it would bring your Pygmalion and Majorbarbara back to you.

Esther You don't even know what they're like.

Shaw It doesn't matter. It doesn't matter. I had a foolish idea. I wrote my plays for posterity, but posterity doesn't really want them. They sit in bookshops beside overflowing cookery sections. But your Pygmalion, your Majorbarbara... they *are* posterity. They are the future I wrote for. And that you could do that, that you could create the future, whilst I just wrote jokes about flower sellers and munitions factories – it leaves me speechless with awe. You are the true artist, Esther, not me. You are. ...Or rather, you're better than that. When it comes down to it, I suppose I made art my life. But art isn't as important as life.

Esther *(gently)* You need to let go.

Shaw Yes. I need to let go. So I can move on at last.

(And she kisses him on the lips.)

Esther I'm sorry.

Shaw No, it's all right...

Esther I couldn't help myself.

Shaw I haven't been kissed like that for over a hundred years.

Esther A hundred years feels about right for me too.

(They kiss again.)

Are you all right, dearest?

Shaw You remind me of Charlotte.

Esther ...That's not a very tactful thing to say.

Shaw And yet it's true.

Esther Did she kiss like this?

Shaw I don't remember. We didn't kiss much. I was too busy with the writing.

Esther I think I could love you. I really think I could love you.

Shaw I tell them. I always tell them. Don't fall in love with me.

Esther Why not? What else have I got?

Shaw You don't love my plays.

Esther They're not the same thing, Bernard.

Shaw But that's just it. I'm rather afraid they are. I'd give them all up now, for Charlotte's sake.

Esther Would you give them all up for me?

Shaw ...Why not? They're worthless.

*(And he turns away from her. **Esther** looks at him, surprised and slightly hurt. Then reaches for him, turns him around, and kisses him again. It is a very deep kiss, and he responds. Hold this for a little while.*

*(Enter **Norman** in striped pyjamas – who freezes in surprise at what he sees.)*

Norman *(softly)* Bernard? Esther?

(And they pull apart.)

Esther Norman! What are you doing here?

Norman *(weakly)* I thought I'd have a think.

Shaw Mr Trent. I can promise you. This is not how it looks.

Esther *(boldly)* I've been having an affair with Bernard, Norman. For the last two weeks you've been at work, we've been at it hammer and tongs. In the garden, on the settee, right beneath your bookshelf of

Shaw memorabilia.

Shaw Esther!

Esther It's true. I'm in love with George Bernard Shaw.

Shaw Mrs Trent! I do protest!

Norman Well. I don't know what to say. ...I don't know what to say.

Shaw Mr Trent, I do assure you...

Norman I think this is splendid news. Really. I couldn't be happier.

(Pause)

Shaw *(puzzled)* What?

Esther *(dangerously)* What?

Norman I never thought I could be prouder than to have had George Bernard Shaw inside my house. But now I find out he's been inside my wife as well. I'm over the moon. Just wait until I tell the Shaw Society about this!

Esther *(quietly)* ...You bastard. I can't believe... You *bastard.*

Norman But, darling. I know you don't want me any more. I knew you'd have an affair one day. And if you have to have one, I'm just glad you picked the author of *Heartbreak House.*

Esther I've wanted you for years. Absolutely bloody years.

Norman *(sadly)* If only that were true. But you sleep as far away from me as possible, right on the edge of the bed. You flinch if I even accidentally brush against you. No, Esther. I know I'm not much of a husband. You'll be better off with the founder of modern drama.

Shaw Mr Trent. I haven't touched Esther. I wouldn't, I assure you.

Norman Oh, Bernard, there's really no need to spare my feelings.

Shaw I'm not! She's clearly desperate and neurotic, and probably on the verge of some sort of breakdown! Even if I had a mind for a fling, I think I'd choose someone just a little more stable!

Norman Are you saying that Esther is a liar?

Shaw Yes. At last. Well done.

Norman I don't like you calling my wife a liar. Sleeping with her is one thing. Insulting her is quite another. I don't know if she still loves me any more, I don't know if she even *likes* me, but I love her. I do love her.

And I would defend her against all the masterminds of world literature.

Shaw All that she has said is a complete fabrication...

Norman Right. That does it. George Bernard Shaw or not, I'm going to ask you to step outside.

Esther *(gently)* Norman, we already are outside.

Norman Then inside then. I can fight you inside just as easily.

Shaw This is ridiculous...

Norman I love Esther! Do you hear me? I love her!

Esther Oh, Norman...!

Norman Do you hear me?

Shaw Loud and clear, Mr Trent.

Norman And you did sleep with her, didn't you? Come on, I'll knock your block off! You slept with her and liked it!

Shaw Yes, Mr Trent. I slept with her. It was very... nice.

Norman Good. I'm glad to hear it.

Esther Norman, of course I wanted you. I always wanted you. But I thought you loved George Bernard Shaw far more than you ever loved me...

Norman Well, why do you think I loved Shaw so much?

Esther I haven't the faintest idea. He's dull, and dry as dust.

Shaw *(faintly)* Oh dear.

Norman For you, of course. Only for you.

Esther I don't understand.

Norman Because it's how we met. Acting in a Shaw play together. And we fell in love. I always wanted to keep the memory sacred, preserve it forever.

Esther But it didn't need preserving! I'm here, aren't I? I've been here all along!

Norman Except you put all your time in the children. All your love too. Pygmy and little Majorbabs. And I needed to remind myself more and more of what we once had. Bernard Shaw. All those productions of *Overruled, The Devil's Disciple, The Shewing Up of Blanco Posnet.* All little love letters to you.

Esther Oh, Norman. You've been so silly.

Norman I love you. I always have. Even with the children taking you away from me.

Esther I'll let go of my Pygmalion and Majorbarbara, if you let go of his.

Norman I promise. I've missed you so much.

Esther I've missed you too.

(They kiss.)

Shaw *(softly)* I miss... I miss Charlotte.

(And the lights slowly narrow on him as he begins to talk. **Norman** *and* **Esther** *are left in half light, holding each other, no longer listening to him.)*

I wondered if I ever would. When she died, I really only felt an overwhelming sense of relief. That her suffering was over, of course, because she *did* suffer, Charlotte, she was a martyr to her arthritis, she used to say when she moved she could feel her bones cracking, even when she breathed out, her bones cracking and splintering.

Esther *(softly)* I love you.

Norman *(softly)* I love you too.

Shaw But mostly I was just relieved to be *free.* Whenever Charlotte had fallen ill and thought she was dying, I'd simply fall ill myself. That would always force her out of bed to look after me. But there came a time when she couldn't get out of bed any more.

Norman *(softly)* I'll throw all Shaw's plays on the fire in the morning.

Esther *(softly)* Oh, not all of them. Leave *My Fair Lady.* I always liked that one.

(And arm in arm they return to the house.)

Shaw And then one evening I went in to see her. I dreaded seeing her, this woman I had been married to for so long, for too long, her face permanently etched with pain, her mouth always curled to give complaint. And I was shocked. There in her bed I saw *my* Charlotte. The Charlotte I had married forty years before, looking young and fresh and... Her face looked up at me from the pillow, and beamed a perfect smile. And I took her by the hand, and told her she was beautiful. I had no choice. She was. She couldn't reply, or did, but what she said made no sense to me, she babbled like a child. But she smiled that perfect smile I never knew she had, and it broke my heart she'd never given me that smile before. I sat on the bed, nearly ninety years old, and looked down on my wife who seemed to be growing younger by the hour. I told her she was beautiful, and that I loved her, because I had fallen in love with her all over again. She died thirty hours later, and by that time her face had become younger still, my dead wife had the face of a young child. Pure and brilliant and innocent. I talked to her. I held her cold hand and talked to her for hours, who had never talked to her whilst she could still hear me. At one point I thought I saw her eyes flicker, so I held a glass to her lips to check for breath. Just as Shakespeare had King Lear do to Cordelia, I had taken the idea from Shakespeare. And I held my beautiful wife in my arms, who had been so plain whilst she lived, and I said goodbye. And I let her go. I let her go. And I refused to miss her. I didn't miss her. I didn't miss her. Until now.

*(During the above **Charlotte** has entered from the house, and moved to sit in the same chair we discover **Shaw** in at the beginning of the play. She has her eyes closed. **Shaw** now approaches her.)*

Charlotte?

(Short pause)

Are you asleep, Charlotte? Or are you dead?

(Short pause)

I do hope you haven't died. Not just yet. I do so want to speak to you first. I need to tell you... I need to tell you I love you. After all. Who would have thought it? 'I love you'. You could knock me down with a feather.

(Short pause)

I don't know why I wrote all those plays. I suppose I thought they meant something at the time. But I promise you this. For your sake, the Devil can have them all. He can destroy them, every last one of them, I'll never have written a single line. And maybe all those years I spent in my study with the door closed to you, maybe I will have spent them with you instead.

(Short pause)

I'll let go. I'll give in at last. And let go of them all.

(Pause. Then firmly, without yet opening her eyes:)

Charlotte Don't you dare do anything so bloody stupid.

Shaw Charlotte?

Charlotte You think those plays are yours alone? And who typed them and collated them and prepared them for publication? Who had to listen to you agonise about them every day, when a story wasn't going well, when a character just wouldn't say what you wanted him to?

Shaw You were too good to me.

Charlotte Rubbish. They were my plays as much as yours. Don't you dare destroy my life's work.

(Short pause)

Shaw I could have done so much more with my life. I thought I had. But it was nothing. Nothing at all.

Charlotte We do the best we can. In your life you wrote some plays. That's what your life was. Some were good. Some were... less so. But it's still a life. And at the end of the day, it's worth a life. You did the best you could. It was worth both our lifetimes, Bernard.

Shaw I love you.

Charlotte I know.

Shaw I should have said it more often.

Charlotte Yes. But never mind, darling.

Shaw I'm going to miss you.

Charlotte No, you're not.

Shaw I will. Eventually. I will.

*(**Charlotte** gets up, offers **Shaw** the chair.)*

Charlotte Here.

Shaw No, Charlotte. You must sit down. You must rest.

Charlotte I'm dead, Bernard. I'm dead.

Shaw ...I know.

Charlotte I'm done waiting for death. Sit down. It's your turn now.

*(And he does. **Charlotte** stands behind him, kisses his head.)*

Goodbye, my dear. I'll see you soon.

(And she exits.

*(**Shaw** closes his eyes. And lights as before, at the beginning of Act One.*

*(Dressed as the **Germ** was, a **Reporter** enters. He stands by the sleeping*

Shaw *warily.)*

Reporter   Mr Shaw? Mr Shaw, sir?

(Short pause)

Mr Shaw? Are you asleep, Mr Shaw?

*(And **Shaw** opens his eyes.)*

I'm sorry to disturb you, Mr Shaw... I was wondering if I could ask you a few questions...

Shaw   Where am I?

Reporter   Beg pardon, Mr Shaw?

Shaw   I asked you where we are.

Reporter   Well. We're in your garden, Mr Shaw.

Shaw   And would you be so good as to tell me when as well?

Reporter   When?

Shaw   The year. I'm hazarding a guess that you know.

Reporter   ...It's 1950.

Shaw   Still in 1950?

Reporter   Well. Yes, sir.

(Short pause)

I hope you don't mind me intruding, sir. I have some questions to ask...

Shaw   You're not a Germ, by any chance?

Reporter   I'm a journalist from the BBC.

Shaw   Ah. Jolly good.

*(Short pause. The **Reporter** looks around awkwardly, then back.)*

Reporter   So how about it, Mr Shaw?

Shaw   I'm sure you'll understand. I'm rather tired of questions. Of discussing my life, and my life's work.

Reporter   Oh, I see.

Shaw   I think we've had enough of that, don't you?

Reporter   I wanted to do the definitive interview. The one that finally made sense of the enigmatic Mr Shaw. Answered all the questions, unravelled all the mysteries. After mine, there'd be no need for any other.

Shaw ...This would be the last interview I'd ever give?

Reporter Well. Yes.

Shaw No more questions. For the rest of my life.

Reporter If you like.

Shaw And beyond. No more questions for the rest of my life – and beyond.

Reporter Whatever you want, Mr Shaw.

(*Shaw leans back in his chair, relaxes. Short pause*)

Shaw Very well then. What is it you want to know?

(*Blackout, music.*)